CW00734416

STEADY AS SHE GOES

An order to the man on the wheel to steer the course on which
the ship is, at that instant, heading.

The title has been chosen as being a free translation of the motto
'PER STET' (Let it stand firm), which appears in the crest of the
Admiralty Compass Observatory.

The compass is the soul of the ship.
Victor Hugo

HMS Sovereign at the North Pole, 23 October 1976.
Mr W. L. Thomson of the Admiralty Compass Observatory receives his 'Polar Plaque' from the Commanding Officer, Commander M. G. T. Harris.

STEADY AS SHE GOES

A History
of the
Compass Department
of the Admiralty

by A. E. Fanning

LONDON
HER MAJESTY'S STATIONERY OFFICE

ISBN 0 11 290425 4
© Crown copyright 1986
First published 1986
Printed in the UK for HMSO
by Robert Hartnoll 1985 Ltd
Dd 718117 C12

Acknowledgements

Grateful acknowledgement is made to the following authorities for permission to reproduce photographs: Mr. J. Chaffer (No. 62), the Commanding Officer, HMS Victory (No. 10), Mrs. R. Creagh-Osborne (Nos. 53, 56, 57, 58), the Imperial War Museum (No. 46), the Keystone Press (No. 118), the National Portrait Gallery (Nos. 17, 31), the Royal Greenwich Observatory (No. 18), the Rutherford Appleton Laboratory (Nos. 77–79, 81), the Science Museum (No. 27), the Sperry Gyroscope Company (No. 63), HM Submarine Museum, Gosport (Nos. 52, 91, 93), Mr. Wilfred P. Trotter (Nos. 35, 44, 45).

All other photographs are either Crown Copyright or the property of the National Maritime Museum or have been offered by past or present members of the Staff of the Admiralty Compass Observatory. Again, I am very grateful for permission to reproduce them.

Contents

Foreword

This is a book that deserved to be written.

The Admiralty Compass Observatory is one of the oldest Government Scientific Establishments, giving precedence only to the Royal Greenwich Observatory and to the Royal Ordnance Factory. Today, the 'history' of an establishment can so easily be lost, particularly after a change in its status. As a result, errors in the priority of scientific discovery and development appear all too frequently in the technical press. It is therefore gratifying that Commander Fanning was able and willing to undertake the mammoth task of going through the archives of the establishment (many of which had never before been sorted and catalogued) and writing this book, which covers an important aspect of scientific development during an exciting period of naval history.

Commander Fanning's time as Deputy Director at the ACO covered much of the crucial period of its expansion during the 1960s and 1970s while much invaluable background information was gleaned from the work of Commander May, himself a naval historian and former officer of the Compass Department. Future historians will benefit from Commander Fanning's work and from the orderly arrangement of the archives which he has left us.

Official funding for this book was provided by the Admiralty Research Establishment and by the Caird Fund of the National Maritime Museum (which also sponsored the writing and publication), but of course this covered only a nominal part of the real cost. The rest was provided as a labour of love by the author who spent long hours of his own assembling the material, travelling and interviewing people, and finally, of course, in writing the text. As with many topics, there is a fine line to be drawn between the extremes of producing a ten-volume work which nobody will ever have the time to read and condensing the text to such an extent that important milestones are lost. Commander Fanning has steered an excellent course between these two dangers to produce this valuable and interesting history of an important phase of the art, or should it be science, of navigation.

E. Hoy
Head of the Admiralty Compass Observatory

Author's Preface

'. . . ignorance is the first requisite of the historian –
ignorance which *simplifies and clarifies*, which *selects and omits . . .*'

(From the Author's Preface to *Eminent Victorians*
by Lytton Strachey).

Twenty-six years in Naval uniform and a further eighteen on the staff of the Admiralty Compass Observatory combined to give me a keen interest in the history of the Royal Navy in general and of the Compass Department of the Admiralty in particular. When the time came for retirement I found myself with a strong urge to write the story of this unique department which, from simple beginnings in 1842, when it was formed to improve the lot of the Mariner's Compass, developed over the next century and a quarter to embrace the whole range of Naval navigational equipment, much of it based on the most advanced aspects of modern technology. When I began work I had little idea of the enormous wealth of historical material that would come to light during my research and, indeed, had only a superficial acquaintance with the story. In fact I had in full measure the first requisite of Lytton Strachey's historian, ignorance. Coincidently, many of my early heroes were, in their own sphere, Eminent Victorians.

At the start of the nineteenth century the state of compasses at sea was generally deplorable with weakly magnetized needles and very poor craftmanship. The trouble was further compounded by the increasing quantity of iron that was being introduced into ships, seriously affecting compass accuracy. Yet seamen in general had little understanding of these matters and paid scant attention to the dangers they implied, regarding the resulting disasters simply as Acts of God, to be accepted as part of the hazard of their calling. Fortunately, however, there were also enlightened men prepared to address the problem and, in this field, the pioneering investigations of Flinders, Barlow, Johnson and Airy were of particular significance. Brief accounts of their work have been included in the Introduction to this volume as together they give a comprehensive picture of the state of compass management at sea during the early part of the century, when men were still groping for the truth. This forms an appropriate springboard from which the story of the Admiralty Compass Department can be launched.

Much has been written about the early history of compasses, while technical libraries abound with information about modern navigational systems. My aim has therefore been to include only sufficient detail of equipments to enable the reader to appreciate the scope of the department's work, the significance of any breakthrough or milestone as it occurred or, conversely, the effects of opportunities missed. I have tried to explain the reasons for the major decisions taken and to show how, over the years, the department has developed to meet the changing needs of the Navy as it evolved from sail to steam, from paddles to screws and from wooden walls to iron-clads. In the twentieth century aircraft, submarines, missiles and nuclear power have all made their impact. Above all, I have tried to relate the story to the personalities involved, upon whom lay the burden of its success or failure.

Today, thanks to the wonders of modern navigational science, submarines can safely remain submerged for weeks on end and can routinely navigate under the ice-cap, penetrating to the North Pole itself. It is the story that lies between the simple beginnings in the 1840s and the department's wide ranging responsibilities of the 1980s which forms the subject of this narrative.

In writing this history I have received help from many quarters for which I have been extremely grateful. The work was sponsored jointly by the Ministry of Defence and the Trustees of the National Maritime Museum, from whom I enjoyed the privilege and support of a Caird Fellowship as well as considerable assistance from the Staff of the Navigation Department. I was fortunate, too, in being able to consult many past members of the Admiralty Compass Observatory in addition to those who carry the torch today, particularly Ted Hoy, its present Head. Many of these have kindly read appropriate sections of this book, often offering helpful criticism, anecdotes and photographs. In particular, the two Directors under whom I served, Captain C. J. Wynne-Edwards and Captain T. D. Ross, gave me much valuable information about the problems as seen from the top, as also did my predecessor as Deputy Director, Commander A. V. Thomas. Special mention must also be made of the great help I received from Lieutenant Commander Andrew David, whose knowledge of the Archives of the Hydrographic Office must be encyclopaedic.

My particular thanks go to Maurice Wooller for painstakingly reading the story as it developed and for making many helpful suggestions; also to the ladies of the typing pool of the ACO who typed the manuscript – some sections many times over.

Finally I wonder whether this story would have been written without the unstinted help and encouragement of Commander W. E. May, himself a world authority on compasses, who had already done much original work on the early history of the Compass Department. Although my own research was done from primary sources whenever possible, he allowed me unfettered access to his papers which were of the utmost assistance. He, too, read my manuscript, meticulously checking detail.

To Commander May this book is dedicated, with deep gratitude.

May 1985
A. E. F.

Introduction

'Who was the first inventer of this instrument miraculous, and endued, as it were with life, can hardly be found.' (W. Barlowe, *The Navigator's Supply*, 1597)

'The compass being an instrument of the utmost consequence to Navigation, it is reasonable to expect that the greatest care and attention should be used in its construction . . . but so careless are the generality of Commanders of this most useful instrument . . .' (*The Complete Dictionary of Arts and Sciences*, 1764)

Early in the eighteenth century it was recognized that the compass, the most vital instrument in navigation, was inadequate. Incredibly, another century was to pass before any effective steps were taken to remedy a state of affairs that was losing the country hundreds of ships – and countless hundreds of lives – every year.

The Compass Department of the Admiralty came into being on 14 March 1842, following the recommendations of the Compass Committee set up in July 1837 to investigate 'an evil so pregnant with mischief'. This story traces the fortunes and development of that small department from its early struggles to improve the performance of the magnetic compass, through many vicissitudes, wars, economies and expanding horizons, up to modern times. It shows how, by meeting each new challenge, the natural successor of that new department, now known as the *Admiralty Compass Observatory*, has emerged as a lively, forward-looking organization that is still responsible for 'everying that matters' in navigation equipment in Britain today, as was its forebear in 1842.

Early history

The origins of the magnetic compass are obscure, and claims to its invention appear in the legends of several nations. It is probable that the directional property of the lodestone ('leading stone') or a piece of iron 'touched' by a lodestone, was well known to the Chinese, Indians, Arabs and Turks, as well as to many European nations during the Middle Ages and possibly considerably earlier.

Certainly some crude form of magnetic compass was in use at sea in the twelfth century, probably consisting of a magnetized needle stuck through a straw or piece of wood and floating in a bowl of water. Descriptions occur in many languages and the following, taken from an early Arabian manuscript[1] of AD 1240 is typical:

> The Captains who navigate the Syrian Sea, when the night is so obscure that they cannot perceive any star to direct them, take a vessel full of water which they place sheltered from the wind . . . They then take a needle which they enclose in a piece of wood or reed formed in the shape of a cross . . . so that it floats. Then they take a magnet stone . . . and give to the hand a movement of rotation towards the right, so that the needle turns on the surface of the water. Then they withdraw the hand suddenly, and at once the needle, by its two points, faces to the south and to the north. I have seen them, with my own eyes, do that, during my voyages at sea from Tripoli to Alexandria in the [Arabian] year 640 [or AD 1240].

The development of the mariner's compass from such early beginnings has been ably traced in many works of scholarship and it is not my intention to add to their number. Nevertheless a brief mention of the significant milestones in its history may serve as a useful background to the formation of the Compass Department and enable the improvements and developments which followed to be viewed in their true perspective.

The Chinese were using primitive compasses in ships by AD 265,[2] and although some sources credit Marco Polo (1254–1324) with their introduction into the Mediterranean, there is ample evidence that they were in use in Europe considerably earlier. Alexander Neckham (1157–1217) in 1187 describes a floating needle for use in a ship[3] while, in 1269, Pierre de Maricourt, writing from Italy, provides the first known description of a magnetized needle mounted horizontally between upper and lower pivots.[4] The idea that the needle was somehow attracted to the pole of the heavens or to the polestar appears in various works[5] and the instrument was often referred to as a *stella maris*, the name compass not being generally used until early in the fifteenth century.[6]

The points of the compass came originally from the names of the winds which blew from the various parts of the horizon. Homer

(c. 900 BC) mentions four winds, Boreas, the north wind; Euros, the east wind; Notos, the south wind; and Zephuros, the west wind. Later, around 100 BC, these had increased to eight and were depicted in the famous Temple of Winds in Athens. As the requirements of navigation made further sub-division necessary, we find a convenient Italian twelve-wind system being widely used in the Mediterranean throughout the Middle Ages. By the sixteenth century, however, the more general use of the compass in sailing led to a further sub-division of the original eight winds into sixteen and then thirty-two. Although different countries often used different names, that for the north wind, *Tramontana*, seems to have had wide acceptance and led to the habit of marking the north point with an elaborately embellished letter T. Sometime after 1500 this gave way to the fleur-de-lys, which it closely resembled, and which is now universally employed. At the same time the east point was frequently marked by an ornamental cross.[7]

The naming of the thirty-two points, which are now accepted throughout Europe and the Americas, appears to have been developed during the sixteenth century by the pilots of Bruges, using abbreviations of an early French version of the four cardinal points (winds), north, east, south and west.[8] As the accuracy of navigation improved so half and quarter-points were introduced, but although Pierre de Maricourt had, in 1269, described a compass graduated with 360° this practice was not widely adopted for the mariner's compass until well into the seventeenth century.

Ornamental wind roses (*rosa ventorum*) began to appear on charts late in the fourteenth century but there is no evidence that this was directly connected with the introduction of the compass card itself. Indeed it seems more likely that the directions (winds) were at first marked on the inside of the vessel or box in which the compass needle was pivoted. Exactly who took that all important step of transferring these directions to a compass card attached to the needle cannot be firmly established, but suggestions that it occurred as early as 1302 at Amalfi, in Italy, are normally associated with the name of Flavio Gioja.[9] Certainly the town boasts a most imposing statue in his honour.[10] It was, however, this change which marked the essential difference between an ordinary compass with a pivoted needle for use on land and the mariner's compass which, by showing at a glance the direction of all points of the horizon, could be used to indicate a course and would be of use at sea. The introduction of a lubber's line (or lubber's point) to indicate the direction of the ship's head, against which the course is steered, came much later. It is mentioned in occasional seventeenth- and early eighteenth-century documents,[11] but it does not appear to have been widely used until about 1790.

The practice of decorating the compass cards themselves also began during the seventeenth century and many beautiful examples still survive, including some on which the *eight* principal points are colourfully illuminated with connected motifs – the Sun, Moon and planets, animals and birds, ships, nautical instruments, the muses, and so on.[12]

The fact that the compass needle deviates from true north was known to the Chinese in the twelfth century[13] and it was certainly recognized in Europe well before the time of Columbus. Navigators learnt to allow for the north-easting or north-westing of their compasses and some compass-makers, particularly in northern Europe, adopted the habit of slewing the needles relative to the fleur-de-lys so that their compasses would read true. Later it was shown that this variation differs widely in different parts of the world (some credit Columbus with this discovery) and also that its value alters from year to year. Nevertheless, compasses in which the angle between the card and the needle could be adjusted were still to be found at sea until well into the nineteenth century.

Between 1698 and 1700, at the request of the Royal Society, Edmond Halley made two voyages to the South Atlantic in the *Paramour* to study magnetic phenomena, and in 1701 he published the first chart showing lines of equal magnetic variation (isogonic lines).[14] This chart was of the Atlantic Ocean only but it was followed in 1702 by a more ambitious edition which also covered the Indian Ocean. During the eighteenth century the most intractable problem in navigation was that of finding *longitude* and to this end in 1714 the British Government, through its Board of Longitude, offered a prize of £20,000 for a successful solution. As is well known, the answer ultimately lay in finding a method of keeping accurate time at sea and the prize went to John Harrison for the invention of the marine chronometer. In the meanwhile many other means had been tried including the use of 'lunars', the occultation of stars by the Moon or the eclipses of Jupiter's satellites. Halley's chart was yet another attempt at solving the problem. By charting the variation in different parts of the world, it was hoped that mariners could obtain their longitude by observing the errors of their compasses. Although this method never proved entirely satisfactory there are many examples of its successful use and the hope persisted until well into the 19th century[15]. By that time other errors connected with the introduction of iron into ships had rendered it quite impracticable. The variation charts were, of course, also of great value for correcting compass courses.

Azimuth compasses, with sights for observing the bearing of an object or of the sun and stars, began to appear late in the sixteenth century, generally with the sights fixed to the box or bowl, the whole of which was rotated. Later these sights were fitted on a bar or ring which could be rotated on top of the compass bowl itself. Azimuth compasses were, however, used sparingly until late in the eighteenth century, and in the Navy were normally only issued to ships when proceeding abroad.

Some form of binnacle[16] in which to house the compass has been in use from earliest times and the term may originally have referred to the house or shelter provided for the pilot in which he also kept his instruments. At first, compasses were used mainly for checking the direction of the wind rather than for steering and it was probably prudent that pilots should keep so mysterious an instrument hidden from the ordinary sailor who might be superstitious. The earliest description which refers to a stand for the compass itself is dated 1627: 'a square box nailed together with wooden pinnes, called a bittacle ... this is built so close that the lamp or candle only sheweth light to the steerage, and in it always stands the compass.'[17]

The basic design of the binnacle appears to have altered little during the seventeenth, eighteenth and early nineteenth centuries, and this description given in 1764 will be readily recognizable to those who have visited HMS *Victory* at Portsmouth: 'BINNACLE, in Naval Affairs, a wooden case standing immediately before the helm on deck, and containing three divisions, the middle one of which is for a lamp or candle, and the two side ones for the sea compasses, by which the course is steered.'[18] Such a binnacle provided a compass on each side of the wheel, for use when sailing on either tack, and in the Navy a second binnacle was often provided 'for him who *cons*, or superintends the steerage'. A separate azimuth compass, normally mounted on a stand or tripod, was set up when required in the most convenient part of the ship from which to observe the bearings of headlands, or of the Sun and stars. Compasses without azimuth fittings were therefore generally referred to as binnacle compasses. From about 1550 onwards, compasses were always hung in gimbals to keep them level, against the motion of the ship.[19]

Compasses during the eighteenth century

Despite its unique importance to their trade, seamen in general gave little thought to either the care or improvement of the mariner's compass for several hundred years after its introduction. Apart from the modest practical advances so far described, few important changes were made to its basic design or performance. At the start of the eighteenth century compass bowls were still extensively made of wood, with a detachable bottom so that the needle could be removed for re-touching without breaking the water-tight seal on the glass.[20] Although brass bowls came into limited use in the middle of the seventeenth century, they were expensive and in the Navy were only issued to flagships or ships proceeding abroad. Compass needles were often of wire and their magnetism was weak and far from permanent. Frequently, two needles were used, bent on either side of the pivot and joined at their ends. Their attachment to the card was often inaccurate and the general workmanship was crude, even by the standards of the day. Yet it was with such primitive instruments that the intrepid seamen and explorers of the fifteenth, sixteenth and seventeenth centuries accomplished their historic voyages of exploration and trade.

On 27 October 1707 six ships out of a squadron of twenty-one, commanded by Sir Clowdisley Shovell, ran onto the rocks to the west of Scilly and four were lost. After suggestions that the disaster had resulted from the poor state of their compasses, an examination revealed that out of 145 carried in the squadron (136 with wooden bowls) only 3 were fully serviceable. The Board decreed that in future only brass bowls were to be purchased for the Navy, but a century later many wooden bowls were still in use.[21]

The first real improvement in the mariner's compass came from the work of the celebrated Dr Gowin Knight of London who in 1745 devised a method for magnetizing steel bars far more strongly than was possible with the simple touch method. He demonstrated its effectiveness to the Royal Society[22] and was subsequently elected a Fellow, but for a long time he insisted on keeping his method a secret, hoping, it seems, that his monopoly in strong magnets would make his fortune. In 1749 Dr Knight was called upon to advise when the ship *Dover* was struck by lightning which had reversed the polarity of her compass needles and magnetized the iron spikes, unforgivably used in the construction of her binnacle. He was appalled as the crudeness of her compass equipment which, on investigation, he discovered to be typical of the items then generally available, and he determined to design and market a greatly superior instrument. Knight's compass had a single, flat, *steel* magnet, fastened above the card to avoid the necessity of piercing it and balanced by a brass circumferential ring below. Examples of this compass, which were made for him by John Smeaton,[23] were tested at sea in several HM Ships, and later he was permitted to conduct a trial himself in the *Fortune*, with a view to improving the performance in rough weather. Although he seems to have been the first man to have undertaken a scientific study of how to make a compass steady at sea, he never really solved the problem.[24] Nevertheless, his improvements had a considerable influence on other manufacturers of the day and his compasses were even copied by the German manufacturers of Hamburg during the 1760s.[25] They were widely adopted by the Navy and remained the best available until the Admiralty's Standard Compass appeared in 1840. In 1766 Knight took out the first patent for a compass ever granted in England.

During the eighteenth century the arrangements for the supply and repair of compasses for the Royal Navy had a chequered history. In 1728 the Navy Board decided, partly as an economy measure, to employ its own compass-maker in Deptford Dockyard rather than relying on contractors, but the experiment was not a success. The supply of serviceable compasses never kept pace with the demand and when, in 1758, the *Torbay* passed through the Channel Islands having shaped a course to make Portland Bill, it was clear that urgent action was necessary. Dr Knight was appointed Inspector of Compasses to the Royal Navy and thirty more of his compasses were ordered immediately. However, although they were popular with the larger ships, these compasses were still very unsteady in a seaway and the commanders of smaller vessels found them 'too ticklish'. Captain Cook, who took one of Knight's improved compasses with him on his first voyage (1768–71) had a very poor opinion of it. Knight was succeeded as Inspector of Compasses by

Mr Magellan but on the latter's death in 1790 the appointment appears to have lapsed.[26]

Deviation

Towards the end of the eighteenth century another factor, far more insidious than poor manufacture, began to make itself apparent in the behaviour of compasses at sea. This was the increasing use of iron in ship construction. No magnetic compass can work accurately unless it can freely sense the earth's magnetic field, undistorted by magnetism from other sources. The presence of iron produces such a distortion and causes an error in the indication of the compass which was initially referred to as the local attraction (of the iron) but which is now called deviation.

Because so much of the early work of the Compass Department was intimately concerned with the problems arising from the deviation of the compass on board a ship, a brief description of this phenomenum is given in appendix 1, in order that those not familiar with the subject may more readily understand the background to the story which follows. Whilst the deviation of the compass is a subject which has been exhaustively researched and which today raises few new problems, this has not always been so. The wide variety of sources in a ship which can cause deviation were introduced very gradually as iron became more widely used, and an understanding of the laws governing the way in which a magnetic compass can be disturbed came only after much groping and painful experience. In the late eighteenth century, when these effects first began to assume serious proportions, such an understanding lay many decades in the future.

The earliest report of the disturbing effects of iron on the compass comes from the pen of a Portuguese naval commander and explorer, Don Joao de Castro, who, in 1538, after finding that his observations for variation were inconsistent, recorded: 'This kept me very irresolute until I found the cause, that is a cannon which was close to the spot . . . The set of observations . . . which I found very contradictory . . . was troubled by the proximity of artillery pieces, anchors and other iron.'[27] Similar comments crop up at intervals during the next two and a half centuries but without apparently exciting much concern among mariners. It is probable that the effects were generally small. However, it was on Captain Cook's second voyage (1772–75) that the astronomer aboard the *Resolution*, William Wales, first became seriously worried about the behaviour of his compass. Wales was an astute and systematic observer who kept detailed records. In the introduction to his report on the astronomical observations of the voyage, he wrote: 'throughout the whole voyage I had great reasons to believe that variations observed with the ship's head in different positions, and even in different parts of her, will differ very materially from one another; and much more will variations observed on board different ships.'[28]

William Wales also accompanied Cook on his third voyage (1776–80) and seems, from a careful analysis of his records, to have gained a fair understanding of the systematic way in which the errors of the compass varied. Somewhat surprisingly he failed to establish the connection with the iron in the ship and seems to have concluded that the errors observed lay in the instruments themselves. Thirty years later Matthew Flinders, in his epic work, *Voyage to Terra Australis* stated: 'It seems indeed extraordinary that with the attention paid by Mr Wales to the subject, he should not have discovered or suspected that the iron of the ship was the primary cause of the differences so frequently observed.'[29]

But the significance was missed and we are told that Captain Cook, normally 'the most Scientific of Naval Officers', used to keep his iron keys next to the compass, while Captain Bligh, who as a lieutenant had been the navigator on Cook's third voyage, used later to store his pistols in the *Bounty*'s binnacle. It appears that even experienced seamen regarded unexplained errors in the compass simply as acts of God which, like storm and tempest, they accepted as a hazard of their calling.

In 1794 Murdo Downie the Master of HMS *Glory* was invited by the Admiralty to test a device invented by Ralph Walker of Jamaica, the latest and probably the best of a long line of instruments designed to determine variation and hence, it was hoped, longitude. The compass itself was excellent but Walter's hopes of a reward for solving the 'longitude problem' were quickly dashed when Downie showed that the instrument gave different readings in different parts of the ship. He wrote to the Admiralty as follows:

I am pretty well convinced that the quantity and vicinity of iron in most ships has an effect in attracting the needle; for it is found by experience that the needle will not always point in the same direction when placed in different parts of the ship; also it is rarely found that two ships steering the same course by their respective compasses will go exactly parallel to each other; yet these compasses, when compared on board the same ship, will agree exactly.[30]

Downie's report was probably the first official information the Admiralty received on this important subject, but the warning went unheeded. Despite mounting losses through wrecks and scattered convoys, many of which could only be attributed to compass errors, Their Lordships failed to recognize the danger. Experienced masters and pilots of the period used sometimes to make an allowance when shaping their courses on regular passages, although they were generally unaware of why it should be necessary to do so and could not have explained why it might be required when sailing in one direction but not in another. This allowance was often referred to as 'in draft' and we are told that in HMS *Victory* it sometimes amounted to one and half points (17°). Of the many factors which contributed to inaccurate and often disastrous navigation, the error of the compass was fast becoming the most potent, but it was still the least understood.

Captain Matthew Flinders

The first man to attempt to give a logical explanation of the phenomenon was Matthew Flinders (1774–1814) who, while surveying off Tasmania in HMS *Reliance* in 1798 became aware not only that his compass bearings were frequently in error but that they changed with each alteration of course. He soon realized that it was the iron in the ship which was affecting the compass and during his next voyage to Australia in 1801 in command of HMS *Investigator* he set about determining its laws. Appreciating that his compasses gave different readings in different parts of the vessel, he made it a rule only to observe with the compass in the binnacle.

When in northern latitudes Flinders noted that the errors in his observations for variation were greatest when on easterly or westerly courses and more nearly agreed with the correct values as the ship swung to north or south. Much later, from a careful inspection of his results, he wrote: 'the excess or diminution of the variation was generally in proportion as the ship's head inclined on either side from the magnetic meridian.'[31] Flinders also noted that the errors decreased as the ship approached the equator and later, off the Cape of Good Hope, that they had reappeared but with the opposite sense. In his subsequent analysis of his results he wrote:

> After much examination and comparison of the observations and some thinking on the subject, I found that the errors had a close connection with the dip of the needle. When the north end of the needle had dipped it was the north point of the compass which had been attracted by the iron in the ship; and as the dip diminished, so had the attraction until, at the magnetic equator where the dipping needle stands horizontal, there seemed to be no attraction. After passing some distance into the southern hemisphere, and the south end of the needle dipped, our observations again showed errors in the compass . . . (but in the opposite direction) . . . These errors increased as the dip augmented, and in Bass's Strait, where the south dip is nearly as great as the north dip in the English Channel, the attraction produced almost as much error as when I left England, but it was of an opposite nature.[32]

The rules of compass behaviour were beginning to form in Flinders' mind, and during the two years he spent surveying the coasts of Australia from Cape Leeuwin to the Torres Strait and the Gulf of Carpentaria he was continuously at pains to improve the accuracy of his charts by eliminating compass errors. Yet despite his magnificent accomplishments his expedition was dogged by ill fortune. His astronomer, Crossley, had had to leave the ship at the Cape due to ill health while his navigator, Thistle, was lost early in the survey in a boating accident. Finally the *Investigator* herself became unfit for further service and the survey had to be abandoned. In December 1803, while returning to England in the elderly schooner *Cumberland*, Flinders himself was interned in Ile-de-France (Mauritius) where he had called for repairs, unaware that England and France were again at war.

Although he remained a prisoner for more than six years he was well treated and was allowed to keep his charts and papers. Never a man to be idle, he settled down to develop his theory of compass errors, using it to correct and redraw much of his survey and considerably improving its accuracy. When, in November 1804, an opportunity arose to send letters to England, he addressed a paper to Sir Joseph Banks (1743–1820), the President of the Royal Society, entitled 'Concerning the differences in the magnetic needle on board the *Investigator*' in which he set down the progress he had made and for the first time attempted to explain the nature of ship magnetism. Although Flinders had had no scientific training this remarkable paper aroused considerable interest when it was read to the Royal Society on 28 March 1805.[33] At the Admiralty, alas, it produced no impact whatsoever.

Flinders was released from captivity in January 1810 and reached England in October where shortly afterwards he was promoted to captain with seniority 7 May 1810.[34] In April 1812, realizing that no action had been taken to follow up his investigations, he wrote again to Their Lordships giving a brief account of his discoveries and stressing that until compass errors could be accurately ascertained, observations of variation taken at sea would be of little value. It was, he said, a matter of the utmost importance for the perfection of hydrography, navigation and natural philosophy.

In this letter Flinders[35] suggested that experiments to confirm his findings should be made in one ship of each class in order that 'the errors in the compass arising from changing its place, and also from altering the ship's head or course, might be clearly ascertained, and a place might be found in every ship where the direction of the needle was not liable to any error'. These proposals were strongly supported by the Hydrographer, Captain Hurd, and six ships were made available for the trials. The *Starling*, a 12-gun brig, the *Helder*, a 40-gun frigate, and the *Reasonable*, a 64-gun ship, were at Sheerness; the *Loire*, a 48-gun frigate, and the *Devastation*, a bomb, were at Portsmouth; and the *Orestes*, a 16-gun brig, was at Plymouth. Flinders attended the trials in all except the last. In his full and detailed report[36] he begins by giving an account of his compass experiences in *Investigator*, explaining how he came to formulate definite rules for its behaviour. He then lists the results of his latest experiments and after drawing ten deductions concerning the magnetic character of a ship and its effect on the compass he again states his conclusions that the strength of the magnetism of a ship depends on her geographical position and is proportional to the angle of dip of the earth's magnetic field.[37]

Generally his results confirmed his earlier ideas but in one important respect they were at variance. His report to the Royal Society in 1804 had stated: 'I suppose the attractive power of different bodies . . . to be collected into something like a focal point . . . and that this point is nearly in the centre of the ship, where the shot are deposited.'[38] He now realized that every item of iron exerts its own influence and that the effect produced upon the compass is the combined result of all the attractions in the ship.

The next section of his report is particularly significant for it explains how the errors of the compass can be ascertained, how they might be obviated by discovering the neutral point in the ship where the compass would have no error and finally how it might be possible, by means of a 'counter attractor', to correct the errors of the compass caused by the attraction of the iron in its vicinity. Whilst Flinders made it clear that he had not actually tried the counter-attractor ('Upon this subject I speak with the utmost diffidence'), he nevertheless gave clear instructions for placing it, viz: 'Take a strong bar of old iron, of such a length as that when one end is let into the deck, the other will be nearly upon a level with the compass card.' He also explained how it should be adjusted to produce the right amount of correction. Although he was exactly describing what we now call the Flinders Bar,[39] this form of correction was not in fact introduced for another fifty years.

Flinders turned next to the compasses themselves and here he subjected the Admiralty to a most seering attack. He told them; 'the fact is, so far as my experience has gone, that amongst the nautical instruments taken to sea, there are not any so ill constructed, nor of which so little care is afterwards taken, as of compasses.' After developing this theme, he went on: 'Such is the general state of the instruments upon which the safety of every one of His Majesty's Ships, more or less often, depends . . . can it be a subject of surprise that the most experienced navigators are those who put the least confidence in the compass?'

The dockyards too were severely censured for their careless treatment of the compasses in store, and he was equally scathing about the situation afloat where, at this time, compasses were still under the charge of the Boatswain. With a rare touch of sarcasm he wrote:

The Boatswain of the ship, who has nothing to do with the accuracy of the course, receives the compasses into his charge; and puts them away, with other things, into his store or sail room; or if he is a careful man and has the means, he places them upon a shelf or in a locker in his cabin; perhaps with his knives and forks and a few particular marline spikes.

And turning to the compass manufacturers he said: 'Compass making is now at that pitch that neither reputation nor an adequate profit being (able) to be obtained from it, the best instrument makers generally refuse to have anything to do with them.'

To remedy such a deplorable state of affairs Flinders proposed the appointment of an Inspector of Compasses who would examine all compasses purchased and would prepare a specification for a standard design. This man would also 'take such steps with respect to obviating the errors of the compass and finding *neutral stations* as Their Lordships may think proper to direct'. He went on to suggest safeguards to ensure the proper care of compasses both in dockyards and on board ships where, he proposed, they should be placed in the charge of the Master.[40]

This was a truly magnificent report, and its recommendations anticipated by a quarter of a century the findings of the Admiralty Compass Committee that was to be set up in 1837 to remedy a situation that had scarcely changed in the interval.

On the advice of the Hydrographer, Flinders' report was sent to Sir Joseph Banks, who had taken an early interest in his work and who passed it to a Major Rennell, an acknowledged expert in magnetic matters. Rennell had been Surveyor-General with the East India Company and had earlier served for a few years in the Royal Navy, but he was now aged 70 and his remarks did little to help the report on its way. While grudgingly agreeing with Flinders' conclusions about the ironwork of a ship he remarked that he had never noticed any deviation of the compass when he was at sea! It was a reaction that was typical of many. Nevertheless, Banks urged upon the Admiralty the importance 'of furnishing some few intelligent Captains or Masters of the King's ships with copies of Captain Flinders' report, with orders to transmit their observations on it to the Board'.

Flinders had clearly expected that the whole report would be printed and circulated so that his discoveries and theories could be given wide publicity for the benefit of seamen and so that the opinions of more learned men could be obtained. Instead he was invited by the Admiralty to prepare an abbreviated statement which was sent to the Fleet on a single sheet of paper dated 26 August 1912, calling for observations.[41] Some months later three further pages, giving the 'general deductions' of the report were sent out by way of explanation. Of the 613 vessels then in commission, only 2 appear to have bothered to reply!

Matthew Flinders died on 19 July 1814, at the early age of 40, having been in poor health for some time and his superb report has never been published.

1814–37

Had all Flinders' pioneering work been in vain? It was fortunate that his abbreviated statement had been taken up by the *Naval Chronicle*[42] and printed in full whilst an appendix to his book *A Voyage to Terra Australis*, which was published just after his death, contained a resume of all his compass experience in the *Investigator* together with an account of the trials of 1812. Soon other essays began to appear and over the next few years interest in the subject grew rapidly. In 1818 William Scoresby (1789–1857), then the captain of a whaler, not only observed the huge deviations experienced by ships in Arctic regions from the magnetic induction in vertical soft iron but also commented on the diminution of the earth's directive force on the compass needle.[43] He thus very nearly obtained the true law which Flinders had missed. Similar observations were also obtained by Edward Sabine[44] who had accompanied Commander John Ross on his search for the North-West Passage in 1818 and had made a second expedition the following year under Lieutenant Edward Parry. However, it was Dr Thomas Young, the secretary to the Board of Longitude who, in 1819, finally showed that the deviation due to induction in vertical soft iron is proportional not to the dip but to the tangent of the dip (see p. xliii). In the same paper[45] Young was the first to explain a further component of the deviation, that caused by induction in soft iron acting on a level with the compass. This is now called quadrantal deviation, and Young showed that its effect would not change with latitude.

In 1819 Professor Peter Barlow of the Royal Military Academy endeavoured to represent the magnetic effect of a ship by a mass of soft iron near the compass. Initially he used a ball, but this was later changed to a disc, known as Barlow's plate, which he placed so that it doubled the error of the compass. Thus by observing the bearing of an object both with the plate in position and without it, the correct reading could be calculated. It is reported that Barlow was later asked about the effect of fitting steel masts in a ship and, having determined that they would probably reduce the deviation, he realized that by positioning his plate on the opposite side of the binnacle it would be possible to use it to correct the compass instead of doubling its error. In 1824, he sent a report to the Admiralty giving the results of experiments conducted in HM Ships *Levan*, *Griper* and *Conway* over a wide range of latitudes from 80°N to 61°S.[46]

As none of these men was likely to be aware of the full content of Captain Flinders' great report of 1812, Barlow probably never knew that with his plate he was achieving much the same result as the bar suggested by Flinders, but with considerably less efficiency. Although Barlow's plates continued to be fitted until the middle of the century they never wholly lived up to their inventor's claims.

Despite the growing awareness in certain quarters of the problems of deviation, very little official action appears to have been taken by the Navy Board to improve the situation or to alert the Fleet to an ever growing danger. Compass errors caused by the increasing use of iron were becoming appreciable yet the great mass of seamen remained blissfully ignorant of the threat to their safety, let alone its cause, and were largely unaware of the imperfections of the compasses themselves. Two examples from the many recorded must serve to illustrate this sorry state of affairs.

First, in 1820 Professor Barlow was requested by the Lords Commissioners of the Admiralty to examine the state of the compasses in store in the Royal Dockyard at Woolwich. His report tells how, having constructed a simple testing apparatus, he began to determine their errors. But he records:

> I soon found that it would be useless to examine the cards indiscriminately: for out of the whole number (not less, I conceive, than 150) more than half of them would be considered *mere lumber*, and which ought to be destroyed on the same principle as we clip base coin, being wholly useless while in store and *extremely dangerous* if suffered to pass out of it. I determined, therefore, to select thirty only, which appeared to be the most perfect in their construction.[47]

Barlow examined these 30 – 'the most perfect in their construction' – yet still found only 8 out of the original 150 that were accurate to better than 1°. It is small wonder that he described them as 'generally speaking wretchedly defective . . . would have disgraced the arts as they stood at the beginning of the 18th century'. His excellent report analyses the sources of error, almost all of which could be attributed to poor design, indifferent workmanship or the careless and indiscriminate way in which the compasses were kept in store.

Two years later, when again called in by the Admiralty, he found the situation virtually unchanged and reported: 'It is constantly to be regretted that while all the other appointments in the British Navy are so excellent, the compass, (an instrument of unquestionable importance and the least expensive in a ship) should be so very inferior as it is at present.'[48] Yet it was to be another twenty years before the Inspector of Compasses, first proposed by Captain Flinders, was to appear to remedy this shameful situation.

The second example concerns the 'melancholy wreck' of HMS *Thetis* of which the following account was given in the *United Service Journal*.[49]

> The Thetis sailed from Rio Janeiro on 4th December (1830) with a million dollars on board, besides other treasure, and every prospect of a fine passage, stretching away to the South East. The next day, the wind coming rather favourable, they tacked, thinking themselves clear of land; and so confident were they that the top mast studding sails were ordered to be set, the ship running at a rate of nine knots; and the first intimation they had of being near land was the jib-boom striking against a high perpendicular cliff, when the bowsprit broke short off, the shock sending all three masts over the side.

In his letter of proceedings the commander of the *Thetis* stated that 'from the precautionary measures taken, nothing but the strongest currents . . . can be pleaded in extenuation'. Alas, among 'the precautionary measures taken' no mention is made of observing and allowing for the error of the compass caused by the local attraction and, as a result, a fine vessel, twenty-five valuable lives and a cargo worth nearly a quarter of a million sterling were lost.

Trials in the Garryowen

In 1835 a series of trials was conducted in the iron paddle-steamer *Garryowen* which was to have a profound influence on the future of the magnetic compass at sea. In that year the directors of the firm of Laird of Liverpool, the principal builders of iron ships in the country, became alarmed lest increasing compass errors should adversely affect their business, and suggested to the Admiralty that some experiments should be made. A few years earlier Lieutenant Edward J. Johnson, an officer with surveying experience, had on his own initiative carried out some experiments with magnetic needles, the results of which he had communicated to Their Lordships.[50] He was promoted to Commander in 1829, and for a year and a half commanded the ten-gun sloop *Britomart*, principally on the Lisbon station, during which time he received the approbation of Their Lordships for his exemplary conduct. In the summer of 1835 he was continuing his magnetic experiments whilst on half-pay and was thus an obvious choice for this new task.

Although Johnson's experimental work had been partly concerned with reducing the disturbance of the compass needle, he had had no experience of experiments in ships and there was little previous work to guide him. He was probably unaware of Flinders' report of 1812 and although naval captains had, since that time, occasionally swung their ships to observe deviations, it is doubtful if Johnson himself had ever done so. However, after consulting two of the leading experts, Professors Barlow and Christie of the Royal Military Academy, and equipping himself with two Gilbert's Azimuth compasses, a number of common binnacle compasses, a theodolite and the necessary instruments for measuring dip and magnetic intensity, he set off for Ireland.

The *Garryowen*, which had been loaned for the trials by the City of Dublin Steam Packet Company, was built by Laird's. She was an iron paddle-steamer of 210 tons, 130 feet long, schooner-rigged and carrying the immense funnel of the period, 28 feet in height. Her two paddle-wheels, 15 feet 6 inches in diameter, were driven by separate 85 hp engines. As she was lying at Limmerick on the River Shannon, with no convenient wet dock, Johnson had her moved to Tarbert Bay where she was tautly moored, using anchors other than her own so that all iron on board should be in its correct seagoing position. Preparations were then made to enable the ship to be warped round to all points of the compass and a temporary poop was erected on the stern similar to that normally found in HM ships, on which compasses could be mounted for trial.

Having determined the magnetic bearing of a distant mountain peak from a station ashore, the theodolite was placed in that position and the two azimuth compasses were set up on the quarter-deck and the forecastle. In order to determine the positions of greatest and least deviation and the general magnetic state of the vessel no less than thirteen other stations were established at which compass errors could be obtained by comparison with the azimuth compasses. These ranged horizontally from the tip of the bowsprit to a stage rigged over the stern, and vertically from stations between decks to positions on the foretopmast and below the mizen gaff. Although compasses were also mounted amidships, between the paddle-boxes, the proximity of moving machinery and of the great funnel made these positions unstable. It is an interesting reflection on the state of knowledge at the time that amongst the compasses used was one mounted on glass pillars. While Johnson's report does not say whether, in this way, he hoped to achieve insulation from the effects of local attraction, his references to insulation on other occasions makes this probable. Their Lordships' instructions had included the requirement to conduct trials with Barlow's correcting plate, but these were not pursued, partly due to the adverse weather but mainly because in the position chosen for the azimuth compasses the deviations were too great for the plate to correct.

Trials commenced on 21 October and continued until 18 November 'after frequent interruptions, sometimes for several days together, by rain and gales of wind'. Many of the trials were repeated both with the ship cold and with steam up. The very remarkable deflections observed at the compass positions over the stern led Johnson to conduct a series of experiments in which he caused first the bow and then the stern of *Garryowen* to be warped towards instruments set up on the quay, arrangements being made to measure accurately the distance offshore. It was immediately apparent that the ship was producing a marked disturbance in the compasses on the quay and that the effects produced by the bow and stern were in *opposite directions*. Johnson concluded 'that the deflections alluded to were caused by the magnetic influence of the iron in the vessel; . . . the effects on the different needles being precisely similar to those which would have occurred *had a magnet been placed in the position of the vessel*' (emphasis added).[51]

This was a most significant conclusion. Hitherto it had been generally assumed that the local attraction was due primarily to induced magnetism, what today we call the soft-iron effects. Johnson's experiments suggested for the first time that permanent magnetism (i.e. the hard-iron property) was also involved. He went on to explain:

> As in the construction of iron vessels, hammering the numerous rivets might elicit magnetic influences, it would be well to note, by compass, the direction of their heads and sterns when building, with a view of ascertaining whether . . . any distinct magnetic properties indicated by those parts are due to the line of direction of the vessel with respect to the magnetic meridian.

In other words, he was suggesting that the ship's magnetic state was largely determined *by the direction in which she lay on the building slip*, a conclusion that was not fully explored until a quarter of a century later.

A full report was submitted to Their Lordships on 16 January 1836. In his conclusions Johnson pointed out that the normal place for a steering compass on board a wooden ship was no longer suitable in an iron ship and that in *Garryowen* the compass was so much in error as not to be depended upon. He recommended that as far as practicable a site should be selected above the general mass of iron on board and he listed the considerations which determined a good compass position, all of which hold good today. Finally he suggested a number of additional experiments which he thought might have a bearing on the way the magnetic condition of a ship could affect the behaviour of the compass, including 'whether the causes that affect the direction of the magnetic needle on board an iron vessel are constant or variable', whether 'the directive power will be sufficient for all the purposes required', what would be the effect of remaining for some time on the same heading and whether the compass would be affected by the heat of the furnace.

Looked at with hindsight, these suggestions show clearly that Johnson was developing a sound grasp of the problems involved. His report even contained a tentative suggestion about the possibility of *correcting* the compass, when he said;

The elevation above the deck should be such as to remove the needle from the separate action of particular portions of iron work so that . . . the *joint effects* of all the iron in the vessel (may) be resolvable into one force, the power of which might be discovered and perhaps controlled. If that of simple iron, by Professor Barlow's correcting place, and if that of the pole of a magnet, it might be useful to *ascertain how far another magnet in a given position was capable of correcting for the deflections* (emphasis added).

Already he appreciated the necessity of correcting 'like with like', still a vital axiom in all compass correction.

Johnson's experiments represented the most significant breakthrough of all the practical investigations hitherto undertaken in the long and chequered history of the Magnetic Compass at sea. His report led directly to the next two major advances, the far-reaching series of experiments carried out in 1838 by Professor George Biddell Airy, from which he developed his system of compass correction, largely along the lines tentatively suggested by Johnson, and the setting-up of the Admiralty Compass Committee in 1837, which finally led to the establishment of the Compass Department with Johnson himself as the first Superintendent. Johnson's full report was read to the Royal Society on 19 March 1836, by Captain Francis Beaufort FRS, Hydrographer to the Admiralty, and two months later Johnson was elected a Fellow. He was thus firmly established as a leading authority on compasses and the magnetism of ships, subjects he was to pursue, for the benefit of seamen, for the remainder of his life.

Airy's system of compass correction

The investigations by Flinders, Barlow and others had shown that a compass is influenced by magnetism *induced* in the iron of a ship, while Johnson's experiments in *Garryowen* had established that an iron ship would also act in the manner of a permanent magnet. Although Johnson had recommended a number of further trials which he thought advisable, he had made no attempt to establish the laws governing the magnetic disturbances observed.

In 1837 Professor Airy, the Astronomer Royal, had begun regular magnetic observations at Greenwich. When, therefore, in January

1838 the Admiralty was offered the use of another steamer 'at £50 a week', they decided to ask Airy for his opinion. After studying Johnson's report Airy concluded that the additional experiments proposed were unnecessary but instead recommended 'a train of observations expressly directed to theoretical points'.[52] When, in July, the iron ship *Rainbow* was placed at the Admiralty's disposal by the General Steam Navigation Company, it was Airy who was invited to conduct the experiments. The ship was moored in the basin at Deptford and observations were made during July and August under most favourable conditions. Airy's aim, as he stated in his report to the Royal Society, was 'ascertaining the laws of the deviation and the neutralization, if possible, of the deviating forces.[53] As behove a senior wrangler, he believed that any problem could be solved if it could be reduced to one of mathematics.

The eminent French mathematician Poisson had treated the subject of magnetism in depth in a series of papers to the French Academy of Science between 1824 and 1838, but his work on the deviation of the compass in a ship had been based almost exclusively on his theory of transiently induced magnetism. Although recognizing the possible existence of a certain degree of permanent magnetism in a ship, he did not include this in his calculations, believing that its effect would be small and wishing to avoid unnecessary complications in the solution. Poisson's decision was justified when considering the wooden ships of the 1820s but could not of course be admissable when dealing with an iron ship. Airy had to consider not only the induced magnetism but also what now proved to be the more dominant influence, the permanent magnetism. In his paper to the Royal Society he starts his discussion of induced magnetism by explaining that the difficulties in the application of Poisson's theory to complicated cases are great and that he prefers to use a simpler theory which 'will give the same comparative results though not the same absolute results as Poisson's'. Again when dealing with permanent magnetism Airy says: 'It is supposed in the following investigations that the existence of permanent magnetism produces no modification in the induced magnetism, their effects being simply combined by algebraic adding.' Although neither assumption was fully justified, this simplified treatment enabled Airy to develop an entirely new and practical approach to the correction of compasses in ships. His supporting mathematical discussion is fully set out in his report to the Royal Society which he read on 25 April 1839,[54] and need not be further considerred here.

Airy chose four separate positions in the *Rainbow* in which a compass might be placed and then determined, by a comprehensive series of measurements and observations, the way in which the magnetic forces in the ship acted at each. When analysed his results enabled him to establish certain constants for each position which indicated the way that a compass in that position would be affected. It was then comparatively straightforward for him to calculate how the correctors should be placed in order to produce the required compensation. Airy used a single 2-foot bar-magnet and a scroll of iron plate 'tolerably free from permanent magnetism' for the main compass, with a 14-inch bar magnet for each of the others. When writing about these trials in his autobiography he said: 'On August 20th I carried my magnets and iron correctors to Deptford, mounted them in the proper places, tried the ship and the compass, which had been disturbed 50 degress to the Right and 50 degrees to the Left, was now sensibly correct.'[55]

In October 1838 Airy was invited to carry out further trials in the 300-ton iron sailing vessel *Ironsides*, building at Liverpool. His reaction was interesting. He was a very busy man and had not wished to become further involved in compass correction. As a scientist he no doubt considered that he had solved the problem and it was now up to others to apply his solution. He wrote to the owner, Mr Cairns, as follows:

> The increasing trouble in a matter in which I have no interest compels me to make the following offer. I will undertake to attend to the necessary correction myself if you will agree to pay me a net fee of £100, with expenses of every kind. This shall be considered payable . . . either when I am satisfied or when it is proved to you that the error does not exceed three degrees. (This, I may mention, would not satisfy me). If I fail, my expenses only to be paid.[56]

The correction was achieved and the fee duly paid, but it was subsequently returned when Airy was reimbursed by the Admiralty, the trials being regarded as a continuation of those carried out in the *Rainbow*. The results of both sets of trials were published in the *Philosophical Transactions of the Royal Society* for 1839. Airy's

'Concluding remarks' in this paper summarize the situation as he saw it so clearly that they merit inclusion just as he wrote them:

1. It appears from the investigations above, that the deviations of the compass at four stations in the Rainbow, and at two stations in the Ironsides, are undoutedly caused by two modifications of magnetic power; namely, the independent magnetism of the ship, which retains the same magnitude and the same direction relatively to the ship in all positions of the ship; and the induced magnetism, whose force varies in magnitude and direction while the ship's position is changed. It appears also that, in the instances mentioned, the effect of the former force greatly exceeds that of the latter.

2. It appears also that experiments and investigations similar to those applied above, are sufficient to obtain with accuracy the constants on which at any one place the ship's action upon the horizontal needle depends (namely,

$$\frac{H}{I\cos\delta} + \tan\delta, \quad N, \quad \frac{S}{I\cos\delta} \ M, \text{ and P});[57]$$

and that by placing a magnet so that its action will take place in a direction opposite to that which the investigations show to be the direction of the ship's independent magnetic action, and at such a distance that its effect is equal to that of the ship's independent magnetism, and by counteracting the effect of the induced magnetism by means of the induced magnetism of another mass (according to rules which are given), the compass may be made to point exactly as if it were free from disturbance.

3. It appears also that by an easy tentative method, the compass may now be corrected without the labour of any numerical investigations, or any experiments, except those of merely making the trials.

4. It appears also that the permanent vertical disturbing force, as far as the examination of the Rainbow authorizes us to draw any distinct conclusion, is not great, and therefore that there is no fear of great disturbance of the compass by the heeling of the ship.

5.   But it appears that one of the magnetic constants consists of two parts, which cannot be separated by experiments on the horizontal magnetism at any one place: and that the effect of the impracticability of separating these parts will be to render the compass incorrect in one magnetic latitude when it has been made correct in a different magnetic latitude (though there is good reason to think that the term on which the variation depends is so small that it may be neglected, except in the case of a ship sailing very near the magnetic pole). And it appears that though in theory the term in question could be determined from observations of the dipping-needle, yet in practice the method fails, because the observations cannot be made with the requisite accuracy. It appears, however, that this term may be determined by observations of the horizontal needle at two places whose magnetic latitudes are different, and that the correction may then be made perfect for all magnetic latitudes.

6.   To these considerations we may add the following: that though the uniformity of the induced magnetism, under similar circumstances, is to be presumed, yet the invariability of the independent magnetism during a course of many years is by no means certain.

Airy originally envisaged that every iron ship would have the four constants determined for each compass position at the beginning of its life and that these would be checked periodically, it being 'probable that the independent magnetism of the ship will change with time'. While experimenting in the *Ironsides* he hit upon the idea of using *two* permanent magnets, one fore-and-aft and one athwartship, instead of counteracting the whole of the ship's permanent magnetism with a single magnet set at an angle, as he had done in the *Rainbow*. This enabled him to suggest a greatly simplified procedure for correcting the compass (paragraph 3 above) which follows precisely that normally employed today (i.e. correcting the athwartship magnetism with the ship's head on north and the fore-and-aft magnetism with the ship's head on east). The permanent bar magnets used for correction were secured to the deck and, when the adjustment was completed, were counter-sunk into it and embedded in tallow or whitelead for protection, the whole being subsequently shut in by fillets of wood and caulked.[58] Initially Airy used 'scrolls' of iron for correcting the effects of induced magnetism (paragraph 2) but he later suggested boxes filled with iron chains, so that any retained permanent magnetism would be randomly distributed.

Although Airy's method of compass correction at first appeared to be entirely successful, in two respects its theory was seriously at fault. His conclusion 'That there is no fear of great disturbance of the compass by the heeling of the ship' (paragraph 4) is, he admits, based on experiments in the *Rainbow* where it is probable that the vertical magnetism was small. Elsewhere in his paper Airy does briefly discuss the use of a vertical magnet to correct the compass when the ship is heeled, and even the use of a 'graduated slider' to simplify adjusting it with change of latitude. However, he clearly did not consider that the errors experienced would be large enough to cause inconvenience and he does not mention this aspect when describing his simplified procedure for correcting the compass. In the *Ironsides*, however, after the compasses had been corrected her captain complained that 'in heavy weather they ran round and round'. Although he blamed this on the compasses themselves it is probable that a contributory cause was a large heeling error. It was to be another twenty years before this subject was fully investigated by the *Liverpool Compass Committee* of 1855–60,[59] and appropriate compensation provided.

The second flaw in Airy's method of correction was potentially far more serious. He had correctly concluded (paragraph 5) that it was only possible to separate the two parts of his first constant by making observations in two widely differing magnetic latitudes, but he believed that the error resulting from not doing so would be 'so small that it may be neglected except in the case of a ship sailing very near the magnetic pole'. As was pointed out by Archibald Smith,[60] this assumption was totally unjustified. It was certainly possible to correct a compass in England by using magnets alone to compensate both for the deviation due to the ship's permanent magnetism and that caused by induction in the vertical soft iron. While the ship remained in home waters the compensation would hold good. If, however, it were to sail to the southward, whilst the correction of permanent magnetism would still be valid, the deviating effect of the magnetism induced in the vertical soft iron would gradually reduce, becoming zero on the magnetic equator before increasing again with the opposite sign as the ship entered southern magnetic latitudes (see p. xxv). The compensating effect of the magnets used to correct this part of the deviation would thus become increasingly less accurate and, once the ship had crossed the magnetic equator, would actually *increase the deviation* to a far greater extent than Airy believed possible. This mistake of Airy's adversely affected the practice of compass adjustment for at least twenty years.

With hindsight such errors and shortcomings may seem obvious but at the time there was still much that was not fully understood; nor had Airy previously been involved in ship magnetism to any great degree. Despite its imperfections his system must surely be regarded as a magnificent achievement, a real breakthrough which laid the foundations of the method that was later to be introduced in a more practical way by Sir William Thomson in 1876 and is still, with modifications, in use today. It was unfortunately some years before Airy himself appreciated the importance of these flaws in what he regarded as his 'perfect' system, and this led him into much bitter controversy.[61] Although in 1855 he wrote 'I am now inclined to think that my estimate of the possible magnitude of this term was too low', confidence in the whole system of correction, even by those who fully understood it, had been badly shaken. Brilliant as were his achievements in so many fields, ship magnetism must be counted as one in which he never enjoyed the approbation he richly deserved.

Initially it was with the Merchant Navy that Airy's system of correction found greatest favour. Merchantmen were increasingly being built of iron, and captains, who generally understood very little of the problems involved, tended to accept the boon of an 'apparently accurate compass' without question. This undoubtedly led to many a shipwreck. In the Royal Navy the introduction of iron ships was more gradual and for some years large deviations were rare. Airy's system was probably only partially understood by those in authority and it is doubtful if its shortcomings were fully appreciated. Nevertheless it was justifiably mistrusted as engendering a false sense of confidence in the permanent accuracy of the compass. The official Admiralty policy was therefore directed principally to discovering that part of the ship in which the Standard Compass might most advantageously be placed without correction, believing that it was safer for the general purposes of navigation that the errors should be obtained by frequent observation in each ship and then allowed for when determining the ship's reckoning.

These two opposing points of view were to dominate all ideas and discussions on the management of compasses at sea during the first fifty years in the life of the Admiralty Compass Department. In the late 1830s, however, the controversy had not yet started. At sea ships were being navigated as best they could with compasses which were generally of poor quality and were seldom properly cared for. They had errors due to *local attraction* which varied in an apparently random fashion. Although much was understood by the savants, seamen in general were unaware of their predicament. It was small wonder that shipping losses in England alone averaged more than one a day.

NOTES

INTRODUCTION

1 Baylak ibn Muhammed al Qibaqi, *Kanz at-tugger fi ma'rifat al-ahgar*, dated AD 1240, Bibliothèque Nationale, Paris.

2 See the eleventh-century *Paei Wang* dictionary.

3 Alexander Neckham, *De Naturis Rerum*, c. 1187.

4 'Epistle of Pierre de Maricourt' (Petrus Peregrinus), 1269, Bodleian Library.

5 Ibid.; Roger Bacon, *Opus Minus*, late thirteenth century.

6 During the thirteenth century the word *compasso* was used in the Mediterranean to denote what we would now call sailing directions.

7 See Silvanus P. Thompson, *The Rose of the Winds. The Origin and Development of the Compass Card*, 1913.

8 Ibid.

9 Dr Breusing, *Flavio Gioja and the Mariner's Compass*, Bremen, 1871.

10 This was erected in 1903. A request for financial support for the project received little encouragement from the Admiralty. Hydrographer's Minute Book, No. 55, p. 105.

11 Claude F. M. Dechalles, *L'Art de naviger*, 1677; Joseph Harris, *Treatise of Navigation*, 1730.

12 W. E. May, *Ornamental Compass Cards*, 1950.

13 See Ken Tsung Schi, *Pang Thsai You I* (Medical Natural History), 1111–17.

14 Earlier charts of the mid-sixteenth and early seventeenth centuries are recorded by May, *A history of Marine Navigation*, 1971, p. 84, but these are believed to have been of limited scope.

15 Ibid.

16 Originally 'bittacle', with various spellings, possibly derived from the Latin *habitatus*, a dwelling. The name binnacle first appears early in the seventeenth century, although 'bittacle' is still occasionally found at the end of the nineteenth century.

17 Captain John Smith, *The Seaman's Grammar*, 1627, p. 15.

18 T. H. Croker, in *The Complete Dictionary of Arts and Sciences*, 1764.

19 A compass recovered from the *Mary Rose*, sunk in 1545, appears to have been supported in gimbals.

20 It was the custom for ships on long voyages to carry a lodestone for the purpose of remagnetizing their compass needles and this practice continued well into the eighteenth century.

21 May, *History of Marine Navigation*, p. 76.

22 *Philosophical Transactions of the Royal Society*, Vol. LXV, Table VII, p. 397.

23 Smeeton was already an experienced compass-maker. Later he achieved fame as the builder of the third lighthouse on the Eddystone Rocks off Plymouth.

24 The reason for the unsteadiness of Dr Knight's compass, although not at the time appreciated, lay in the fact that a single heavy needle will tend to turn into the plane of motion as the ship rolls. This can be overcome if the card is balanced so that its moments of inertia in the north-south and east-west directions are the same.

25 A. Schuck, *Alter Schiffskompasses und Kompassteile im besitz Hamburger Staatsanstatten*, 1910.

26 W. E. May, 'The compass makers of Deptford', *Nautical Magazine*, June 1950.

27 João de Castro, *Roteivo de Lisboa & Goa*, 1538.

28 James Cook, *A Voyage towards the South Pole and round the World*, 1777.

29 Captain Matthew Flinders, *Voyage to Terra Australis*, 1814.

30 Ralph Walker, *A Treatise on Navigation, with a description and explanation of a meridional and azimuth compass, for ascertaining the quantity of variation . . . with tables of variation for all latitudes and longitudes*, 1794. Walker was paid the sum of £200 by the Admiralty for his invention.

31 Flinders, op, cit.

32 Ibid.

33 *Phil. Trans. Royal Society*, 1805, Part 2.

34 Had he reached England in 1804, as planned, he would have been promoted then. The regulations would not, however, permit his seniority to be backdated beyond the date when the current First Lord had taken office!

35 ADM 1/1809, No. 80.

36 ADM 1/1809, No. 130A.

37 In this Flinders was mistaken. The deviation produced by vertical soft iron is proportional to the sine of the dip and inversely proportional to the horizontal component of the earth's field, which varies as the cosine of the dip. The deviation produced thus varies as *sine dip/cos dip = tan dip*, but the difference is not significant except

in high latitudes. This was first pointed out by Thomas Young in 'Computations for clearing the compass of the regular effect of a ship's attraction', *Journal of Arts and Sciences*, 1819.

38 *Phil. Trans. Royal Society*, 1805, Part 2.

39 This type of corrector was again suggested by the Liverpool Compass Committee in 1859 (see page 59) and was eventually introduced by Sir William Thomson in 1876. (See page 000).

40 An instruction was issued to the Fleet on 10 December 1813, placing the azimuth compasses under the care of the Master. Binnacle compasses, however, remained as boatswain's stores until 1843.

41 ADM 1/1809, No. 178.

42 *Naval Chronicle*, Vol. XXVIII (1812), pp. 321-23.

43 Scoresby's (later the Rev. W. Scoresby, DD, FRS) results will be found in *Phil. Trans. Royal Society*, 1819, p. 91; and also in his *Account of the Arctic Regions, with a History of the Northern Whale Fishery*, London, 1829.

44 Later General Sir Edward Sabine, RA, KCB, president of the Royal Society (1861–71). See *Phil. Trans. Royal Society*, 1819, p. 120.

45 'Computations for clearing the compass of the regular effect of a ships attraction', Journal of Arts and Sciences, 1819.

46 National Maritime Museum, Magnetic Compass Collection, Item R1 (5).

47 Report by Professor Barlow to the Lords Commissioners of the Admiralty, 31 January 1820, ADM 106/2531.

48 ADM 106/1465, B. Pro. 44.

49 *Phil. Trans. Royal Society*, 1831.

50 ADM 1/2967, No. J29. Johnson first reported to the Admiralty on 21 April 1826 on the magnetic experiments carried out at his home at Bywell in Northumberland and at St Petersburg. He later returned to these investigations and forwarded a further report on 23 May 1835 from his London address at 13 Cambridge Terrace. This report has unfortunately been lost, although recorded in the Public Record Office.

51 *Phil. Trans. Royal Society*, 1836, Part 2.

52 Wilfred Airy (ed.), *Autobiography of Sir George Biddle Airy*, Cambridge U. P. 1896.

53 *Phil. Trans. Royal Society*, 1839, Part 1.

54 Ibid. In 1848 Archibald Smith, also a senior wrangler, whose extensive contributions to the theory of the deviations of the compass are discussed in chapter 2, presented a paper to the Royal Society in which, in his words, he 'modified Poisson's Formulae so as to adapt them to the form in which the data generally present themselves, viz; a vessel having hard as well as soft iron – both unsymmetrically distributed'. See ibid., 1848, p. 347; and W. Scoresby, 'Introduction', *Journal of a Voyage to Australia and Round the World, for Magnetical Research*, Longmans, 1859.

55 *Autobiography of Sir George Biddell Airy*.

[56] Archives of the Royal Greenwich Observatory, Vol. 1258.

[57] The symbols used are fully explained in Airy's paper (*Phil. Trans. Royal Society*, 1839, Part 1). A brief description of each is given below with, in brackets, the symbol normally used today, when applied to a well-placed compass.
H is the effect of permanent magnetism on the compass, directed towards the ship's head. (P)
S is the effect of permanent magnetism on the compass, directed towards the starboard side. (Q)
M, N and P are constants, referring to induced magnetism and depending solely on the construction of the ship.
M is the coefficient on which the absolute diminution of directive force depends. (a)
N is the coefficient on which depends the force similar to permanent magnetism. (c)
P is the coefficient on which depends the transversal force, changing signs in each successive quadrant. (e)
I is the intensity of terrestrial magnetism. (T)
δ is the angle of dip.

[58] Examples of this method could be found at sea half a century later.

[59] *Third Report from the Liverpool Compass Committee to the Board of Trade*, HMSO, 1861.

[60] *Phil. Trans. Royal Society*, 1848.

[61] Charles H. Cotter, 'The Airy – Scoresby controversy', *Annals of Science*, Vol. 34 (1977).

How it all began:
The Admiralty Compass Committee and the Compass Department under Captain E.J. Johnson F.R.S., 1837-53

'Many instances of HM Ships having been endangered and their service delayed through the badness of their Steering Compasses have become so notorious that it is a matter of surprise that more serious mischief has not been the result. The necessity of providing a better description of instrument is therefore obvious and the additional expense can be but trifling . . . perhaps Their Lordships would appoint a Committee of Officers who are qualified to give an impartial judgement on this subject and who, without any expense to the country, would examine the compasses now supplied to HM Ships.' (From a minute to Their Lords Commissioners of the Admiralty, from Captain Francis Beaufort, the Hydrographer, 15 July 1837)

The year 1837 saw a new queen on the throne of England and, in the Navy, the start of a new era in navigation which was to have a profound effect on the safety of Her Majesty's ships upon the high seas. Anxiety about the poor state of the Navy's compasses had been growing for many years, and the mounting toll of losses at sea told its own story. When, in 1820, Professor Peter Barlow of the Royal Military Academy was invited to examine the compasses in store at Woolwich, he had described the majority of them as 'mere lumber'. Yet sailors at the time paid scant attention to the care of these vital instruments. Barlow's report contains the telling sentence: 'I am aware that many Nautical Men set very little value on the compass, but this I consider to arise from the constant defects it is found to exhibit.'.[1]

Some years earlier Captain Matthew Flinders had been equally critical. In his report to the Admiralty in 1812 he had stated 'amongst the nautical instruments taken to sea, there are not any so ill-constructed, nor of which so little care is afterwards taken, as of compasses'.[2]

To find the reason why no positive steps had been taken to remedy this sorry state of affairs we need look no further than the organization of the Admiralty during the period. The Navy Board, which had been responsible for building, supplying and manning the ships of the Navy, was abolished as a separate authority in 1822 and placed directly under the Admiralty, which by tradition had responsibility for strategy and the commissioning and operating of the Fleet. However, the original Navy Board staffs remained at Somerset House and although, under a reorganization in 1832, the superintendents of the five major departments each became answerable direct to one of the Lords Commissioners of the Admiralty, communication between Somerset House and the Admiralty was minimal.[3] The only 'technical' department was that of Surveyor of the Navy. Most stores, and this included compasses, were purchased by the Storekeeper-General and it is probable that he was more often influenced by the price than the performance. In many instances no one appears to have had responsibility for checking the quality of the goods supplied.

On 15 July 1837 Captain Beaufort, the Hydrographer, drew Their Lordships' attention to the growing danger to the safety and efficiency of Her Majesty's ships through the inferiority of their compasses. Perhaps it was the inclusion of the phrase 'without any expense to the country' which caught their attention on this occasion for they reacted with commendable promptness. On 18 July the following letter was sent to each of the gentlemen recommended by Beaufort as 'qualified to give an impartial judgement':

The Lords Commissioners of the Admiralty having had under their consideration the defective state of the Magnetic Compasses usually supplied to Her Majesty's Ships, and deaming it necessary to apply some remedy to an evil so pregnant with mischief, have determined to have the subject investigated by a Committee of Officers conversant with Magnetic Instruments; and understanding that you are willing to contribute your assistance to this object, Their Lordships have commanded me to acquaint you that they have fixed upon Monday the 24th instant for this committee to meet in the Admiralty Library at Noon, and to request you to be a member thereof.[4]

The Storekeeper-General was instructed to provide the Committee with two specimens of each type of compass in store. This letter was signed by John Barrow, who was the Second Secretary to the Admiralty from 1804 to 1845.[5]

The Admiralty Compass Committee

The six members of the committee were: Captain (later Rear-Admiral Sir) Francis Beaufort (1774–1857), who had been Hydrographer since 1829, and was responsible for all navigational matters; Captain (later Rear-Admiral Sir) James Clark Ross[6] (1800–62), who was already famous as an Arctic explorer and as the discoverer of the north magnetic pole; Major (later General Sir) Edward Sabine (1788–1883), who had acted as scientific officer and astronomer on two Arctic expeditions, under Commander John Ross (1818) and Lieutenant Edward Parry (1819–20). He had specialized in terrestrial magnetism and was later to become President of the Royal Society (1861–71); Samuel Hunter Christie (1784–1865), professor of mathematics at the Royal Military Academy, Woolwich, and a leading investigator into magnetic phenomena; Captain Thomas Best Jarvis, an experienced surveyor, late of the Bombay Engineers. He returned to India in 1838, having been provisionally appointed Surveyor-General in India (a post he never achieved) and thereafter took no further part in the committee's affairs; and Commander Edward John Johnson (1794–1853), who had conducted extensive experiments for the Admiralty in the iron paddle-steamer *Garryowen* in 1835. All except Jarvis were already Fellows of the Royal Society, and so this was a powerful body. Initially the task of guiding its work as chairman was undertaken by Captain Ross but, on his departure for the Antarctic in 1839 with HM Ships *Erebus* and *Terror*, the job fell to the redoubtable Beaufort.

The committee's work extended over three years. They examined specimens of the available compasses of the day[7] and subjected them to tests from which it was quickly apparent that no material improvement had taken place since Professor Barlow's devastating report of 1820.[8] The magnetism of the needles was generally too feeble to give a proper directive force to the compass, the construction of which often revealed crude workmanship and unsound principles. Compasses were also obtained from the French and Danish navies and were subjected to similar scrutiny.

The committee then conducted experiments to determine the best form and material to use for compass needles, cards, bowls, pivots, caps, gimbals and so on, dividing the work between them. Professor Christie, who had some years earlier carried out a wide-ranging series of experiments with magnetic needles, undertook to study this vital aspect. His conclusions showed that clockspring was the best material and that the most satisfactory results were obtained by laying two strips together with a segment of mica between their ends. Initially the strips were bent apart at the centre to make a space for the cap. Later, when it was decided to go in for multiple needles, this became unnecessary and the mica was then found to be superfluous even in needles made up of more than one lamination.

Johnson undertook the experiments with cards and with what he termed 'the suspension of a ship's compass', by which he meant the pivot and cap, a vital aspect on which it was important to obtain experience from sea acquired over lengthy periods. Views were sought from seagoing captains amongst whom was Robert Fitzroy, Captain of the *Beagle*, who had recently returned from a five-year voyage of circumnavigation (1831–36). He considered one of *Beagle's* compasses (by Stebbing's of Portsmouth), with a ruby pivot working in a hard metal cap, to have been so successful that it had been retained on board for the next commission. Johnson also worked with Ross on experiments with compass bowls which they conducted in the magnetically clean area of Regent's Park, demonstrating the superiority of copper both as a means of damping the oscillations of the card and as a way of avoiding the magnetic inclusions so often found in brass. *Eddy-current damping* had been demonstrated by Sir William Snow Harris in a series of experiments in 1830–31, the results of which had been presented to the Royal

Society in a paper entitled 'On the transient magnetic state of which various substances are susceptible.'[9]

Views and opinions were also sought from manufacturers and other workers in the compass field, among whom must be mentioned the Reverend William Scoresby, an acknowledged expert whose interest in the compass had been excited twenty years earlier when, as a whaling captain, he had observed its strange behaviour in high latitudes. Since then he had closely studied the subject of magnetism, conducting numerous experiments of his own. Although he and Christie had crossed swords at the meeting of the British Association for the Advancement of Science in 1836, his dealings with the committee over the first year were cordial and productive. He gave freely of his time and intellect, supplying them with much useful material. He had designed a laminated compass needle of very hard steel for which he claimed great things, and at the request of the committee samples were supplied for test. It seems, however, that the results did not prove as favourable as he had expected. Further, he appears to have insisted that the committee, in their report, should recognize and acknowledge his claim to originality regarding both the principle of constructing his needles and his methods of magnetizing them. The committee declined to do so, maintaining that it had been

> appointed for the practical purpose of improving the compasses of the Royal Navy, in the fulfilment of which purpose it is their duty, in addition to the improvements which they may themselves devise, to avail themselves of any suggestions which they may obtain from others; acknowledging, of course, in their report, the quarter from whence they may have received any useful suggestion, but it is *not* their duty, nor their intention . . . to decide any questions of priority of discovery or invention.[10]

The committee had abundant evidence that Scoresby's principles of construction had been applied many years earlier, while his technique for magnetizing 'does not appear to differ in any respect from the method practised by the late Dr Gowin Knight' (in 1745).

Scoresby was a man of many talents. Sea captain, explorer and scientist, he had also just been granted the degree of Doctor of Divinity and appointed to the vicarage of Bradford. He had other work to pursue and realized there was little point in pressing his claim. Relationships with the Compass Committee were abruptly severed and although he remained active in the field of magnetism, William Scoresby does not figure in our narrative again for another two decades.

It soon became apparent that no compasses then on the market remotely approached the standards the committee were seeking. Accordingly, using the results of their wide-ranging experiments, they decided to develop their own design. Through the good offices of the Hydrographer their compasses were sent to sea for evaluation in the survey vessel, HMS *Fairy* under Captain Hewitt who, over two years, conducted many valuable trials before, in November 1840, the *Fairy* was tragically lost with all hands in a North Sea gale. Two compasses of the committee's latest design went down with her. A third and similar compass was by that time on trial in the Antarctic, with Captain James Ross in the *Erebus*.

From these early designs the committee developed, by gradual stages, what became known as the Admiralty Standard Compass, Pattern 1, a dry-card compass with a fairly thick copper bowl, designed to calm the oscillations of the needles. In construction and refinements it was far ahead of any compass of its day and so it remained for many years. It was adopted by many foreign governments and in the Royal Navy it was to be the principal compass for almost fifty years. Eventually, in 1888, it was re-designated a 'landing compass' and although it was removed from the Rate Book shortly before World War II it is known to have still been in operational service as late as 1944, over a century after its introduction.

Some of the notable features of this compass deserve special mention. The card, slightly over 7.5 inches in diameter, was of mica covered with paper.[11] It was divided into points and quarter-points and, on an outer circle, also graduated in degrees from 0° at north and south to 90° at east and west, with sub-divisions to 20 minutes. Engraved plates for printing the cards were provided by the committee and one of these was still in use in the 1930s. Obtaining the best arrangement for the needles was the subject of lengthy experiment and the compass collection at Greenwich contains no less than thirty-five different designs that were tried out during the period 1837–40.

At first Johnson, in common with many others, opposed the use of multiple needles, fearing that they would destroy each other's power, but this proved to be unfounded. Indeed, multiple needles had been in use in the Danish Navy for more than half a century. It was the mathematician Archibald Smith who pointed out to Major Sabine that by using several needles, spaced so as to balance the card north-south and east-west, it was possible to obviate the tendency of a single needle to align itself with the direction of roll. This had been the main fault with Gowin Knight's otherwise excellent compass of 1750 (see p. xxi) and many others.[12]

The final arrangement had four edge bar needles, two of them 7.3 inches long and two 5.4 inches long, disposed so as to give a uniform displacement of mass about the centre of the system. The card was balanced by a brass circumforential ring suspensed below it, as in Knight's compass and by sliding balance weights on bars radiating from the centre. A card-lifter was also incorporated, operated by a screw at the side of the bowl. Facilities were provided for changing the pivot which screwed into a pillar and was adjustable by tangent screws for centring. After lengthy trials the committee found that under normal conditions the best performance was obtained by using an iridium pivot working in a sapphire cup. This was known as card 'A' but in rough weather or when firing guns it was the practice to use a special, heavy card (card 'J') which had a cup of speculum metal bearing on a pivot made of ruby, the arrangement favoured by Fitzroy. The belief that heavy cards were best in rough weather probably originated from an early trial in the *Fairy*, but this was a false premise and had an adverse effect on compass design for many years.

Special attention was also given to the design of the azimuth circle which incorporated many refinements. A circle of silver was let into the verge ring, as in the arc of a sextant, and graduated every half degree to 360°. It was fitted with two verniers, capable of recording angles to one minute of arc. The circle was mounted on a central boss and carried an elaborate prismbox with dark shares as well as a folding sight vane and black-glass reflector for taking bearings of celestial objects. The committee considered that azimuth and steering compasses should be interchangeable, the only difference being in the verge ring and azimuth circle. A compass could thus readily be converted to either use.

Although some liquid-filled compasses were also considered, the committee appear to have dismissed them rather lightly. Johnson was afraid that 'under the combined motions of pitching and rolling the fluid itself might partake of an oscillation unfavourable to the needle denoting the true magnetic meridian', (now called 'swirl error')[13] He was also concerned that 'when an accident occurs or a derrangement takes place, it seems more difficult to remedy than in other compasses'. Several manufacturers were marketing liquid compasses at that time and one compass in particular, made in accordance with Crow's patent of 1813, incorporated many highly desirable features. By placing the needle inside a float it gave buoyancy and stability to the directional system, while the use of a card with a diameter considerably smaller than the bowl greatly reduced the error caused by the swirl of the liquid. Other improvements included a hide bottom to the bowl to allow for expansion and a good azimuth circle. It is regrettable and indeed surprising, in view of the thoroughness of the committee's work, that this compass was not given a serious trial. Although liquid compasses were of necessity introduced later for a number of purposes, their design was not given the same careful and imaginative attention, and the most important features, the float and the reduced diameter card, were not incorporated again for many decades. This was the first of many missed opportunities.

In April 1838, while the committee was engaged with its experiments, Captain Ross wrote to Their Lordships stressing the need for accurate information on *variation*. The committee had resolved

> that it is extremely important for the benefit of navigation that a series of magnetic observations should be made at several parts of the coasts of the United Kingdom, especially those points from whence the variation of the compass would be determined . . . and that in order to unite these observations with each other and thus to ascertain the direction of the curves of equal variation, it would be desirable that a few connecting observations should be made in the interior of the Kingdom.[14]

On the bottom of this letter the Secretary to the Board, John Croker, enquired of Beaufort, 'Who is the most competant person for this in the Admiralty?' to which the Hydrographer replied, 'There is no one I think so fully competant and so well prepared for this important service as Captain J. Ross himself'!

Thus the peripatetic chairman and Arctic explorer, who had until recently been engaged on Major Sabine's magnetic survey of the British Isles,[15] immediately set out to visit his former observing stations, covering the length and breadth of the Kingdom in a remarkably short time. Some six months later, when he was in southern Ireland, he received a letter from Beaufort informing him that Secretary Barrow had queried his claim for £100 expenses. Beaufort went on, 'I did not hesitate in saying that of all the scientific expeditions of the last 100 years, I would pledge my credit this would return the most for the expense.' [16]To Barrow, Beaufort wrote, 'When he completes his mission we shall know for the first time since Halley the actual state of the magnetic variation in England.'[17]

By the time the survey was completed, plans for a more far-reaching expedition were already taking shape. At a meeting of the British Association in Newcastle, the Committee of Physics and Meteorology under Sir John Herschel had noted: 'Great and notorious deficiences exist in our Knowledge of Variation lines generally, especially in Antarctic seas, and the true position of the South Magnetic Pole can scarcely even be conjectured from the data already known.'[18]

At the suggestion of Major Sabine this committee proposed that a scientific expedition for the purposes of magnetic research and geographical discovery should be despatched to the Southern Ocean and that Captain James Ross should be its leader. Britain had not mounted an expedition expressly equipped for magnetic observation since Edmund Halley's voyage to the South Atlantic late in the seventeenth century. The Royal Society strongly supported the idea and the government gave it their backing. On 21 September 1839 Captain Ross set sail with HM Ships *Erebus* and *Terror* and thereafter, apart from sending back occasional reports on the experimental compass supplied to the *Erebus*, he took no further part in the Compass Committee's activities.

The expedition nevertheless had an important bearing on the work of the future Compass Department which, under its second Superintendent, Staff Commander Evans, was to become the authority responsible for co-ordinating information on terrestrial magnetism. Magnetic observatories were established in St Helena, the Cape of Good Hope and Van Diemen's Land whilst continuous observations were taken on board both ships and in any port or island where it was possible to land including, on one occasion, on an ice floe. Although it was not possible to approach nearer than 160 miles to the South Magnetic Pole, its position was established as 75°05'S 154°08'E, some 600 miles from the theoretical position calculated by Gauss only a few years earlier, based on the very limited data then available.[19]

During three seasons Ross's expedition pressed to the southward as far as the ice would allow, penetrating the Ross Sea to latitude 78°10'S, some 200 miles nearer the Pole than any man before him. He christened the newly found continent *Victoria Land* and its active volcano, *Mount Erebus*. When naming the many new features on his chart he seems often to have been mindful of his colleagues on the Compass Committee; thus we find Beaufort Island, Mount Sabine, Cape Johnson and Cape Christie.[20]

After circling the globe from west to east the expedition reached England again in September 1843. In addition to its valuable contributions to botany, zoology, geology and meteorology, the magnetic phenomena of the southern hemisphere were for the first time placed in a clear light before the world. James Ross was knighted and received many honours including the Founders' Medal of the Royal Geographical Society and the Gold Medal of the Geographical Society of Paris. The historian, Commander L. S. Dawson, said of him in his *Memoirs of Hydrography*[21]:

> Sir James Ross had more experience of Arctic service than any other officer that ever lived. He endured nine Arctic winters and passed sixteen navigable seasons in the arctic regions. He was, without comparison, the fittest man to command this expedition.

Forty years later the explorer Sir Joseph Hooker, who had been assistant surgeon in *Erebus*, referred to his former commander as 'the greatest navigator since the days of Cook'. A modern account of this exceptional expedition is given in *Ross of the Antarctic* by Rear Admiral M. J. Ross,[22] a great grandson of Sir James. The results of the magnetic observations were published in the *Philosophical Transactions of the Royal Society*.[23]

On the departure of Captain Ross, chairmanship of the committee devolved naturally onto Beaufort and he and Johnson were to work in close harmony for the next fourteen years. The Hydrographer already had a high opinion of Johnson's abilities. Some years earlier he had commented very favourably on his survey of the coasts of Northumberland and Durham, undertaken on his own initiative in 1831, while on half pay. Later, in July 1837, Beaufort wrote to him: 'I can with equal truth and pleasure say that of the numerous surveyors which have been at work under this office, there is not one who has ever performed this task with more scrupulous minuteness nor with a more anxious desire to do it full justice than yourself.'[24]

Captain Johnson (he had been promoted on 27 December 1838) was the only member of the committee with no other major duties to preoccupy him. Consequently to him had fallen the lion's share of the practical work and it was he who drew up most of the detailed reports on the experiments carried out. These documents, together with two reports by Christie on his extensive work with compass needles, were attached as appendices to the main report of the committee, which was prepared by Major Sabine. The whole was bound into one volume, together with numerous letters covering the committee's activities (several more of which were added at a later date). After three years work the story was at last complete.[25]

The report was signed on 29 June 1840 and was forwarded by Beaufort to Sir John Barrow with a proposal that twelve of the new compasses should be purchased for more extensive trials. In approving this suggestion Their Lordships stated that they were 'very sensible of the indefatigable perseverance with which the committee devoted themselves to their task' and, with due prudence, enquired about the probable cost of the compasses.

Finding a suitable manufacturer for the new compasses caused the committee some concern. Most of the trial items had been made by John Charles Robinson, an instrument-maker of 38 Devonshire Street, London, who had been very helpful in carrying out many little experiments for them. His proposal to charge the apparently excessive sum of £25 for the new compasses now put them in a quandary. They were loathe to go elsewhere yet, in a letter to Sabine, Beaufort said 'I know that an estimate like this would much discompose the Board.' Eventually, however, although some orders were placed with other manufacturers, Robinson's price appears to have been accepted for when he died early in 1842 we find William Gilbert of 138 Fenchurch Street being given a large order for 200 compasses at the same price.[26]

The twelve new compasses were sent for trial in vessels serving in all parts of the world. Three went to ships of the Niger expedition, others to the America and West Indies station, South Africa, the Torres Strait and the East Indies. Two of the officers who thus received early practical experience of this revolutionary instrument were Lieutenant Strange of the *Wilberforce* (Niger) and Frederick John Evans of the *Fly* (Torres Strait), both of whom were destined later to serve in the Compass Department – Evans as its very distinguished Superintendent.

Throughout 1841 the committee continued to meet occasionally to consider compass problems and Christie, in particular, continued his experiments on needles. Johnson was largely employed supervising the manufacture and testing of the trial compasses, arranging their despatch and getting to know the capabilities of the individual instrument-makers, knowledge that was to prove invaluable to him in the years ahead.

In March 1842, in response to a request from Their Lordships, the committee prepared a set of *Practical Rules for Ascertaining the Deviations of the Compass which are Caused by the Ship's Iron.* This little pamphlet went through no less than eleven editions and was still in use with only minor changes in 1899.[27] The first paragraph of the *Practical Rules* read as follows:

> Every ship should be provided with a good Azimuth Compass, which may be called the *Standard Compass*; with it the Binnacle Compasses are to be frequently compared, and by it all bearings ought to be taken. It must be placed on the midship line of the quarter-deck or poop, and as far as possible from any considerable mass of iron, whether above or below it, such as the spindle of the capstan, the chain peak haulyards, the iron quarter-davits, etc. It should be fixed on a permanent support or pillar, and at such a height as will permit amplitudes and bearings to be observed with it over the hammock-nettings, or bulwarks. This pillar might be hollow, so as to admit, in some vessels, of a transparent compass-card being lighted from below. No stand of arms or other iron, subject to occasional removal, should be placed within at least fourteen feet of this Standard Compass.

The concept and prime importance of the Standard Compass was thus firmly established. The pamphlet also described the various methods that could be used for 'swinging ship' to obtain the deviations of the compass, and gave instructions for applying these to courses and bearings. The importance of frequently checking the deviation by observing azimuths was repeatedly stressed so that officers should not think that once the ship had been swung that was the end of the matter.

Beaufort's letter, dated 10 March 1842, laying the draft of the *Practical Rules* before the Admiralty, included the following significant paragraph;

> I would further beg of you to represent to Their Lordships that the officers of Her Majesty's Service having hitherto been little accustomed to the operation of swinging their ships for the purposes of detecting the errors of the compass, and it being very desirable that a practice which must soon become general throughout the Navy, should be satisfactorily and judiciously commenced, I would respectfully submit to Their Lordships' consideration the propriety of appointing some intelligent person to superintend the performance of that opperation until it become habitual to the officers.[28]

Beaufort suggested that this officer should also assist the ship-builder in determining the best position for the pillar, in each ship and should be responsible for examining all compasses received from the makers. Thirty years earlier Captain Flinders, in his famous report of 1812, had recommended an Inspector of Compasses with precisely these duties, but nothing had ever been done.[2]

This time Their Lordships reacted promptly. It was decided that Johnson should carry out these duties, being paid as a surveyor, and his appointment, dated 14 March 1842,[30] only four days after Beaufort's letter, read as follows:

> My Lords Commissioners of the Admiralty having received from the Committee on Magnetism a set of Rules for ascertaining and applying the Deviation of the Compass which are caused by iron in Ships; and having determined that all Her Majesty's Ships and more especially all steam vessels shall be fitted with such a Pillar as is mentioned in those Rules, for the support of a Standard Compass, by which all bearings of the land shall be taken, and all the Courses regulated; and My Lords being also desirous that Officers in Command of H.M. Ships should become accustomed to the operation of swinging their ships for the purpose of detecting the errors of the Compass, they are pleased to entrust you with the execution of this service, in the course of which

Their Lordships conceive it will be necessary for you, not only to afford your advice and assistance in the performance of the operation of swinging the ships until it become habitual to the Officers, but also, (as the proper position of the Standard Compass must depend in almost every ship on local circumstances) personally to assist the Master shipwrights of the several Dockyards in determining the most advantageous place for the Pillar, and corresponding orders will be given to the officers of the Yards on this point. Two hundred improved Compasses on the principles set forth in the Magnetic Committee's Report of 29th June 1840 are now being manufactured by Mr Gilbert of Fenchurch Street the construction and adjustment of which will require severe examination, and to this point also your attention is to be directed.

My Lords will cause you to be supplied with copies of the proposed Rules for ascertaining the Deviation of the Compass, when they shall be printed.[31]

Birth of the Compass Department

Captain Johnson acknowledged his appointment and thanked their Lordships 'for the confidence reposed in me to execute a duty of such importance'. He now had a busy time ahead of him. Following his experiments in the *Garryowen* and his experience on the committee he had acquired a very thorough grasp of the problems of managing magnetic compasses in iron ships. He was also a man of immense energy and conscientiousness. For two years he was to be the sole member of a new department charged with the following tasks:

1.   The testing of the new compasses. This would entail setting up a new organization for the purpose.

2.   Arranging for the custody and proper treatment of compasses, both in store and afloat.

3.   The proper installation of compasses in ships.

4.   Instructing the officers of the Fleet in compass matters and the swinging of ships to determine the errors of their compasses.

The enthusiasm with which Johnson tackled his new duties comes out very clearly in his correspondence, over which he was extremely methodical. (His correspondence registers are a researcher's dream. His successors, alas, were less punctilious.)[32]

There was at the time no official organization for testing compasses, as had been suggested by Flinders, and Johnson had some difficulty in finding a satisfactory site for the purpose. Greenwich Park ('in the gravel pits near Maize Hill') was objected to by the Commissioners of Woods and Forests 'on account of the beauty of the scenery and the great enjoyment derived by the public . . .', while the grounds of the Royal Observatory, where regular magnetic and meteorological observations had been made since 1837, were already fully occupied. Eventually a suitable house in Maryan Road, Charlton, only a quarter of a mile from Woolwich Dockyard, was leased from Sir Thomas Maryan Wilson and a wooden observatory some 15 feet in diameter was erected in the large garden, 100 yards from the house and clear of any magnetic material. Negotiations had, however, taken over two years and, in order not to jeopardize the supply of compasses to the Fleet, Johnson had been forced to continue testing in Regent's Park 'until in December the weather rendered that place no longer eligible'. In September 1844 he was authorized to engage a pensioner Sergeant of Artillery named James Brunton at 2/6d per day (plus accommodation and fuel) to do the actual compass testing, a task he faithfully performed for almost forty years.

The Compass Department at last had a home, the house acting as a dwelling for Mr Brunton, an office for the Superintendent and a store both for instruments awaiting test and for the fine collection of compasses originally put together by the committee, to which Johnson was adding year by year. The official address of the establishment was 'The Compass Observatory, Woolwich'.

On the advice of Major Sabine equipment for monitoring the earth's magnetic field was based on that developed for the many magnetic observatories recently established at home and abroad. Johnson, however, personally designed the compass-testing stands and standardized the tests. He wrote to Beaufort that he was determined that proving a compass should become an exact science 'with measurable results, instead of trusting to the guesswork of opinion'! Testing in the new observatory started early in 1845 but the *Register of Examination of Instruments* has many entries before this period, those in 1842 being marked 'At the Royal Botanic Gardens, Regents Park'. Late in 1845 approval was obtained to build a castellated wall on the top of Cox Mount (for which the Admiralty paid 4/- a year rent) to act as a sighting mark from the Observatory.

Each section represented a known fraction of a degree and allowance could thus readily be made for the diurnal changes in the variation, greatly simplifying testing.

Although no illustration of the Observatory has survived, Captain E. W. Creak has left a brief description of the building at Deptford (whence it moved in 1869), after it had been largely rebuilt in 1895:

> The Observatory. – On a grass plot in HM Victualling Yard at Deptford, as far removed from neighbouring iron as possible, stands the Compass Observatory. It is an octagonal building, constructed entirely of wood and copper.
>
> Of the three windows, one lights the Unifilar Declination Magnetometer standing on a stone pier, and capable of being moved on it as the Variation of the needle changes from year to year. By means of this instrument the Variation (or Declination) can be exactly observed from the theodolite placed on a second stone pier in the centre of the building.
>
> A second window, opposite the first-named, lights a revolving base plate, graduated to minutes of arc, and carrying a sprang for mounting the compass to be examined, the whole of these being supported on a third stone pier. From this window a special mark on the wall opposite can be seen bearing from the centre of the base plate N. 10° W. (true). Hence, knowing the Variation, the magnetic bearing of the mark can be obtained exactly at any time.
>
> (*Elementary Manual for the Deviations of the Compass*, 1903, p.38)

A more detailed account of the original equipment and of the working procedures of the Observatory is given in Johnson's book *Practical Illustrations of the Necessity of Ascertaining the Deviations of the Compass*.[33]

The care and proper treatment of compasses on board ship naturally demanded Johnson's special attention. In 1813, following the representations of Captain Flinders, azimuth compasses had become the responsibility of the Master, but all other compasses still remained as Boatswain's stores. Under an order dated 11 April 1843 (see appendix 2) the Admiralty Standard Compass was placed under the personal charge of the captain, in the same way as chronometers, and in the following year all other compasses became the responsibility of the Master. Neither officer was to receive his final bill for full pay until Johnson had certified that the compasses had been returned in good order, or a satisfactory explanation given. Detailed instructions were prepared to accompany each Standard Compass and transactions were monitored by special forms, each of which required a report 'should [the compass] have received any injury in its conveyance'. With the agreement of the Storekeeper-General, Johnson personally controlled the allocation of Standard Compasses, and even Admirals Superintendent were not immune from censure if he found that one had been transferred without his authority!

Believing that compasses should be 'given the same care as Chronometers' Johnson arranged that each ship should have a special compass closet, the key of which was to be kept by the Master. Detailed instructions were given about stowing spare compasses and cards with their needles end for end (north and south polarity), and compass closets were still being built into ships as late as 1906. Similar storage arrangements were made in dockyards so that compasses 'could be kept separate from common ships stores', and Johnson frequently inspected the stock, throwing out anything he considered 'mere lumber' and breaking any weak compass needles so that they could not be reissued.

The number of compasses carried by different ships varied widely and it was not until 1848 that Johnson was able to standardize an official establishment for each rate of ship. Generally, however, ships would have a Standard/Azimuth compass (occasionally both were supplied), port and starboard binnacle (steering) compasses, one or more hanging compasses for use between decks, and a selection of boats compasses, with spare compass bowls and cards for each. The Compass Committee had recommended that the Admiralty Pattern 1 should be provided both as a Standard/Azimuth compass and for steering (without an azimuth circle) and 200 new compasses had been ordered from William Gilbert (for which he was paid an advance of £300). As the build up of stocks naturally took some time it was at first necessary to limit the supply of new compasses to one per ship, selecting the best of the ordinary compasses in store for use in the binnacles and endeavouring always to have a binnacle compass of the same size as the standard, so that they could be interchangeable. When Gilbert died in 1844, after a lengthy illness, only forty had been completed. A request from Mrs Gilbert to be allowed to carry on the contract was refused and the work was transferred to Henry Barrow who had succeeded to the business of Robinson. (This firm held the monopoly for the manufacture and repair of the Admiralty Pattern 1 compass until the 1880s, after which no more of these compasses were made.) Although a steady flow of new compasses was maintained for the first four years, the original plan was never fully met. The Admiralty, who had never liked the price, soon decided against their use as steering compasses and later even cut down on the supply of Standards. Whilst a limited number of commercial compasses were bought as replacements, Johnson was forced to make the best use possible of the compasses available in store, taking care that each ship had at least one good instrument. Thus a proliferation of different types remained in service for many years and examples of Walker's Meridional compass, first produced in 1795, were still to be found at sea during the 1850s.

A look at the Compass Department estimates for this period is revealing. In 1843 these amounted to £3745, which included £2550 for new Standard Compasses, much of which was not spent due to Gilbert's illness. In the following year the total fell by about a third (with £1550 for new compasses), after which it decreased steadily until 1847 when it stabilized for two years at £2198 (with £1250 for new compasses). Further cuts in 1849 reduced the total to £1118, all purchases of new compasses being cancelled, and although this was later rescinded to allow compasses on order to be supplied, no new orders were placed for many years.

The introduction of iron ships and steam propulsion

Before discussing the other tasks which faced Captain Johnson on assuming his new responsibilities, it would be as well to look briefly at the progress made towards modernizing the Navy prior to 1842, particularly with regard to steam propulsion and the building of iron ships. Both had been approached with great caution by Their Lordships despite the notable enterprise shown by some commercial concerns. The first paddle-wheeler had demonstrated its capabilities before the battle of Trafalgar, and by the year of Waterloo (1815) much improved, compact steam engines were being fitted into iron-built ships. The Admiralty was kept informed of these developments and in 1821 purchased its first steamship, the *Monkey*, a wooden paddle-tug which proved invaluable for assisting large sailing ships in confined waters. It was followed by others and by 1832 the

Admiralty owned some twenty steamships, all of low tonnage. The year 1837 saw the launch of HMS *Gorgon*, a steam frigate of 1111 tons and 6 guns, the first of a line of eighteen wooden-hulled paddle-frigates which continued to appear until 1851.

Meanwhile, on the commercial front, the first crossing of the Atlantic by a paddle-wheeler had taken place in 1827 and ship-owners were quick to realize the potential. The maiden voyage in 1837 of the *Great Western* (a wooden paddle-steamer of 1778 tons) was followed a year later by the laying down of the Great Britain, an iron ship of 3490 tons, driven by a screw. This was the very year in which George Airy carried out his pioneering experiments into compass correction in the *Rainbow* and *Ironsides*. Believing, as he did, that the problem which had plagued iron ships for so long could now be completely solved, he was able with confidence to reassure ship-owners. In the same year the Admiralty purchased the iron steam packet *Dover* for the cross-Channel run and it is interesting to note that five years later, and with Johnson's agreement, Airy was called upon to correct her compasses.

At first the Admiralty had good reasons for its cautious approach to steam in warships. The paddles sacrificed much broadside fire power, while the early engines were often very unreliable. Indeed in 1821 an order had been issued forbidding the use of steam in men-of-war.[34] Furthermore, the Admiralty was understandably opposed to changing the basic structure of its ships. Would not the introduction of steam quickly render an all-sailing Navy obsolete and put an end to Britain's naval supremacy? There were of course men of vision who thought otherwise. Admiral Hardy, Nelson's flag captain, who was First Sea Lord from 1830 to 1834, was one who believed wholeheartedly in steam and envisaged a new modern navy with complete mobility, but there were also powerful but less enlightened authorities who were reluctant to accept the change. In particular, the Surveyor of the Navy, Captain Sir William Symonds, still preferred to build fast sailing ships, possibly fitted with auxiliary engines to drive paddles. Although the introduction of the screw, about 1830, would have overcome the fire-power problem it was soon to become apparent that the wooden hulls into which it was fitted were being seriously strained by vibration. Despite a number of convincing demonstrations of its efficiency, the screw was not widely adopted by the Navy until the middle of the century.

Meanwhile, following a series of trials to test the effectiveness of iron as a protection against gunfire, a few composite vessels had been built with wooden hulls, protected by iron belts. The introduction of armourplate followed and the next logical step was to build an iron ship to provide both adequate protection and strength for the engines. At this point however public opinion took a hand. Centuries of naval supremacy had led the nation to honour its woodenwalls. The announced intention to build naval ships of iron was greeted by an immediate outcry in the press and caused the Admiralty to hesitate – possibly with some relief! Although they again moved cautiously forward between 1842 and 1844 when a number of iron warships were ordered (including the *Birkenhead* and *Trident*, both of which were to figure significantly in the affairs of the Compass Department in the following decade), as late as 1850 a report to the Admiralty was still of the opinion 'that iron cannot be beneficiently employed as a material for the construction of vessels of war'.[35] Their Lordships no doubt felt that their caution had been justified. The iron frigates already built were converted to troopships and seventeen more which were then under construction were scrapped.

Such was the background and climate of opinion when Johnson began organizing 'the proper installation of compasses in ships' and 'assisting the master shipwrights in determining the most advantageous position for the pillar'. Initially he concentrated on steam vessels which, although still mainly of wood, already contained a considerable quantity of iron. Within a fortnight of his assuming his new duties we find a succession of letters to Their Lordships requesting the removal of offending ironwork fitted too close to the compass. Moveable iron whose effect on the compass was variable, was particularly objectionable; such items as steering gear, especially iron tillers, large iron hoops on the boom, awning stanchions and boats davits were notably troublesome, as were the after captstan and the 'great funnel', which could be either up or down. Johnson thus embarked on the campaign to achieve a magnetically stable position for the compass which, as every compass-adjuster will confirm, is still being pursued with the same frustrations today, not only in ships but also in aircraft. An order had been in existance since 1805 that no iron was to be placed within 7 feet of the compass (the first known 'safe-distance' instruction) but it appeared that dockyards either knew nothing of the rule or widely disregarded it. Johnson therefore prepared a comprehensive statement covering both the care of compasses and the safe-distance regulations and this was eventually issued as Admiralty Circular, No. 9, dated 20 November 1845 (see appendix 3) the first of a series of such instructions which have been continued to this day.[36]

Although hulls were still built mainly of wood, the 1840s increasingly saw the introduction of structural iron to provide greater strength. This generally took the form of knees or diagonal riders (strengthening pieces, fitted slantwise across the sides of the vessel) which could produce enormous differences between the port and starboard compasses. Occasionally even the wooden crossbeams were reinforced with iron and the situation eventually became so bad that, following some experiments in the *Conflict* in 1846, Johnson reported to the Admiralty that 'when these iron riders are multiplied they form an iron network which, as far as the compass is concerned, renders the ship as difficult to navigate as if she were entirely built of iron'.[37] In January 1849 he was instructed to consult with the Surveyor of the Navy 'on the subject of the removal of iron work from the vicinity of the compass on board ship', as a result of which an order was issued that iron riders should never come nearer to any compass than 20 feet; also that boats davits, large stanchions and knees within that distance should always be of wood or 'mixed metal' (alloy). It was a notable triumph.

The *Practical Rules* required that the Standard Compass should be 'fixed on a permanent support or pillar' and dockyards were invited to prepare suitable designs, a task in which Johnson, whose letters were often illustrated by beautiful sketches, frequently took a hand. This resulted in many pleasing arrangements. In its simplest form a wooden pillar some 10 inches in diameter was surmounted by a heavy brass ring to take the compass gimbals and capped by a hexagonal, glass-panelled hood which could hold a small lamp. A hollow pillar and transparent compass card could be provided if it was desired that the compass should be lit from below. Photographs show that elegantly carved pillars became quite a feature, although regrettably few have survived. In an attractive alternative design which appeared some years later the wooden pillar was replaced by four brass stanchions, either of full height or forming a dwarf binnacle which could be mounted on a solid mahogany table. In brigs, where the boom was generally too low to clear the compass at a working height above the deck, a telescopic binnacle was provided which could be raised and lowered. This was surmounted by a pleasantly ornate copper, japanned 'urn' to take the compass, which became very popular and was much in demand by other ships.

Obtaining a satisfactory site for the Standard Compass, where the deviations would be small, frequently necessitated raising the pillar still further by placing it on a platform or pedestal or, if the magnetic conditions were very bad, mounting the compass on the mizenmast or placing it in one of the tops. Although this had sometimes to be accepted, the utility of a compass in such a position was doubtful in any but fair weather and Johnson was not normally in favour of it.

Swinging ship

Perhaps the most important duty assigned to Captain Johnson was that of 'Instructing the officers of the Fleet in compass matters and the swinging of ships to determine the errors of their compasses'. Instructions for swinging were contained in the *Practical Rules* and ships were normally swung on completion of building or refitting which, on the Thames, took place at Sheerness, Woolwich or Deptford. Johnson found that Greenhithe Reach was the most suitable place for swinging and arranged for a set of five buoys to be laid in a position clear of the fairway and screened from the flood stream by the curvature of the land. The position chosen had a well defined distant mark (the Severndröog tower, 11 miles away) and here ships were wharped round the 32 points of the compass and their deviations observed.[38]

Before long swinging was extended to the ports of Portsmouth and Plymouth and, on occasions, was undertaken at Sheerness although tidal conditions there made the operation extremely difficult. Hawsers were often broken and swings could take several days to complete. When Johnson was not available the Admiralty sometimes ordered captains to swing their own ships, a task which some achieved with great credit. In March 1843 Captain Vidal of the survey vessel *Styx* submitted a description of a swing, using the theodolite technique employed by Johnson in the *Garryowen* (see p. xxxiii), which was a model performance. Others were not always so successful.

The results of all swings carried out were bound into volumes which are now held by the National Maritime Museum and which, although not quite complete, give a remarkable record of the behaviour of the compass from 1842 to modern times. The special swinging forms prepared by Johnson for recording the observations differ little in format from those in use today.

It must be remembered, however, that the operation of swinging to obtain the deviation did not entail any compass adjustment. Despite Airy's experiments which provided an excellent first attempt at correcting the compass with magnets and soft iron, there was still much that was not fully understood, even by the experts, and there was a real danger that correcting the compass would encourage officers to believe that once adjusted it would remain right for all time and under all circumstances. Hence the Admiralty's policy was to obtain the best possible position for the Standard Compass, where the deviations would generally be small, and to compare all compasses on board with the Standard, at the same time stressing that constant checks on the deviation were essential, particularly after any significant change in the ship's geographical position.

There is no doubt that initially this policy was sound. Despite the tentative introduction of steam most naval ships were still built mainly of wood, and their deviations were easily manageable. It was with evident satisfaction that Johnson wrote to Their Lordships in March 1845 'that when the Standard Compass is properly placed . . . and the regulations respecting the iron-work observed . . . the deviations are reduced to a small amount. The greatest deviation on any of the 32 points in the *Vindictive* was 1°35'.'[39]

After being swung a ship was given a table of deviations which it was expected would hold good, at least in home waters, for many years. The requirement for ships to be swung annually was introduced by an Admiralty circular dated 12 May 1852, and this policy has continued to this day.[40]

Although Johnson was not in favour of correcting the compass he nevertheless kept an open mind on the subject as more iron ships came into service. Large deviations were a nuisance, particularly when a ship was required to alter course frequently in inshore waters. Thus in 1844 Johnson agreed to the compasses of the iron steam-packet *Dover* being corrected by Airy and the practice was continued sparingly whenever it proved impossible to find satisfactory positions, especially for the binnacle compasses which had, of necessity, to be placed near the wheel. Amongst the vessels whose compasses were corrected we find the screw-yacht *Fairy* in 1845, the iron paddle-ships *Birkenhead* in 1846 and *Undine* in 1847, and an increasing number in later years. It is doubtful, however, whether Johnson fully understood Airy's method for not until 1852, when he employed a Barlow's plate while adjusting the compass of the screw-ship *Horatio*, did he attempt to use soft-iron correctors in addition to magnets. Indeed as late as 1850 when writing to the Master of the *Victory* at Portsmouth after swinging the *Birkenhead* he had said, 'for it must be taught that these magnets are not permanent correctors but, on the contrary, merely deviation reducers'[41] Shortly after Johnson's death in 1853 an instruction was issued that deviation should be reduced if the errors exceeded a point, but it was many years before this became regular practice.

Meanwhile many iron merchant vessels had had their compasses corrected by Airy's method and Johnson was frequently asked by the Admiralty to comment on letters from ship-builders or -owners. He was consistant in his conviction that Airy's plan was by no means as perfect as was widely accepted. Not only could he point to 'the record of the accidents to Iron Steam Vessels which have occurred in consequence of the errors of their Compasses' but it was apparent that ships with correctors frequently had greater errors in their compasses on change of latitude than those without. On one occasion he drew attention to the case of an iron sailing vessel bound for Calcutta which, after having its compass closely adjusted by Mr Gray of Liverpool, found an error of $4\frac{1}{2}$ points (51°) when south of the Cape of Good Hope.[42] Such was Johnson's reputation amongst seamen that both the P & O Steam Navigation Company and the Royal Mail Steam Packet Company invited him to undertake the swinging of their ships. Whilst the Admiralty was not prepared to authorize this, he was allowed to train an officer from each company. In 1847 in reply to an enquiry from the Privy Council for Trade he recommended that the *Practical Rules* and the Admiralty memorandum on safe distances (appendix 3) should be adopted as statutory regulations for the Merchant Service and that swinging officers should be appointed at the principal ports after examination by Trinity House. He also pointed out that it was indispensable for safety that ships proceeding abroad should be swung at both ends of the voyage.[43]

At first nothing was done about these eminently sensible proposals but four years later, at the request of Captain (later Rear-Admiral) F. W. Beechey, FRS, a very experienced surveyor who was attached to the Board of Trade, Johnson drafted the compass clauses for a Parliamentary Bill regulating steam ships. These covered the requirement to carry good compasses including, where possible, an azimuth compass, and laid down the rules concerning their siting, safe-distance considerations and the necessity for continual observations for deviation, whether or not the compass was corrected by magnets.[44]

The following year Beechey again sought Johnson's advice about 'the examination of certain persons claiming to be qualified in compass adjustment', all of whom were employed by the compass manufacturers, including a Mrs Janet Taylor of the Minories. Johnson's opinion was: 'There can be no proper examination of such people as Instrument Makers who undertake to swing ships, but by seeing them perform the operation and explain the results obtained.'[45] He therefore again recommended the appointment of 'some intelligent and responsible officer to see that it is correctly done'. But Beechey was feeling his way against considerable prejudice. (He had even written, 'I am afraid an Azimuth Compass on board a Merchant Steamer would be too much to insist on.') The Board of Trade would not accept Johnson's recommendation and the subject appears to have been dropped. Further suggestions along similar lines were made by the Liverpool Compass Committee (1855–60) and by the Royal Society, supported by the Admiralty, in 1865, but it was not until the turn of the century that the practical examination and certification of compass adjusters were introduced, very much along the lines that Johnson had originally proposed.

One aspect of compass correction that had received only cursory attention by the Astronomer Royal was that of heeling error (see appendix 1). Indeed, although it was briefly discussed in his paper to the Royal Society in 1839, Airy had confidently assured ship-owners that this error was unlikely ever to exceed one degree. Swinging a ship heeled was first attempted by Commander William Walker, the Queen's Harbour Master at Plymouth when, in 1844, he swung the 120-gun, first-rate *St Vincent*, heeled at an angle of 8° by means of 100 tons of water ballast and the weight of her crew (1000 men). Johnson was in attendance. This, however, was a wooden ship and the effect, though noticeable, was small. Of far greater significance was a similar trial conducted the following year in the iron brig *Recruit* which clearly exhibited considerable heeling error, and in which a new scheme of correction devised by Walker was employed. Although Johnson makes several references to Walker's plan in his reports to the Admiralty, he does not describe what was done and no record of the precise method of correction appears to have survived. It is clear, however, that he thought it worthwhile to try the apparatus over an extensive change of latitude for in his report[46] dated February 1847 he suggested that if 'at any time when Their Lordships may require the services of a brig at Rio de Janeiro' the *Recruit* might be sent. He was aware that the problem was becoming serious for his report goes on:

> There may however be many magnetic peculiarities in Iron Ships yet undiscovered and every careful observation respecting them cannot fail to be advantageous . . . From the numerical results obtained it is evident that the heeling of an Iron Ship produces differences in the deviations of her Compasses, which are very considerable at the Binnacle but much less at the elevated position of the Standard.

Johnson even went so far as to add the rather forlorn proposal that 'in furtherance of the object of keeping the Standard always at its elevated position it appears to result that no Iron vessel should be rigged as a brig'.

The serious effects of heeling error shown in the *Recruit* were confirmed a few months later by trials conducted in the iron steam vessel *Bloodhound*, in conjunction with some experiments to ascertain 'whether the heating action of steam upon the hull of an Iron Vessel affects a Compass . . . in any degree which may be of practical importance to the purpose of Navigation'.[47] Although the trials showed that such effects were insignificant, Johnson nevertheless proposed that iron ships navigating in regions of very high temperature should pay attention to the possibility of the magnetism being affected by the sun's rays. The errors introduced by heeling were, however, of 'quite a different character, being very marked and of an amount which may not safely be disregarded on board an Iron Sailing Ship'.

It is probable that, despite these trials, Johnson did not fully understand the significance of heeling error. While its effect on the Standard Compass could be reduced if the compass was elevated, its effects on the binnacle compasses and the oscillation that would result when the ship rolled must often have been considerable. Airy had suggested that this might be corrected by the use of a vertical magnet but Johnson does not appear ever to have attempted this. Instead he recommended that all iron sailing ships should be swung both upright and heeled, not apparently appreciating that the magnitude of the error varied in direct proportion to the angle of heel. In the event swinging ships heeled was seldom done and it was another decade before the problem was thoroughly investigated by W. W. Rundell, the energetic secretary of the Liverpool Compass Committee.

The appointment of an Assistant Superintendent

Swinging ships and siting their compasses entailed an immense amount of travelling and although Johnson's instructions were to give precedence to steam vessels he had frequently to refer to Their Lordships for guidance as to priorities. The following note from his correspondence is typical of many. On returning from a visit to Portsmouth he found a letter from the Admiralty telling him that the *Trafalgar* at Sheerness was ready for her swing that day. He minuted this letter as follows:

> Received this day, on arrival from Portsmouth, and being summoned to Greenhithe to superintend the observations of the 'Vesuvius', at the same time also to Devonport and again to Portsmouth for the observations of the sailing ships. Received Admiral Bowles' authority to proceed to HMSV 'Vesuvius'.[48]

Other examples from his letters show that Johnson sometimes had as many as five simultaneous calls for his attention and it was eventually decided that he should have an assistant. Commander James Newbury Strange was appointed as Assistant Superintendent of Compasses on 14 August 1845. The choice was a happy one. Strange was an experienced officer with more than fourteen years at sea, who had been the First Lieutenant of the iron vessel *Wilberforce* during the Niger expedition (1840–42) to suppress the slave trade. It will be recalled that the *Wilberforce* was among the ships to receive one of the committee's twelve prototype compasses for trial in 1840. As she was an iron ship, large compass errors had been expected and, a year before the formation of the Compass Department, it had been decided to correct her compasses by Airy's method, an operation which, according to the ship's log, took eight days to complete. Commander Strange thus needed no introduction to the new compasses or to the problems to be found in iron ships. For three and a half years he and Johnson had a most harmonious working relationship.

Strange, who lived in Southsea, took over the bulk of the work at Portsmouth and Plymouth, leaving Johnson free to concentrate on the Thames. Whenever possible he took passage to Plymouth in one of HM ships as there was at that time no direct line from Portsmouth and the journey via London was slow and tedious.[49] Accordingly his visits to Plymouth normally lasted several days so that he could deal with as many outstanding ships and other tasks as possible, also supervising the work of the local compass manufacturer, Mr Cox, with whom excellent relationships appear to have existed.

The correspondence covering Commander Strange's service in the Compass Department[50] gives an illuminating insight into the many technical and human problems with which he had to contend. His dealings with the Commanders-in-Chief, the captains of HM ships and the dockyard authorities are all recorded and Johnson was kept fully informed of his work, his movements and the difficulties and obstructions he encountered. At Devonport, for example, we learn that the dockyard initially insisted on receiving a separate Admiralty authority for repositioning every compass. Nor were things made any easier by the conservatism of naval officers themselves, many of whom still did not believe that a magnetic compass could be in error, no matter where it was placed. In one acrimonious exchange the captain of *Hermione* refused to have his azimuth compass secured in a fixed position and was supported in his opposition by the Master Attendant, clearly another 'old salt'. However, Johnson was able to enlist Admiralty support to clear up these and many similar problems and on this occasion he sent an encouraging note to Strange, which read:

Any system which bears hard upon old prejudices, particularly if it be attended with additional labour, mental or bodily, is sure to meet with opposition, but we must not mind that; the rough edges of the pebbles are worn away by their chafing on the beach and in the end they become polished. We must persevere, reason and persuade and, if that will not do, insist upon the carrying out of the plan.[51]

In 1848 the cuts in naval expenditure brought in by Lord Russell's Whig government hit the Compass Department severely. A circular to dockyards calling for suggestions to reduce its running costs, led to an enquiry under Captain Alexander Milne, a Lord Commissioner of the Admiralty, the main result of which was that the post of Assistant Superintendent should be discontinued and the swinging carried out by the Masters Attendant in the dockyards and the Masters of flagships. In addition, a large order for new compasses was to be cancelled (see p. 18). Strange was, however, allowed a quarter's grace and remained in post until March 1849. After a year on half pay he found himself back at sea in command of the *Archer*, once more bound for West Africa.[52]

Before leaving his appointment Commander Strange endeavoured to ensure that the Masters Attendant were fully trained in swinging and in the examination of compasses, a task that had been placed on them following the appalling results of Johnson's early surveys of the compasses in store. Dockyards had been supplied with a deflecting apparatus for checking the power of the compass needles both on receipt from the manufacturers and periodically thereafter. Swinging was to be shared with the Masters of flagships but none of these officers appear to have relished their additional tasks nor, on many occasions, were they very good at it. A number of near disasters resulted from wrongly named deviations and Johnson spent much time correcting the errors in the tables they prepared, a problem which remained with him to the end. His last recorded letter, written to the Master of the *Waterloo* only a week before he died, was devoted entirely to this subject.[53] He must have sadly missed the reliable, helpful and intelligent service he had enjoyed and his assistant, Strange, whose approach to all compass matters appears to have coincided so exactly with his own.

A wide range of activities

In addition to the time-consuming tasks of inspecting and swinging ships, Johnson found the necessary leisure to pursue a wide range of activities connected with compasses and magnetic matters. He was constantly preoccupied with the problem of making the committee's compass steadier in bad weather and the compass collection at the National Maritime Museum contains many examples of devices designed to 'calm the movement of the card'. Essentially broad-minded, he did not consider that the Navy was irrevocably committed to the Admiralty Standard Compass and frequently sponsored trials of instruments by other makers, notably Sir Willian Snow Harris, E. J. Dent, Commander Walker, John Syeds, Grant Preston and West & Co. As early as 1845 it had been found necessary to supply liquid steering-compasses to ships for use in rough weather, to be placed in the binnacle of 'such vessels as from the violence of their motion and nature of their construction may cause such application to be necessary'.[54] Favourable reports on these liquid compasses soon began to reach the Admiralty and caused Beaufort to write to Johnson: 'The accounts which I every day hear of the good work done by Mr Dent's compasses make me more and more urgent with you to carry out, without any further delay . . . a thorough trial of their merits compared with our compasses, in unsteady vessels.'[55]

Comparative trials were conducted early in 1847 on board the steam mail packet *Garland*, a lively vessel capable of 14 knots. Six different compasses were carried, three of which were liquid, by Dent, Preston, and J. Gray and R. J. Keen of Liverpool, and three were dry. In addition to the Admiralty standard there was a binnacle-compass fitted with small ivory knobs just below the glass to dampen the movement and a compass specially constructed to Walker's plan, with the pivot passing through a bell-shaped brass collar and fitted with treble gimbals.[56] The passage to Ostend was calm and all compasses behaved perfectly. However, on the return crossing to Dover, to quote Johnson's report:

> A strong gale having sprung up . . . and raised a considerable sea . . . afforded an excellent opportunity for testing all the compasses . . . as in crossing the Flemish banks obliquely (tide against wind) there was a continuity of broken water which, combined with the velocity of the vessel, produced a variety of motions most favourable for our purpose.[57]

Under these conditions the two liquid compasses by Dent and Preston proved by far the steadiest. Vibration from the buffeting on one occasion caused the Admiralty compass to swing 12 points while Gray's compass 'swung half round'. The other two compasses 'were sufficiently steady to steer by' although both swung up to a point and a half ($17°$).

The superiority of liquid compasses was impressively demonstrated again the following year during trials on board HMS *Excellent*, the gunnery training ship. A number of compasses were placed within 7 feet of the breach of a 32-pounder gun when firing and, as in the *Garland*, it was the liquid compass of Dent which was by far the least affected.[58]

It will be recalled that the Admiralty Compass Committee had dismissed the use of liquid compasses after only a cursory consideration and without giving them a thorough trial, yet within five years they had had to be introduced for use in rough weather. Johnson may well have been considering the wider introduction of Dent's compasses for he had already arranged for a number to be fitted with 'Azimuth Circles, Prisms and vanes' for use as azimuth compasses. However, he seems to have been concerned lest steadiness under severe conditions might imply reduced sensitivity at other times. On one occasion when asked to comment on a favourable report on Preston's liquid compass in heavy weather he informed Their Lordships:

> I beg to observe that the said liquid compass was expressly supplied to meet such exigencies, experience having shown that no compass yet invented possesses the desirable properties of being both accurate and steady under all circumstances – steadiness being the result of the application of additional friction, as in the case of the liquid compass, . . . which, although rendering them steady and useful under the conditions described, renders them sluggish, inaccurate and not to be relied upon under general circumstances.[59]

Further, both Johnson and Beaufort were constantly mindful that the Admiralty had invested large sums of money in the committee's compass which, under favourable conditions, was still the best in the world. Whatever the reasoning, the chance was allowed to pass, as was a similar chance fifteen years later, when the United States Navy changed to liquid compasses. These events were to have a profound effect on the development of marine compasses in England during the second half of the century.

Boats compasses were also in serious need of attention. In 1845 Johnson had conducted a trial on the Thames which showed that Dent's and Preston's compasses were greatly superior to the 'Common Boats Compass' then in use which, when the boat was rocked, simply 'went round and round'.[60] It appears, however, that despite the favourable reports from captains who were fortunate enough to be issued with a liquid compass (once an officer had seen a liquid compass in a boat he never wanted another) their introduction was slow. Ten years later, during the Baltic campaign, we find the Hydrographer complaining to the Secretary to the Board that, 'The Common Boat's Compass supplied to HM Ships is worthless and spins round at every stoke of the oars.' He asked that all ships about to proceed to the Baltic where they 'will have to encounter foggy weather . . . and have much use of their boats . . . should be provided with at least one of Dent's liquid boats compasses, and that the issue of the common boats compass to HM Ships should be discontinued'.[61]

Satisfactory lighting for the compass was another subject to which Johnson gave much thought. In line-of-battle ships and frigates the provision of hollow supports to enable the compass to be lit from the main deck below, as suggested in the *Practical Rules*, was desirable whenever the siting of the compass allowed. However, it raised many difficulties such as the provision of adequately transparent cards (these were usually made of satin) smokey lamps (the poor quality of the storekeeper's oil was generally held to blame), ventilation and the fact that 'cards with four needles cause confusion upon the face of the card'.[62] Comparative trials of three improved lighting systems (lamp and reflectors) submitted by Lieutenant Tremlett of the Royal Naval College, Mr Brunton[63] and Professor Snow Harris, were carried out by ships of the Fleet during 1851, but precise details of the equipment have not survived. When illumination from below was not possible the light had to be placed in the binnacle hood where the problems of smoking lamps and dripping oil were only too evident.

Johnson was frequently called upon to conduct trials of 'new inventions', often proposed by gentlemen of rank, both British and foreign, whom Their Lordships considered should be given a fair hearing. Particularly persistent were those with schemes to insulate the compass from the local attraction of the ship's iron. The Superintendent of the Compass Observatory had learnt a great deal since the days when he experimented with a compass on glass pillars during the *Garryowen* trials of 1835. When, therefore, in 1846, Dr Jennings applied to the Admiralty for a remuneration for his patent 'insulating compass' (Patent No. 4259 of 1818) Johnson informed them, 'So far as our present knowledge extends, there is no substance in nature which will cut off the action of one magnet upon another.'[64] Nevertheless, this was a good compass which had been taken by Commander John Ross on his Arctic expedition of 1818 and was again used by his nephew, James Ross, in the Antarctic in 1839, when he had commented "it continued to act when no other compass would".[65] Sir John Ross's report had however shown clearly that it experienced the same deviation as all the other compasses on board.[66] Other ingenious designs by a long list of inventors headed alphabetically by Baron de Bade (one of many barons to submit ideas) were all examined and tested, several specimens being preserved in the compass collection at the National Maritime Museum. Not surprisingly their performance seldom approached the imaginative claims made for them by their inventors. Another suggestion that frequently cropped up was to slew the card on the needle to correct for variation, an idea first tried in the fifteenth century (see p. xviii), and there was also an ingenious steering compass designed by Captain Sparkes, in which the spaces between the graduations on the card were varied so as to allow for the deviation.[67] There was even a compass by Napier with a type of 'off course alarm system' that was many years ahead of its time.[68] All these suggestions were studied and their utility assessed and reported on with the utmost courtesy.[69]

In 1846 an enquiry of a different nature led Johnson to carry out a series of observations at Euston Square and Camden Town stations to determine the likely effect of passing trains on compass testing at Charlton. A proposal by the North Kent Railway to run a branch through Woolwich was being vigorously opposed by Sir Maryan Wilson on whose land the Compass Observatory stood.[70] The line was however successfully opened a few years later and must have been a boon to superintendents of the Observatory travelling to and from London.

Probably one of Johnson's strangest tasks came when he was asked to report to the Admiralty on a 'telephone' being shown in the Great Exhibition of 1851. This consisted of a large trumpet mounted on an air chest from which four metal reeds could produce different sounds. The chest was so constructed that it could also be used for supplying air to divers! Johnson commented favourable on the possible use of the system as an alarm signal, 'instead of using, as at present, the gun, the bell, the drum and the steam whistle', but was doubtful whether the variations of pitch would be distinguishable in a strong wind.[71] Although Captain Beechey of the Board of Trade had informed Johnson that the committee's compass had been adjudged the best azimuth compass in the Exhibition, for some reason the Admiralty does not appear to have figured in the list of successful exhibitors.[72]

In 1849 Lieutenant Colonel Sabine, then Foreign Secretary to the Royal Society, designed 'A small Apparatus to be used with a ship's Standard Compass' which, by means of a deflector, enabled that part of the ship's deviation which changes with latitude to be determined at sea without the requirement to swing.[73] After Johnson had conducted trials at Greenhithe and suggested a number of practical improvements, the apparatus was tried at sea both in northern regions and at the Cape of Good Hope, but it does not appear to have been widely adopted. Possibly Johnson himself was not convinced of its necessity for, as he wrote to Sabine:

> If the regulations for swinging ships on foreign Stations, observing Amplitudes and Azimuths upon the points of No Deviation and those of greatest deviation at Sea, and thus by a most easy, obvious and effective operation reform the Deviation Table for any change of geographical position, will not keep us right: If by constant observation of Azimuths on the course which the Ship may be steering, the bearings of Planets or known Stars when on the Meridian of the place (which in Ships having Chronometers there would be no difficulty about) and if in addition to these most simple means we join those of the Deflecting Apparatus (if successful) we cannot discover the error of the Compass and know the course we are steering, I really do not know what process could be devised.[74]

Throughout Johnson's time as superintendent, no consideration that might further the efficient functioning of the magnetic compass in Her Majesty's ships or improve Navigation appears to have escaped his notice. He was particularly interested in the changes in a ship's magnetic state with change of latitude and constantly stressed the importance of swinging on arrival on a foreign station and frequently thereafter, even listing the ports where deviation tables should be obtained. No new steamship was allowed to go to sea before being swung[75] and he arranged that ships in reserve – Advance ships as they were called – should be swung and a deviation table kept on board so that they could be brought forward at a moment's notice. (Despite this instruction, in 1859 the *Princess Alice* was found to be navigating with a deviation table issued to the *Onyx* in 1846!) Compasses of Advance ships were to be stowed below in the compass closets and examined quarterly. He redesigned the ship's log-book so that 'more space should be allotted to the register of the necessary elements for ascertaining the ship's position and less to the commonplace narrative of proceedings'.[76] In particular the deviation allowed on each course, the set of the tide, bearings and soundings were all to be recorded. In the same year, by an Order in Council dated 20 March 1845, it became the practice that all officers passing at the Royal Naval College should 'in future be examined in the principles and application of local attraction of Compasses'.[77]

On the material side, when in 1848 the Admiralty had curtailed the supply of Standard Compasses, Johnson made strenuous efforts to obtain suitable alternative azimuth and binnacle compasses from manufacturers at reasonable prices, exhorting the Storekeeper-General to buy new compasses and sell off or destroy the worthless items in store, rather than wasting money on their repair. He called for a return of all compasses held in the yards, according to their classification, maker and state of serviceability, which revealed that, with the addition of the 2150 instruments at sea, the 'number of compasses belonging to the Service' then stood at 3256.[78] Only 230 of these were the new Standard Compasses. Shortly afterwards a further personal examination by Johnson of the compasses in store at Woolwich led to almost 50 per cent being condemned to be 'broken or destroyed in such a manner as to render it impossible for them to be used again either in the Royal Navy or the Merchant Navy'.[79] In the following year Woolwich became the main holding-yard for compasses so that those returned from repair could be tested at the Observatory before going into store, and a quarterly return was instituted on the state of all compasses held in dockyards.

But pressure for further economies in the cost of running the Compass Department continued, and at the end of 1852, only six weeks before he died, we find Johnson proposing to Their Lordships a major reform of the arrangements for compass repair. This envisaged setting up at Woolwich 'a Section expressly for the purpose of refitting and repairing compasses'.[80] As in the days of the 'Compass Makers of Deptford' (see p. xxi) all repair work would be concentrated in one place and men of known reliability and expertise could be employed. This time, however, they would work expressly under the directions of the Superintendent of the Compass Department, so that their work could be monitored and the charges compared with those made by instrument-makers. The scheme could have been very effective, but because of Johnson's untimely death, it was never tried.

In 1849 and for several years thereafter, considerable attention was given to the proper equipping of the many expeditions sent out in search of Sir John Franklin who, in 1845 at the age of 59, had sailed with the *Erebus* and *Terror* on his third attempt to discover a North-West Passage.[81] These expeditions presented a unique opportunity for gathering further knowledge of the magnetic conditions in high latitudes. All ships taking part were supplied with Standard Compasses and Johnson himself supervised their swings at Greenhithe. As he wrote in the Admiralty's instructions to the ships concerned:

> The observations made at Greenhithe furnish the requisite preliminaries for ascertaining at any time the correct variation, by placing the ship's head upon one of the points of *no deviation* and observing an Azimuth, thus quickly and effectually accomplishing that object, and in like manner the amount of change of Deviation may be obtained by placing the Ship's head upon the points of *greatest deviation* and observing Azimuths the results of which afford the means of reforming the Tables of Deviation as described in the 'Practical Rules'.[82]

Johnson asked that these observations be taken at every 7 or 8 degrees change of latitude in addition to noting the deflection with Colonel Sabine's apparatus.

That Johnson was supremely conscientious and meticulous comes out clearly from his letter books, now held by the National Maritime Museum. These registers comprise sixteen separate volumes for correspondence with the Admiralty, Naval Officers, Dockyard Authorities, Instrument-makers and, for a short period, with his Assistant Superintendent. This volume was continued after 1849 for correspondence with Master Attendants and the Masters of flagships. There is also an interesting Miscellaneous volume containing letters from inventors, scientists (including Sir Edward Sabine and the Astronomer Royal) and others with 'suggestions' to offer. In each book the letters received are pasted in at one end while at the other Johnson copied his Out letters in his small, neat hand. When, about the year 1850, the electric telegraph became available, these messages were also included to complete the record. Each volume was carefully indexed and the collection gives a detailed and comprehensive account of the compass history of the period as well as an insight into the many administrative problems he had to handle.[83]

Most of Johnson's correspondence was conducted from his home at 13 Oxford Terrace, Paddington, London, where he lived from 1841 until his death. Each year he would apply for leave in October which he invariably took in Northumberland, staying with friends at Eastfield House, Warkworth, near Alnwick, not far from his birthplace at Bywell, where his father had been the vicar. Except during the period when Commander Strange was in post all official correspondence seems to have been redirected to him there and on at least two occasions he returned from leave early to deal with urgent problems.

After Johnson's death the care with which the letter books were kept gradually diminished. Evans, with assistance from Mr Brunton, maintained most of them until he was appointed Chief Naval Assistant to the Hydrographer in 1865. Thereafter his successor, Mayes, took little trouble over them. When, in 1870, an office for the Compass Branch was opened in London, they finally ceased and from then until 1912 all compass correspondence was handled entirely within the hydrographic organization.

Throughout Johnson's time in the Compass Department there were many naval officers who still refused to accept that there could be anything wrong with the indications of the magnetic compass; alternatively, there were those who considered that it could never be anything but capricious and unreliable. Both schools seem to have had difficulty in appreciating the vital importance of ascertaining and allowing for the deviation at all times. In an attempt to highlight the dangers to navigation, Johnson found time to write his book

Practical Illustrations of the Necessity for Ascertaining the Deviations of the Compass, which he initially had printed for private circulation. Later he was persuaded to submit it to the Admiralty and in 1847 it was published with their sanction and issued to all HM steam vessels and all Masters Attendant.[84] A second edition containing much additional matter was published in 1852.

The book shows that Johnson had made a considerable study of the compass problem and of its history, as he quotes extensively from earlier writers. The first part deals with the consequences of ignoring the deviations of the compass and contains accounts of many famous shipwrecks; how the frigate *Apollo* and forty of her convoy were wrecked off the coast of Portugal in 1803; of the *Reliance* which in 1842 grounded off Boulogne, her crew believing themselves to be close to Dungeness; the case of the *Courageux* which grounded in the Baltic in 1812 due to a stand of arms placed on the main deck below the binnacle; and many other well documented cases. Johnson pointed out that Britain alone was losing through stranding, 550 ships a year, or a ship and a half a day. A section on the design of compasses, quoting from Peter Barlow's report on their appalling state in 1820, and containing more recent examples of his own, leads naturally to an account of the work of the Admiralty Compass Committee and a description of the Admiralty Standard Compass. Testing compasses at the Observatory and reports on some of the trials carried out aboard ships is followed by a précis of the current regulations covering their use and care, in which the *safe-distance regulations* and the *Practical Rules* are reproduced verbatim. Typical examples of the deviation tables for actual ships are included to illustrate the magnitude of the error likely to be found even with a well-placed compass, and the changes which could arise through a change of armament, structural alterations to the ship or simply raising or lowering the funnel or propeller. To emphasize the fact that the deviation tables provided were applicable in one locality only, tables are included showing how the errors varied with change in geographical position, thus underlining the warning given in every edition of the *Practical Rules*. There is a cautionary note about the effects of heel on the compass error but no advice as to its cause or how to cope with it, again showing that Johnson had not fully grasped the problem.

The final section contains much additional information on magnetism, listing the principal works on the subject, also an excellent historical section on local attraction, with further graphic examples.

Despite its shortcomings this was a most worthy book which is believed to be the first attempt in any language to write a complete manual on the use of the magnetic compass at sea. Johnson's work provided a sound foundation upon which his successors could build. Alas, his warnings could not have prevented the tragic loss of the *Birkenhead* off Cape Agulhas in 1852, in which 432 soldiers were drowned.

The loss of the Birkenhead

The *Birkenhead* was one of the iron paddle-frigates ordered by the Admiralty in 1842–44. A ship of 1400 tons, she was built by John Laird of Birkenhead and launched in December 1845. Shortly before her completion the Admiralty decided against the use of iron frigates and she was converted to a troopship, being given a high forecastle and poop to increase the accommodation. The latter provided a suitable site for the Standard Compass which was supported by wooden beams 11 feet above the iron top sides. Despite deviations of up to 18°, magnetically this position appears to have been remarkably stable. Johnson took great pains over this ship. No less than five swings were carried out in England during the years 1847–51 and these show almost complete consistency, the points of no deviation and of maximum remaining constant throughout.[85] The ship had a wheel both on the poop and on the quarter-deck, magnets being used as deviation-reducers at the lower position only.

Under Commander Salmon, an experienced Master, the *Birkenhead* made trooping runs to Halifax and the Cape of Good Hope during 1851 and was one of the first iron naval vessels to operate in the southern hemisphere. Although it is known that she was swung while in Canada, there is unfortunately no record of this having been done at the Cape. Early the following year she again sailed for South Africa with urgently needed reinforcements for the Kaffir Wars, and after a brief two-day stay at Simonstown for fuel and stores was ordered on to Algoa Bay. Eight hours later, at 0200 on 26 February 1852 she struck a reef less than two miles off Danger Point, west of Cape Agulhas.

The story of the loss of the *Birkenhead*, from which only 193 persons were saved out of a total of 638, has been eloquently told elsewhere,[86] a tale of heroism and discipline which rang round the world. The mood of the nation was caught in a beautiful if somewhat fanciful poem by Sir Francis Doyle, later professor of poetry at Oxford:

Right on our flank the crimson sun went down,
    The deep sea rolled around in dark repose . . .

The stout ship Birkenhead lay hard and fast,
    Caught without hope upon a hidden rock . . .

and so on for fourteen sonorous verses. Of the cause of the wreck there can be no doubt. The ship was hugging the shore off a coast that had not been fully surveyed.[87] The initial Board of Enquiry at the Cape and the subsequent court martial of the survivors in England both looked at the possibility of the compass being at fault but dismissed it, even as a contributory cause. It is true that the ship had not been swung on arrival at a foreign station, in accordance with the regulations, but her stay had been extremely short. Salmon was a man of considerable experience in whom Johnson had great confidence. He frequently commented on the satisfactory performance of his compass, even mentioning it during his brief stay at the Cape, and it is inconceivable that he had not kept a check on its error. Further, as Johnson pointed out, the ship's course at the time (SSE$\frac{1}{2}$E) was very near one of the points of 'no deviation'.

There the matter might well have rested had not Sir John Ross (now aged 75) written a letter to the *Nautical Standard* blaming the loss unequivocally on the Compass Department and the Admiralty's policy and suggesting that the ship was lost because she was navigating in southern latitudes with a table of deviations given to her in England by Captain Johnson. When Johnson sought Their Lordships' support in answering these damaging allegations they declined, stating that they did 'not think it desirable to notice such communications'.[88] Not surprisingly Johnson was dissatisfied and felt compelled to write to them in his own defence. In a well-reasoned statement dated 4 June 1852, which was supported by much documentary evidence, he firmly refuted the many false statements in Sir John's assertions, drawing attention to the repeated warnings in the *Practical Rules* and elsewhere concerning the change of deviation with change of latitude. When, therefore, in a parliamentary question on 17 June, Sir George Pechell asked the Secretary of the Admiralty 'whether the attention of the Board had been drawn to a letter in the public papers from an Admiral in Her Majesty's service respecting the loss of the 'Birkenhead' steamer, and complaining of the manner in which the duties were performed at Greenhithe by that Scientific Officer, Captain Johnson RN', the Secretary had a detailed reply ready to hand. He had only to add that the Board 'did not feel in any degree disposed to withdraw the great confidence which they had in the gallant officer who had been so truly described . . . as that 'Scientific Officer', Captain Johnson.'[89]

A report of this exchange, published in *The Times* (18 June 1852), produced a measure of support for Johnson in the nautical press and a partial retraction from Sir John Ross. Nevertheless such an accusation by a national figure had already done immense damage to the standing of the Compass Department, so painfully built up over the previous ten years.

Captain Johnson died at his home in Paddington on 7 February 1853, just three months before his fifty-ninth birthday, the cause of his death being given as tubercular disease of the liver. He had begun his work on magnetic compass problems in the early 1820s and had devoted some thirty years of his life to the care and improvement of the compass, constantly drawing attention to its significance and to the dangers inherent in its improper use. For the most part he had had to work entirely on his own and it had often been an uphill struggle against prejudice and obstruction. On matters of policy he had been prudent yet progressive, always keeping an open mind on such subjects as compass design and correction, where experience or new conditions might indicate the need for a change. Their Lordships' confidence in him had indeed been well placed for he had established the Compass Department on a sound footing from which, with enlightened supervision, it could well become a force to be reckoned with in the second half of the nineteenth century. His contribution is admirably summed up by Commander W. E. May in his memoir on this splendid officer: 'He had worked hard and conscientiously to serve the Royal Navy and if his efforts had not always been crowned with success, few could have done as well.'[90]

NOTES

CHAPTER 1

[1] ADM 106/2531

[2] ADM 1/1809, No. 130A.

[3] C. C. Lloyd, *Mr Barrow of the Admiralty*, London, 1970.

[4] ADM 235/20.

[5] Barrow was a man of many interests and had been largely responsible for the Navy's active participation in Arctic exploration. With Beaufort, he had been among those instrumental in founding the Royal Geographical Society and he took an active interest in the compass problem.

[6] It was his great grandson, Captain T. D. Ross, RN, who, 124 years later, became the last naval director of the Admiralty Compass Observatory.

[7] These specimens and a number obtained from foreign navies formed the nucleus of a unique magnetic compass collection which is now held by the National Maritime Museum, Greenwich.

[8] ADM 106/2531.

[9] *Phil. Trans.* Royal Society, Vol. 121, (1831).

[10] Minutes of the meeting of the Admiralty Committee on Ships' Compasses, 9 March 1839.

[11] Johnson's recipe for the cement to be used was: 'Half a drahm of Isinglass, moistened an hour or two with cold water and dissolved in 1/4 of an oz. of Spirits of Wine. One Scruple of Gum Ammonicum, rubbed down with a drahm of water. These ingredients are to be stirred over a water bath and then smoothly and expeditiously laid on the mica or the paper.'

[12] Major Sabine's letter to Baufort is dated 22 December and is referred to again on 19 January, but no year is given. It is not therefore possible to tell at what stage the committee first heard of this important proposal.

[13] Report on the Admiralty Committee on Ship's Compasses, Appendix G (see note 25).

[14] ADM 1/2436, Capt. R (61).

[15] 'Col. Sabine's report on Magnetic Surveys', *Phil. Trans. Royal Society*, 1870.

[16] Hydrographer's Letter Book, No. 8, p. 282.

[17] Hydrographer's Minute Book, No. 3, p. 65.

[18] Sir J. C. Ross, *A Voyage of Discovery in the Southern and Antarctic Seas*, London, 1847.

[19] In 1831 Commander James Ross had also had the honour of planting the British flag on the north magnetic pole, on the west coast of the Boothia peninsula, in position 70° 05'N, 96°47'W, when on an overland journey from his uncle's ship, the *Victory*, which was beset during the ill-fated expedition of 1829–33.

[20] J. C. Ross, *A Voyage of Discovery*.

[21] L. S. Dawson, *Memoirs of Hydrography*, 1885 (reprinted by Cornmarket Press, 1969).

22 M. J. Ross, *Ross of the Antarctic*, Whitby, 1982.

23 *Phil. Trans. Royal Society*, 1843, Part 2, p. x; 1844, Part 2, p.vii; 1866; 1868.

24 Hydrographer's Letter Book, No. 7.

25 ADM 235, No. 20. Additional notes and comments on the work of the committee can be found in W. E. May, 'Compass Department memoirs', 1953–54; National Maritime Museum. Compass Collection, Item 8(b).

26 Half a century later the *Rate Book of Naval Stores* for 1891–92 still quoted the price as £25, 'Complete with 2 cards, 6 pivots, 1 spare cap, Azimuth Circle, Sprang, Reading Glass and Tripod'.

27 National Maritime Museum, Magnetic Compass Collection, Pamphlet P1 (1), 1842. Initially the pamphlet cost 3d. By 1862 it had been considerably expanded, mainly at the suggestion of Archibald Smith, and cost a shilling. The edition of 1899, once more abbreviated, was sold at 2d!

28 Hydrographer's Letter Book, No. 10. p. 354.

29 ADM 1/1809, No. 130A.

30 Captain Johnson's appointment as Superintendent of the Compass Department does not, however, appear in the Navy List until March 1848.

31 ADM 235. No. 20.

32 Correspondence registers, 1842–71, with some letters of more recent date, are held by the Public Record Office under Section ADM 235.

33 1st edn (1847), pp. 38–40; 2nd edn (1852), pp. 70–740.

34 Before 1827 no steam vessel was allowed to be prefixed 'HMS', the first to appear in the Navy List being HMS *Lightning* (1828).

35 A. J. Watts, *Pictorial History of the Royal Navy*, Vol. I, Shepperton, Ian Allen, 1970.

36 Admiralty Circular, No. 9 (20 November 1845). This circular was later incorporated in the *Queen's Regulations and Admiralty Instructions*.

37 ADM 235, M/1, p. 192.

38 As an interesting comment on economy it may be noted that orders were given in 1843 that dockyards were to provide worn hawsers for this operation so that the ships' own hawsers should be preserved.

39 ADM 235, M/O, p. 77.

40 Admiralty Circular, No. 105 (13 May 1852).

41 ADM 235, M/13 (Out), p. 87.

42 ADM 235, M/O (Out), p. 111.

43 ADM 235, M/1, p. 25.

44 ADM 235, M/11, p. 19.

45 ADM 235, M/11, p. 40.

46 ADM 235, M/1, p. 6.

47 ADM 235, M/1, p. 27.

48 ADM 235, M/O (Out), p. 86. Rear Admiral William Bowles was 'A commissioner for executing the office of Lord High Admiral of the United Kingdom of Great Britain and Ireland' (Navy List, 1845).

49 Although the London to Gosport line had been opened in 1842 (largely for the benefit of Queen Victoria's visits to Osborne) and that from London to Exeter, via Bath and Bristol, had followed in 1844, it was not until 1849 that it reached the outskirts of Plymouth.

50 ADM 235, M/13.

51 ADM 235, M/13 (Out), p. 15.

52 Strange was promoted to Captain in 1854 and after further commands eventually achieved the rank of Admiral on the retired list, in 1880. For almost a century he was the only officer from the Compass Department to have reached flag rank. However, in 1971 Captain P. A. Watson, who had served at the Admiralty Compass Observatory as a Temporary Experimental Assistant in 1939–40, before joining the Navy, was promoted to Rear Admiral. He retired in 1976 as Vice-Admiral Sir Philip Watson KBE, MVO, after five distinguished years as Director-General of the Weapons Department, during which he had under his jurisdiction the successors of the original Compass Department.

53 ADM 235, M/13 (Out), p. 106.

54 ADM 235, M/O, p. 93.

55 Hydrographer's Letter Book, No. 14, p. 108.

56 Johnson had tested an early version of Walker's compass at the Observatory and at sea, but had serious reservations as to its accuracy. Nevertheless Walker had persevered and later designs proved more successful. ADM 235, M/O (Out), pp. 49–51.

57 ADM 235, M/1, p. 36.

58 ADM 235, M/1, p. 59.

59 ADM 235, M/1, p. 127.

60 ADM 235, M/O, p. 101.

61 Hydrographer's Minute Book, No. 9, p. 230.

62 ADM 235, M/13 (Out), p. 57.

63 Mr Brunton was later to receive an honourable mention at the International Exhibition of 1862 'for a binnacle lamp securing the efficiency of light and ventilation in strong winds'.

64 ADM 235, M/O (Out) p. 147; M/1, pp. 2, 9.

65 *Catalogue of the Admiralty Collection of Magnetic Compasses*, 1930, Item 14.

66 ADM 235, M/13, p. 59.

67 ADM 235, M/13 (Out), p. 57.

68 ADM 235, M/10, p. 33; M/11, p. 29.

69 The patent specifications of many of these inventions are held with the Magnetic Compass Collection at the National Maritime Museum, Greenwich.

70 ADM 235, M/O (Out), pp. 118, 121.

71 ADM 235, M/1, p. 284.

72 ADM 235, M/11, p. 27.

73 National Maritime Museum, Magnetic Compass Collection, Pamphlet 9/6 (10).

74 ADM 235, M/9 (out), p. 121.

75 Regulations today still require that a new ship should be swung early on the first day of her sea trials.

[76] ADM 235, M/1, p. 17.

[77] Order in council, 20 March 1848.

[78] ADM 235, M/1, p. 102.

[79] ADM 235, M/1, p. 120.

[80] ADM 235, M/1, p. 337.

[81] Between 1848 and 1865 no less than 11 public and 10 private expeditions (the latter mainly funded by Lady Franklin) were sent on this quest. Captain Sir Leopold M'Clintock's search (1857–59) eventually found a tin case near Cape Victoria containing a statement that the ships had been beset in September 1846 and abandoned in April 1848. Sir John Franklin had died in June 1847. Further relics continued to be found until 1879. Dawson, *Memoirs of Hydrography*.

[82] ADM 235, M/1, p. 179.

[83] As a small example, the rates on the property at Charlton involved the county rate, the church rate, the highway rate, the police rate, the poor rate, the sewer rate, and the water rate! Each is referred to separately at different times in the correspondence.

[84] E. J. Johnson, *Practical Illustrations of the Necessity of Ascertaining the Deviations of the Compass*, London, 1847.

[85] Ibid., 2nd edn, 1852. p. 36.

[86] A. C. Addison and W. H. Matthews, *A Deathless Story – The Birkenhead and its Heroes*, Hutchinson, 1906.

[87] ADM 235, M/11, pp. 46, 49.

[88] National Maritime Museum, Magnetic Compass Collection, Pamphlet P10 (7).

[89] Ibid.

[90] National Maritime Museum, Magnetic Compass Collection, Item R8 (2).

The first Ironclads and the development of compass theory under Captain F.J.O. Evans F.R.S., 1855–65

2

The laborious and persevering devotion to the compass problem which has been shown by British mathematicians and practical men, by Sabine, Scoresby, Airy, Archibald Smith, by Captains Johnson and Evans of the Compass Department of the Admiralty, and by Townson and Rundell, who acted as secretaries to the Liverpool Compass Committee, has been an honour to the British nation in the eyes of the world.' (From Sir William Thomson's obituary notice on Archibald Smith, *Proceedings of the Royal Society*, No. 150, 1874)

The spring of 1853 saw war between Turkey and Russia, with international tension mounting further as an Anglo-French naval force was despatched to the Dardanelles to encourage Turkish resistance. When, however, in November of that year a Turkish squadron was annihilated at Sinope, national honour and the impending menace of the Russian Mediterranean fleet ranged Britain and France firmly on the side of the Turks. War was declared on 27 January 1854 and the Royal Navy became involved in hostilities both in the Crimea and the Baltic.

This was the first full-scale war since 1815. Inevitably after almost forty years of peace punctuated by frequent defence cuts the Royal Navy had been badly neglected. Modernization had been cautious and minimal. True there were a handful of ships-of-the line fitted with a screw which gave them mobility, but all were converted wooden sailing-ships. The Navy, which had not got a single iron fighting ship, now faced a war in which the new Paixham's shell would be used in action for the first time, and by the Russians. Iron ships and armour-plate were needed as never before. Suddenly it was apparent that the long supremacy of England's wooden walls, so jealously guarded, was dramatically over.

Meanwhile the Compass Department had been without a Super-intendent for over a year. Ever since its formation in 1842 there had been those in authority who considered the department something of an extravagence. Such people now saw no purpose in its continu-ation. Johnson's methods had often been openly criticized. His system of sending all compasses to Woolwich for test and his meticulous accounting and storage arrangements were foreign to the normal system of naval store-keeping. Attitudes to the compass itself were still divided and many considered that these could as easily be bought from any reputable instrument-maker or ship's chandler; the importance of swinging and constantly checking deviation was not yet universally understood and accepted. More-over, the Compass Department had suffered severely from the cuts made on it in 1848 while the bad publicity which followed the *Birkenhead* tragedy had seriously shaken its prestige. Admiral Beau-fort, the revered head of the Hydrographic Department was now approaching 80 and for some years had had little reason to intervene in compass matters. On Johnson's death, the Admiralty, which had many pressing problems to occupy it, seems to have decided just to let things be and see what happened.[1]

For two years Mr Brunton, the compass-examiner and ex-Sergeant of Artillery, was left to struggle on alone, which he did in a most creditable manner. He continued his testing, corresponding freely with the manufacturers and drawing attention to any shortcomings in their work; he placed orders for repairs and hastened them to keep to promised dates; he checked the prices claimed, challenging any over-charging and generally endeavoured to maintain the same tight control that Johnson had always achieved. If manufacturers thought they might now get away with shoddy work they were gravely mistaken. On one occasion, after examining a batch of compasses for the Board of Trade, Mr Brunton returned them all with a detailed list of faults, finishing with the remark, 'I decline having anything to do with these instruments unless they are in every respect the same as those you supply to the Royal Navy.'[2]

Except on the Thames all swinging was undertaken by the Masters Attendant who still rendered returns to the Compass Department where they were checked by Mr Brunton. Although he was always courteous when pointing out mistakes, it seems that some Masters resented this practice and were reluctant to send him their observations. As a consequence, in March 1854 the new 51-gun screw-steamship *Euryalus* nearly went ashore after being given a card by the Master of the *Wellington* on which westerly deviation was marked east, and vice versa. This was by no means an isolated instance.

During the two years he was on his own Mr Brunton successfully conducted more than thirty swings himself, including the iron steam packet *Dover*, whose compass was corrected by five bar magnets. It was thus a little unfair when, in November 1853, in reply to a question from the Secretary of the Admiralty about his competence to superintend the swinging of ships, the Hydrographer replied, 'I think not. None but a seaman can well superintend the operation which involves the veering and hauling on various guys and hawsers, and none but a seaman can command the requisite attention and obedience.'[3]

Although never given the authority of acting superintendent Mr Brunton was nevertheless authorized to sign the certificates from Masters, acknowledging the safe return of their Standard Compasses so that they could receive their pay. He was asked advice as to what compasses to fit in new ships and he arranged sea trials of new designs, including Gowland's very beautiful spherical compass which had a vertical card and was sometimes fitted as an elevated steering-compass as it could be read from below. He even turned down a number of suggestions by other inventors, basing his opinion on Johnson's register of earlier trials. He examined the quarterly returns of compasses from the dockyards and on one occasion carried out an examination of the compasses in store at Woolwich, condemning many which he considered 'totally unworthy of repair'. However, such was the financial squeeze imposed on the Compass Department during 1853 that no payments were permitted without authority from the Hydrographic Office and three months after Johnson's death Mr Brunton even had to request that he should continue to be paid his salary! The expenses for the whole department for the year 1853–54 amounted to only £373 while the estimates for the following year were originally submitted as £547. 2. 6, of which £370 was for the repair of Standard Compasses.[4] In 1854, however, the demand for compasses increased dramatically to meet the needs of a rapidly expanding Fleet and of the many merchant vessels being taken up for war service. Testing these compasses placed a heavy load on Mr Brunton yet, despite pressure from the dockyards, he was insistent that the choice of firm for their manufacture or repair should remain under the sole control of the Compass Department so that the most appropriate instrument-maker would be employed.

The correspondence registers, which were faithfully maintained by Mr Brunton, show that letters from Beaufort during this period tended to be brief, curt and formal, a style which perhaps befitted an admiral addressing a former sergeant of artillery. A marked change occurs, however, in 1854 when, because of the war, Captain John Washington was appointed to assist Beaufort during his last year in office. He freely sought Mr Brunton's help and received much sound advice. When in 1855 he took over as Hydrographer, one of his first acts was to send the Admiralty a full report on the Compass Department, pointing out that two years after the death of Captain Johnson, the post of Superintendent had still not been filled.

A number of candidates had, in fact, been considered. Captain Robert Fitzroy (of the *Beagle*) had written to Beaufort on 8 February 1853, the very day after Johnson died, to say that he had applied for the post but no reply to this letter can be traced, and Fitzroy went on to found and direct the new Meteorological Department of the Board of Trade. Nevertheless his interest in compasses continued and in 1857 he published an excellent pamphlet on *Swinging Ship for Deviation*, which was subsequently adopted by the Board of Trade.[5] In March 1853 Beaufort proposed the appointment of Mr George Johnston as superintendent, a Master with some thirty years experience, but he appears to have declined as, six months later, did two others[6] after which the subject appears to have been dropped.

Washington's detailed report on the Compass Department[7] began with a brief (and slightly inaccurate) historical survey, listing the duties of the Superintendent and mentioning the excellently designed

Standard Compass and the importance of placing it carefully. Turning to changes since 1842 it pointed to the greater use of iron in ships and the increased speeds encountered, 'the speed with which steamers now dash along at a rate of 10 and 12 miles an hour', underlining the hazards by listing recent notable wrecks attributable to the compass. The controversy over correction was discussed in the light of the British Association meeting of 1854 which had led directly to the setting up of the Liverpool Compass Committee (see p. 58) in which Washington foresaw Admiralty involvement ('To whom should they be referred?'). Finally it emphasized the urgent need to appoint a superintendent immediately to handle the many problems of a fleet involved in a difficult campaign in the Baltic Sea. The full text of this excellent report is reproduced as appendix 4. Accompanying this report was a note from Washington which read: 'Should Their Lordships approve of the above suggestions, I would further submit for approval the name of Mr Frederick Evans, Master RN, long employed in the survey service and the officer who seems to me best qualified for these duties.'

Mr Frederick John Owen Evans was appointed on 16 March 1855, only four days after the date of the report. He was a Master of the old school who had joined the Navy in 1828 at the age of 13 and his career had kept him almost continuously at sea. He had served on almost every naval station, being employed largely on survey duties, and during 1854, had been actively engaged in the Baltic where he was mentioned in despatches for his work in piloting ships into Bomarsund. He was thus a very experienced seaman but, unlike Johnson, he had seldom had contact with the problem of ship magnetism. Nevertheless he set about learning this new science with great enthusiasm and very quickly began to revive the flagging reputation of the department.

Although Johnson had always maintained a close and friendly contact with the Hydrographic Office, he had for the most part acted independently, conducting his affairs directly with the Board through the Secretary of the Admiralty. Evans, on the other hand, had been brought up to regard the Hydrographer as his supreme authority and from the start appears to have behaved as though the Compass Department was under the direct control of the Hydrographic Office, passing submissions through Captain Washington and generally deferring to him on all major matters. Not surprisingly, when in 1856 the staff of the Hydrographer appeared in the Navy List for the first time, it included the Superintendent of Compasses. The Compass Department was thus no longer an independent unit and when, in 1865, Evans was appointed Chief Naval Assistant to the Hydrographer while retaining responsibility for 'The Magnetic Department', integration with the Hydrographic Office was complete. So it was to remain until the year 1912.

It is probable that Evans never ceased to be primarily a surveyor at heart, yet the ten years from 1855 during which he was directly involved in compass matters were of immense significance, covering as they did a critical period in the Navy's history. The Admiralty had at last realized that, much as it had disliked the idea of iron ships, they were here to stay. Moreover, although the Navy had survived the war with Russia, it was not long before relations between Britain and France became seriously strained, and France already had a number of iron warships superior to anything in the Royal Navy. The race to build a modern fleet suddenly acquired a new urgency.

This was a period which called for radical new thinking, but the Compass Department had only recently changed hands and Evans was not cast naturally in that mould. His brief, as he saw it, was to *implement* the recommendations of the Compass Committee of 1840, not to question them. He would proceed with caution, and progress would be gradual rather than spectacular. As a result a number of major opportunities were missed, the effects of which were to be felt by the navy for many years.

But in 1855 all this lay in the future. In other directions there were important advances to be made. Soon after taking office Evans was brought into contact with Archibald Smith, the barrister and mathematician who had first entered the compass field in 1841, when he had advised the Admiralty Committee on the arrangement of compass needles necessary to achieve a uniformly balanced card (see p. 7). Having had his interest drawn to the compass problem by his friend Major Sabine, over the next few years Smith had presented a series of papers to the Royal Society[8] in which he derived, from Poisson's original fundamental equations, a series of elegant and precise formulae which were both practical and easy to apply, enabling the various portions of a ship's magnetism to be analysed numerically. He thus succeeded for the first time in reducing a very complex problem to a set of rules and coefficients which could be readily understood by the intelligent non-mathematician and which, in their essentials, are still in use today. At Captain Johnson's suggestion, this brilliant simplification of the subject was introduced to the Navy in a pamphlet entitled *Instructions for the Computation of a Table of Deviations of the Ship's Compass from Deviations Observed on 4, 8, 16 or 32 Points; and for the adjustment of the table in a change of magnetic latitude*, published in 1851 as a supplement to the *Practical Rules*.[9] A brief explanation of Archibald Smith's coefficients is given in appendix 5.

Evans and Smith clearly took to each other at once and an active and fruitful working relationship developed which, over the next fifteen years, yielded a succession of fundamental papers and publications on the theory and practice of compass behaviour which were of inestimable value to Britain and to the world.

Compass Correction

Since 1852 the *Practical Rules* had included a brief reference to the possibility of reducing deviations by the use of magnets. However, although the 1856 edition drew particular attention to Smith's pamphlet, which showed how the permanent and induced coefficients could be obtained, at no stage was any reference made to Airy's comprehensive system of correction, using magnets and soft iron. The opposing schools of thought on the matter of compass correction were probably even more firmly entrenched than they had been fifteen years earlier. Despite Johnson's fairly liberal views, the official Admiralty policy was still firmly against it. Archibald Smith, who was well aware of the flaws in Airy's system, supported the Admiralty, as of course did Evans.

During 1855–56 three significant and connected events occurred which had a considerable impact on attitudes to this very important subject. The first has often been described as the Airy–Scoresby controversy; the second, which followed it, was the trial of a new type of binnacle, fitted with correctors, in the iron ship *Trident*; and the third was the setting up of the Liverpool Compass Committee by the shipping interests of that Port. Each is of sufficient importance to merit a brief discussion.

It will be recalled that William Scoresby had rendered considerable assistance to the Compass Committee during their early deliberations (see p. 5) and although he finally fell out with them and withdrew his support his interest in the subject never waned. In 1854 he read a paper to the British Association at its meeting in Liverpool concerning the loss of the iron passenger steamship *Tayleur* which, after having her steering compass corrected by magnets, was wrecked in a severe gale when only one day out on her maiden voyage, with the loss of 290 lives.[10] Scoresby was convinced from a series of experiments he had conducted with iron bars and plates that the magnetic character of a ship was capable of sudden and unforeseeable changes and stated that if the compass was corrected by magnets the situation could well be exacerbated. He therefore regarded Airy's system of correction not only as unsound but as positively dangerous and unequivocably blamed the loss of the *Tayleur* on this cause.

Airy had not attended the meeting at Liverpool. However, although he had always accepted that the magnetism of a new ship was liable to change, he believed that this would be gradual and that after an initial period it would settle down and remain fairly constant. His paper to the Royal Society in 1839 had recommended that this aspect should be checked periodically (see p. xxxix). He therefore felt it necessary to reply to Scoresby with all speed and did so in the form of a letter to the editor of the *Athenaeum*, a prominent weekly journal of the period. Details of the exchanges that followed are well documented[11] and need not be repeated here. Neither side gave any ground.

Airy appears, however, to have decided that more positive action was necessary to promote his views. In November 1855 he read a further paper on compass deviations to the Royal Society,[12] following it with a long letter to Their Lordships on the subject of correction, pressing the merits of his system which he said 'has been adopted in nearly every service in the world, excepting only the Royal Navy of Great Britain'.[13] His paper to the Royal Society, clearly showed that he now accepted that the effect of magnetic induction in the vertical soft iron of a ship could be greater than he had at first believed, also that this portion of the ship's semi-circular deviation should not be corrected by permanent magnets but by a mass of soft iron, either before or abaft the compass, as originally suggested by Flinders in 1812. He made it clear that if this were done 'correction would be complete in all parts of the earth'. At the same time he was aware, and had made the point in his paper of 1839, that the two components could only be separated by making observations in widely differing magnetic latitudes. Airy clearly had doubts as to whether this would be done, for he went on to recommend that practically it would be 'easier and safer' to correct the entire semicircular deviation by means of permanent magnets which should be frequently adjusted. In conclusion he appeared to throw down the gauntlet by denouncing the system of not using correction as 'dangerous and I think it ought to be discontinued', and pressing the case for complete correction with magnets and soft iron, although his arguments were still not altogether sound.

For Airy's idea of frequent adjustment to be practicable some simple scheme for moving the magnets was essential. These facilities were provided in a binnacle designed by J. Gray of Liverpool in 1854 (Patent No. 2741 or 1854),[14] and in his letter to the Admiralty of February 1856 Airy proposed that one of these binnacles should be fitted in every iron ship. As the Admiralty now accepted that it was sometimes necessary to reduce the deviation of steering compasses by means of magnets they gave approval for a trial to be carried out in the iron screw-steamship *Transit*. Some months later the iron paddle-wheel steam vessel *Trident* was substituted, a somewhat lucky chance for Airy as his paper to the Royal Society had shown that in this ship the effect of vertical soft iron was small. In other ways, however, *Trident* was a most suitable choice, being of the same class as the *Birkenhead*, with a history of compass problems. Captain Johnson had experienced considerable difficulty in finding a suitable site for her Standard Compass and in 1852 had found it necessary to reduce the errors of her binnacle compasses with two large magnets.

Airy had a high opinion of Gray who had been using his method for correcting compasses in the ships sailing out of Liverpool for some years. Gray's new binnacle provided the means for supporting permanent magnets in the fore-and-aft and athwartship directions so that they could be moved 'by screws, jacks, pinions or otherwise' towards or away from the compass. It also had a vertical magnet directly below the compass which could be raised or lowered but which required the ship to be heeled for its adjustment. The original patent makes no mention of soft-iron correctors but, probably at Airy's instigation, two 68 lb cannon balls mounted on brass pillars were provided for *Trident*.

The original plan had been to fit two binnacles but Evans became alarmed by their size and their cost (60 guineas) and managed to get the order reduced to one. Airy prepared some instructions for their management which he had printed,[15] but for some reason Gray was refused permission to publish them. Airy's plan, as he explained in a letter to Their Lordships, 'embraced three objects, first perfect correction of the compass . . . secondly the supplying a power of maintaining this perfection of correction . . . thirdly the supplying points of reference *at sea* by a Mast-head Compass (there being no difficulty in obtaining them in harbour)'.[16] However, considerable difficulty was experienced with the mast-head compass in *Trident* which, when placed in the main top, 72 feet above the deck, was still found to have deviations of 17°. Moving it to the foretop reduced these to 10° but it was obviously of only limited value as a standard of reference for correcting the steering compass.

Evans conducted the swinging operations at Greenhithe on 22 and 23 December 1856, assisted by Gray. The maximum deviations found before correction were: Standard Compass 24°, steering compass 33°10', and mast head compass 10°. Gray then adjusted the steering compass with three 1 foot magnets fore-and-aft and one 6 inch magnet athwartship, placing the two 68 lb shot at 15 1/4 inches on either side of the compass, which had a 10 inch needle. The ship was then swung again 'without detecting an error exceeding 1°'.[17]

To correct heeling error with the vertical magnet, Gray had asked for the ship to be healed 20°, which Evans considered excessive, suggesting 8°. In the event *Trident* was under orders to sail as soon as possible and this adjustment was never carried out.

Over the next two years regular and consistently favourable reports[18] were made on the working of the compass from as far away as West Africa and the Cape of Good Hope. The captain, Commander Francis Close, took great pains to make the observations and adjustments himself and considered that these were well within the capability of 'a well-informed Seaman'. He further stated, 'I have always used Mr Gray's Compass as the standard in navigating the ship and find it more trustworthy than the Azimuth Compass.'[19] In bad weather the compass was also considerably steadier.

It is difficult to ascertain from the official correspondence why this excellent binnacle was never adopted or at least given a further trial. In May 1858 and again in the following year Airy approached Evans on the subject, suggesting further fittings in iron ships likely to go to the southern hemisphere. Gray also wrote, after seeing a copy of a report from *Trident*, offering a most favourable tender to supply binnacles to Her Majesty's ships at £42 each, complete with adjustable soft-iron spheres.[20] Evans's reply to all these approaches was courteous but evasive. He was still unwilling to commit himself and his attitude was well summed up in a note to the Hydrographer which he appended to Airy's second letter in June 1859:

> 1. As the present system of non-compensation pursued in the Navy is by the recommendation of a Committee of Officers, can it be subverted except by the recommendation of a similar Committee in possession of all the information on the subject up to the present time? Experiments in continuation of the 'Trident's' would be valuable on condition that any Vessel that may be similarly fitted, is certain of proceeding into the Southern Hemisphere, either rounding Cape of Good Hope or Cape Horn.
> 2. It would be desirable before pronouncing finally on 'Trident's' compass to await her arrival home (probably at the close of the year) and then carefully inspect the adjustment in verification of the reports.
> 3. The question of expense is a serious matter for consideration in any extensive changes in the present system.[21]

These comments were entirely prudent, yet it is clear that Evans still considered himself bound by the decisions of the Compass Committee of 1840 which had been opposed to Airy's system. Probably Archibald Smith, who mistrusted the system, was also against the idea and it seems likely that the advantages of having a closely corrected compass were never thought to outweigh the possible risks involved. Evans may also have feared that the additional expenditure would react unfavourably against the department. Whatever the reason, he appears to have made up his mind that the scheme should go no further.

When, in October 1859, *Trident* returned home from West Africa, she was again swung by Evans off Greenhithe but the fact that the swinging form[22] was not even fully completed shows only too clearly that he no longer had any interest in the results of the trial. The ship was paid off at Woolwich in the same month and the Compass Department did nothing further about Gray's excellent binnacle.

Let us now return to the British Association meeting of 1854 in Liverpool at which Scoresby spoke about the loss of the *Tayleur*. It was an emotive subject and the Reverend Doctor once described by Evans as 'That Ancient Mariner and Venerable Pastor', who was no doubt adept at playing on the feelings of his audience, probably greatly over-emphasized the dangers involved. Certainly he aroused serious alarm amongst the underwriters and ship-owners on Merseyside. His paper was followed by one by John Townson, the secretary of the local Marine Board, who appealed to the British Association to give serious and urgent attention to the compasses of iron ships which, in his view, even if 'managed by the most talented individual . . . were still unworthy of confidence'.[23] In the prevailing climate, the Association could not fail to be receptive. With their help and with the backing of the Board of trade, the Liverpool Compass Committee was appointed by the shipping interests of the port 'To investigate the causes of the deviation of the compass in wooden and iron ships, and to investigate the best means of correcting errors arising from this source, especially in iron ships'.[24] Largely through the effects of its energetic secretary, W. W. Rundell, this committee was responsible for many investigations and trials, including sponsoring the voyage of Dr Scoresby to Australia and around the world in the new iron passenger ship *Royal Charter* to study the changes which take place in a ship's magnetism in the southern hemisphere.[25] Of particular concern to them were the effects of magnetic induction in vertical soft iron, first reported by Flinders fifty years before, and the correction of heeling error, first discussed by Airy in his paper of 1839. In both cases the latest theories were verified by practical experiment and a simple means of correction evolved.

A detailed account of the activities and recommendations of the Liverpool Compass Committee is contained in their three excellent reports which cover the periods 1855, 1856, and 1857–60 respectively,[26] of which the principal findings may be briefly summarized as follows:

1. *Magnetic character.* The report dealt with the way in which the magnetic character of a ship is established on the building slip and how it changes with time and position. It found that the resulting deviations were not capricious or erratic as 'many cards of deviation might lead one to suppose' but followed closely the theoretical predictions of Airy and Smith. There was no evidence to support Scoresby's contention that the magnetism might change suddenly although the committee recommended that new ships should be swung before each of their first three voyages.

2. *Correction.* The committee recommended that every ship should have one uncorrected compass elevated as much as possible so that its errors would be contained within small limits. The most favoured arrangement was a mast-head or pole compass. They accepted correction of other compasses as a fact, noting that the strongest argument in favour was the loss of directive force caused by large deviations. They recommended athwartship cylinders instead of boxes of chain and were critical of the majority of adjusters who did not use soft iron to correct quadrantal errors. To simplify swinging they arranged for magnetic bearings of the conspicuous Vauxhall chimney to be painted on the dock walls, at Liverpool, a great boon to adjusters. (The bearings are still given but now refer to the tower of the Anglican Cathedral.)

3. *Compasses.* Although the committee did not specifically consider the design of compasses they stated that they were against the use of long needles, as favoured by Gray.

4. *Heeling error.* This was thoroughly investigated and a number of ships were swung heeled to adjust the vertical magnet.

5. *Vertical induced magnetism.* This was tackled with great diligence, many captains having been sceptical about the large deviations often reported in the southern hemisphere. Several ships were fitted with a corrector in the form of a soft-iron bar, exactly as suggested by Flinders almost half a century earlier.[27]

The Liverpool Compass Committee had done its work with commendable thoroughness. Airy, who was an honorary member of the committee and took a great interest in its activities, said when commenting to the Board of Trade on the second report:

> This report is by far the most important document in reference to the difficult subjects of the magnetism of iron ships, the change of magnetism, the correction of the compass, and the adjustment of the correcting apparatus, that has yet appeared. It does more to remove doubt on several important points than all the discussions which have previously taken place; and generally speaking it explains more completely the difficulties, moral and physical, attending this subject than all other papers known to me.[28]

Evans and Archibald Smith were also appointed as honorary members of the committee but, although Evans had occasional correspondence with Rundell, they do not appear to have taken any active part in its deliberations. Nevertheless they clearly took note of its reports, for in his subsequent papers Evans made frequent reference to the committee's work and quoted widely from its findings. Only on the matter of correction, where there was still a fundamental difference in outlook, do they appear to have disregarded the committee's conclusions, and the Navy was to suffer from the inconvenience of large deviations for many years to come.

Evans's published works

Throughout his time as superintendent Evans wrote and lectured widely on ship magnetism, often in collaboration with Archibald Smith, and much of his work can be assessed from his published papers. His first article appeared in the *Nautical Magazine* in 1857, written in answer to a letter from Captain (later First Sea Lord) Cooper Key of the *Sans Pareil* reporting interesting changes in her deviation on passage to Singapore, largely caused by an iron funnel which had been fitted in place of a copper one. Evans's article was a very succinct review of the state of understanding at the time, including Smith's system of coefficients, and gives a very fair account of Airy's method of correction, whilst making it clear that the Navy did not favour compensation as it might engender a false feeling of confidence. In a further article later in the year he discussed the work of the Liverpool Compass Committee, dealing particularly with the magnetic character of a ship and how it changes after launching. These two articles show that he had already acquired a sound knowledge of the basic theoretical aspects of ship magnetism.

The first major work to come from the new Superintendent was a paper entitled 'Notes on the magnetism of ships'[29] which he read to the United Services Institution in 1859. This contained a broad historical survey of the problem up to that date, including Dr Scoresby's analysis before the British Association in 1854 of a ship's magnetic character, as determined by its heading on the building-slip, and the findings of his voyage to Australia in the *Royal Charter*. Commenting somewhat evasively on compass correction, Evans stated that 'opponents of the system considered it both defective in principle and dangerous in practice'.

The following year saw the publication of a report entitled 'Reduction and discussion of the deviations of the compass observed onboard all of the iron-built ships and a selection of wood-built steam-ships in Her Majesty's Navy, and the iron steam-ship 'Great Eastern'; being a report to the Hydrographer of the Admiralty'.[30]

From an analysis of some 250 tables of deviation, covering 70 vessels, 42 of which were iron ships, Evans drew a number of conclusions concerning their magnetic behaviour. He confirmed that there was a gradual diminution in the ship's magnetic force with time and that the quadrantal deviation (coefficient D) did not depend on the size of the ship, seldom exceeding 7° and generally lying between 2° and 4°.

He pointed to the differing problems which arose when placing the compass in ships built on different headings[31] and recommended that fitting out should always be done on a reverse heading from that of the building-slip, in order to 'shake out' some of the initial magnetism. If a compass was to be corrected he stressed that the ship should always be swung first without magnets to determine her magnetic characteristics. Like Johnson, he considered that the value of mast-head compasses was overrated and that they required too much looking after.

The conclusions drawn from observations he had made with Rundell on board the 18,000 ton *Great Eastern* were especially interesting. In this ship, which was fitted out on almost the same heading as that on which she was built, the maximum deviation was found to have decreased 12° during the first five days after leaving the builders yard, by 19° in the first seven weeks and by nearly three points (32° 10') in the first nine months.[32]

The *Great Eastern* was fitted with a large selection of compasses which, in addition to an Admiralty Standard especially fitted for the trials, included a Gray's azimuth compass as the ship's standard, port and starboard steering compasses, an azimuth compass on the bridge, an overhead compass on the mizenmast, 52 feet above the deck, and a pelorus. In this ship Gray, who had always favoured long needles, excelled himself. The needles of the ship's standard and steering compasses were 11 1/2 inches long whilst those of the masthead compass measured 16 inches. From the errors observed in these compasses, Evans and Smith for the first time identified a new error, 'sextantal' deviation, superimposed on the semicircular, and this, as will be seen later, led Evans to recommend that compass needles should never exceed 6 or 7 inches in length.

With the Admiralty's approval, this excellent paper was read to the Royal Society by Captain Washington FRS on 21 June 1860.

Meanwhile Evans instituted a series of experiments to determine the comparative effects of long and short needles under varying conditions of correction with magnets and soft iron. In all previous mathematical investigations into the deviation of the compass and into the practical methods of applying correctors as suggested by Flinders, Barlow and Airy, it had been assumed that the length of the compass needle could be considered infinitesimal compared with the distance of the nearest disturbing iron.[33] This had been true in the old wooden ships and was still so, within acceptable limits, in most iron ships, provided the compass was carefully placed. It was clearly not true when considering a 16 inch needle or when placing correctors close to the compass.

The results of these experiments showed that if a magnet was placed very close to a single compass needle the formulae would no longer be correct and a 'sextantal' error would result; if however, the disturbing force was a mass of soft iron the errors would be 'octantal' (i.e. the deviation curves would have six or eight maxima respectively). It was further shown that in the case of the Admiralty Standard Compass these errors did not occur. In a paper to the Royal Society entitled 'On the effect produced on the deviation of the compass by the length and arrangement of the compass-needles; and on a new mode of correcting the quadrantal deviation', which he presented jointly with Evans in 1861,[34] Smith commented:

> The remarkable features observed in the deviation of the Admiralty Standard Compass suggested the idea that the arrangement of the needles in that compass might produce, in the case of deviations caused by a magnet or mass of soft iron in close proximity to it, a compensation of the sextantal and octantal deviations and this, on the subject being investigated mathematically, proved to be the case.

Smith was able to demonstrate that by 'a happy coincidence' the arrangement of needles required to produce this result was the same as that which he had proposed just twenty years earlier to achieve equality in the moments of inertia and so improve the balance of the card.[35]

In the same paper to the Royal Society, Smith went on to describe a new method of correcting quadrantal deviation devised by Evans. It had long been known that if two compasses are placed close together they will produce a quadrantal deviation in each other.[36] Because of the very large quadrantal deviation exhibited by the new iron-clad ships, Evans decided to use this fact to correct quadrantal error rather than employing large masses of iron, and he designed a double binnacle in which the distance apart of the compasses could be adjusted to produce the required compensation. The arrangement, which also incorporated facilities for correcting the semicircular deviation of both compasses by means of a single pair of magnets placed between them, was very neat and won the Admiralty a gold medal at the International Exhibition of 1862.[37]

The arms race of the nineteenth century was now gathering momentum, and the year 1860 had seen the launch of HMS *Warrior*, of 6100 tons, the first of the new heavily armoured iron ships. Evans had been experimenting with her compass positions and, despite his opposition to correction, had accepted that the very large deviations he found must be reduced. At the end of Smith's paper to the Royal Society he gave them a graphic account of the problems with which he was faced. The following extract is taken from the *Athenaeum*:

It may be considered interesting to the meeting to receive a brief notice of the magnetism of the first of the great iron war-ships of the day, the *Warrior*, and of the disposition of her compasses. There is but little novelty in the arrangement of those on the upper deck, excepting that it has been deemed desirable to furnish two standard compasses from the unavoidable proximity of the after one to a new feature which, from the special character of the ship, has been introduced, namely an iron-cased tower of rather considerable dimensions for holding riflemen, and of sufficient thickness to withstand the fire of heavy ordnance. This tower is placed on the quarter deck, in the neighbourhood of the steering wheel. The magnetic character of the ship as developed by the two compasses, before the rifle tower was fixed, is quite in accordance with the received principles, as due to the direction of the ship's head, in building, with reference to the magnetic meridian. The foremost compass, which is about one-third of the ship's length from the bow, on the 10th of August last, had a maximum declination of 16°, and the after compass, which is about one third of the ship's length from the stern, a maximum declination of 31°, the ship being built within about 3° of the magnetic meridian (head North, 3 deg East) and the points of no declination consequently at north and south . . . In the fighting ships of what may now be termed a past generation, we did not seek for or expect invulnerability. In 1861 we demand nothing less, and 'more iron' is the cry. It is clear from these new conditions that one compass at least, on which the ultimate safety of the ship may depend, should equally be protected from the fire of the enemy, in the event, which would most likely happen, of every thing standing on the upper deck being swept away by the fire of the enemy. For the management of the *Warrior*, under this probable contingency, an additional steerage wheel has been fitted within the great armour-protected space on the main deck. This space, I need scarcely inform you, is cut off from the ends of the vessel by enormous iron bulkheads.[38]

Evans went on to say that at the steering position on the main deck of *Warrior* the quadrantal deviation amounted to 10° (three times the normal) while the semicircular deviation was almost 40°. He therefore intended to use the new double binnacle, just described, in the 'hope that we have by this method overcome the more serious difficulties of disembarrassing the unfortunate compass which is now so tortured in its action'.

In practice the binnacle was not a success for a number of reasons. Evans had departed from the essential maxim of correcting 'like with like' and the spacing of the compasses had therefore to be altered with change of latitude. The consequent frequent readjustment of the magnets whenever the compasses were moved proved impracticable at sea, while the magnets themselves, not being directly below the compasses, produced a serious heeling-error when the ship rolled. No further ships were fitted although the double-binnacle remained in the manuals as a recommended method of correcting quadrantal deviation for many years.

Warrior's first swing also pioneered new ground. Evans took passage in the ship from Woolwich and, by using precomputed magnetic bearings of the sun, succeeded in obtaining all points on the deviation curve between south and east before reaching Greenhithe. The points between north and west were obtained the following day as the ship swung to the tide. By observing the ship's head by the other compasses at the same time, their deviation tables could thus be completed, so obviating much labour and expense. This is believed to be the first occasion that this technique was used, and Evans enjoyed Their Lordships' approval for his zeal and skill.[39] Today, of course, it is a practice that is regularly employed.

In 1861 Evans also read a paper to the Institute of Naval Architects entitled 'On the deviation of the compass in iron and other vessels, considered practically with reference to material, position and mode of construction and equipment'.[40] In a talk aimed at showing the naval architects how they could contribute to solving the compass problem he gave a very good resumé of the current state of knowledge, paying tribute to the work of Airy, Smith and others for the way they had unravelled 'the apparent inextricably entangled web which . . . appeared to enclose the laws of compass disturbance . . .'; he quoted from Johnson's earlier experiments with iron riders; he remarked particularly on the quality of the iron used in ship-building, pointing to the fact that in a well-built ship permanancy of magnetism, which would result from the use of hard iron, would also result in a small coefficient D;[41] he pointed to the problems of wooden ships which now had 'iron skeletons'; he discussed the best heading on which to build a ship from the point of view of siting the compass. These were all good points for the naval architects to ponder. It was, however, still some years before they were actually invited to provide a suitable position for the compass to be located, as is done today. The compass still took its chance!

This talk was very well received and in the following year the two gentlemen were again invited to address the naval architects, Smith covering the mathematical treatment of the deviations of the compass and Evans following with a short paper entitled 'On the application of the mathematical formulae to the deviations observed on board several iron and iron-plated ships'.[42] In this he analysed the huge deviations found in the iron-plated ships *Warrior*, *Black Prince* and *Defence* which, even at the Standard Compass elevated 10–12 feet above the iron deck, amounted to 28°. At the binnacle compasses deviations were of the order of 40° and in *Warrior*, due to the rifle tower, coefficient D amounted to 16°. Evans had decided to reduce the semicircular deviations of the steering compasses by means of fixed magnets let into the deck but, except in the case of the double binnacle in *Warrior*, he made no attempt to correct the quadrantal deviation nor, despite their large errors, did he touch the Standard Compasses. Although all compasses must have exhibited a considerable degree of heeling error, no reference was made to its possible reduction.

At the end of this paper Evans spoke about the reduced directive force at the compass positions and suggested that the deck immediately under the compass should not be constructed of iron but should be treated as a hatchway, to be subsequently filled in with wood. This was, perhaps, the first tentative suggestion of how a suitable position should be prepared to receive the compass.[43]

The year 1862 also saw the appearance of the *Admiralty Manual for Ascertaining and Applying the Deviations of the Compass Caused by the Iron in a Ship*, edited by Evans and Archibald Smith (at 3/6d it must have been very good value).[44] Parts 1 and 2 contained the original *Practical Rules*, expanded to embrace such modern developments as telescopic funnels, and Napier's graphic method of presenting and allowing for deviation. Part 3 covered the laws of deviation and the theoretical method of computing compass errors, using simplified mathematical expressions. Heeling error was touched on, with a footnote only suggesting its possible correction by means of a vertical magnet. Part 4 dealt with terrestrial magnetism. Three appendices covered the Admiralty Standard Compass, the full mathematical treatment, by Smith, of the theory of deviations (32 pages) and a brief, 2-page explanation of mechanical correction of the compass with magnets, which was to be applied to the steering compass only. Quadrantal deviation was mentioned but its correction with soft iron was considered to be 'attended with great difficulties'. Evans's double binnacle was also included, as an alternative method.

This was the first really comprehensive manual on the subject, and was an immediate success. It was followed in 1863 by an expanded second edition with a number of additional appendices, including details of a method of determining the principal coefficients from observations of the deviation and horizontal force taken on *one* heading only, so that the deviation could be brought within manageable limits before the ship went to sea. The section on mathematical theory was expanded to fifty-eight pages and a short historical appendix was added. Within a year this manual had been translated into French and German and had been adopted by the United States Navy. Later it was also translated into Russian and Portuguese. A new edition of the *Practical Rules*, as reproduced in

Parts 1 and 2 of the *Manual*, appeared at the same time (now costing 1/-).

Evans received a further expression of the Admiralty's approbation for these two excellent publications while Archibald Smith, who had 'pursued the work as a labour of love', was invited to accept a suitably inscribed gold watch as a mark of Their Lordships' deep appreciation.[45]

Late in 1862 Evans and Smith were invited by the British Association to 'Report on the three reports of the Liverpool Compass Committee and other recent publications on the same subject'.[46] After reviewing their own manual as giving the very latest ideas on the subject, they then discussed the most notable of the earlier reports by Johnson, Airy, Scoresby and the Liverpool Compass Committee, highlighting the important contributions or shortcomings of each as they had, in one way or the other, affected the advance of knowledge. Smith had been concerned that much of the progress made by the Liverpool Compass Committee by practical experiment was unsupported by mathematical formulae. These he had now provided in the *Manual*. At the end of this paper he asked again, 'That in the construction of iron vessels, regard should be had to the providing of a proper place for the compass'.

The reputation of the Compass Department now stood higher than ever before, both in the Royal Navy and in the eyes of the world. The Admiralty Standard Compass had been adopted by a number of foreign navies and compasses were being tested at the Observatory for many different countries. In a report to the Hydrographer dated 1859 Evans mentions the Russian, Austrian, Turkish, Portuguese and Netherlands governments[47] to which, two years later, were added the French and Americans. In 1861 Monsieur B. Darendeau, *Ingénieur Hydrographe* in the French Navy, whose position was akin to that of Evans, was sent by his government to examine the compass situation in England, both in the Royal and Mercantile navies. His report, entitled 'Rapport à S.E. le Ministre de la Marine sur un mission accomplié en Angleterre pour étudier les questions relatives à la regulation des compas',[48] gives a most interesting and comprehensive account of the position as it then appeared to an outsider. Four years later Captain J. Belavenetz of the Russian Imperial Navy also came to England to study the compass. He translated the Admiralty *Manual* into Russian and, whilst overseeing the compass interests of the armour-plated battery

Pervenetz, building for Russia on the Thames, was able to reduce her magnetic signature considerably by having her turned end for end for the process of plating.

In the spring of 1862 Evans was elected a Fellow of the Royal Society and shortly afterwards served on its council. Two years later came advancement within the Navy. In 1864, following a review of the status and career structure of the Masters' branch of the Navy, it was announced that all masters of more than fifteen years service should be appointed as Staff Commanders. Mr Evans was accordingly promoted with seniority 11 June 1863.[49]

To conclude this account of the principal papers produced by Evans during his ten years as Superintendent of the Compass Department, special mention must be made of his report to the Royal Society in 1865, again prepared in collaboration with Archibald Smith. Entitled 'On the magnetic character of the armour-plated ships of the Royal Navy and on the effect on the ship's compass of particular arrangements of iron in a ship',[50] this paper was a sequel to that read in 1860 and covered the changes that had taken place during the interval in the construction of warships and in the magnetic disturbances of their compasses. It highlighted the tremendous problems that now had to be faced and is particularly valuable for its account of how the Compass Department was meeting the challenge of ever more magnetic ships by making a far more rigorous analysis of their magnetic character and by introducing new instruments for measuring the forces acting on the compass. Much of its material is still of the greatest importance to the student of magnetic compass theory. It was now customary in a new ship to observe the values of deviation and horizontal force (λ) on one heading before the ship went to sea. Since, in a well placed compass, two coefficients (A and E) could be taken as zero and coefficients D and (λ) could be regarded as common to ships of the same class, it was then possible to calculate the two remaining coefficients B and C and hence to construct a deviation table. When deviations were very large, (e.g. in *Minotaur* they reached 62° at the main deck compasses); they were reduced by magnets built into the ship[51] but no attempt was made to make an exact adjustment. Even the Standard Compass now occasionally needed compensation. In 1864 Evans had sought Admiralty approval to depart (for the first time since 1842) from the rule that the Standard Compass should never be corrected and to use magnets to reduce a deviation of 27° found in the *Prince Consort*.[52] Similar action was also necessary in the *Minotaur*.

Heeling error, too, could now be estimated from a single observation of vertical force, which enabled the heeling coefficient to be calculated.[53] In 1863 an opportunity had occurred to verify Smith's formula for this calculation when *Warrior Defence* and *Black Prince* were swung at Lisbon whilst heeled 7° to clean their bottoms.[54]

This paper is noteworthy for its very clear explanation of the nine soft-iron rods still used in magnetic compass theory, and the separation into constituent parts of the various coefficients; also for its discussion of the magnetism of hollow and solid masses of iron and the mathematical investigation of the very large effect of heavy transverse bulkheads on quadrantal deviation.[55]

Evans followed his paper to the Royal Society by one to the United Service Institution entitled '*On the magnetism of iron and iron-clad ships*'[56] in which he gave a very lucid laymen's account of the problems he was facing. An interesting statement of his cautious philosophy on compass correction shows that while he now accepted the necessity for some compensation, nevertheless, ten years after the *Trident* trials, he still considered it unsafe to adopt Airy's scheme of complete correction. His statement read:

Another generation of navigators will possibly have acquired a sufficient knowledge of the laws of magnetism, and the variety of conditions on board an iron ship, so to manipulate magnets as to render the compass correct at all times and in all places; but at the present time this knowledge is extremely limited and I confess to hesitate (over) the placing of so dangerous a tool as a moveable magnet in the hands of the untrained navigator. My views are now rather to place it beyond his reach, first attending to his convenience by reducing the large errors within easy and effective limits – the residual errors to be constantly determined by observation of celestial bodies – and then securing the magnet as part of the ship, in order that accident or design cannot disturb the effect.'

Evans went on to stress the importance of always having a table of deviations, even if the compass was closely corrected and concluded with a further plea for a prepared compass position. ('I hope the time is not far distant when it will be considered quite as important to prepare a place for the standard compass as for the mainmast').

With the ground thus well prepared, he wrote a long and well-reasoned letter to the Admiralty suggesting the need for a few simple rules on the siting of the Standard Compass for the guidance and attention of the naval architects.[57] These were published with the authority of the Controller of the Navy as 'Rules to be attended to in the construction of iron ships'[58] and for the first time contained the regulation 'a place [is] to be prepared for the Standard Compass, and to be shown in the plans'. This pamphlet, in which the term 'compass platform' was used for the first time, was intended to be read in conjunction with the safe-distance rules contained in the *Queen's Regulations* and with the *Practical Rules*, and these three statements were eventually incorporated into a single comprehensive document which became the charter for the magnetic compass.[59]

The Board of Trade and the Royal Society

The Royal Navy had tackled its compass problems with vigour and Admiralty policy was supported by the necessary regulations. In the Merchant Navy, however, despite the recommendations of the Liverpool Compass Committee, there was still little control over compass matters. The Board of Trade had declined to interfere, preferring to leave matters in the hands of the ship-owners and underwriters. The Merchant Shipping Act required that 'The Compasses of Passenger Steamers shall be adjusted to the satisfaction of the Board of Trade Surveyor', but it is doubtful whether these gentlemen were competant to adjudicate, except in the simplest cases, and there was still no means of assessing the capability of the compass adjusters.

In 1865, at the suggestion of Evans, the President of the Royal Society wrote to the Board of Trade to propose some measure of supervision for the Merchant Navy, drawing attention to the continuing losses at sea and to the recent increase in the understanding of compass problems which now made them amenable to simple rules. This letter made three positive proposals:

1. That every ship should carry a Standard Compass, as distinct from a steering compass.

2. That Masters and Mates should require some knowledge of compass matters to obtain their certificates.

3. That a central expert authority should be established to supervise all aspects of the problem, 'with a proper code of instructions with regulations for their enforcement'.

It was further suggested that the Board of Trade might 'take advantage of the ability and experience of the present Superintendent of the Admiralty Compass Department' by uniting the Royal Navy and Mercantile Marine compass departments under one head, with competant assistants from each branch.[60] It was a bold proposal. At the request of General Sabine, Evans drew up an excellent set of rules for the control of compasses in iron merchant ships, including a scheme for the registration of compass-adjusters by the Board of Trade, as had been suggested by Johnson some fifteen years earlier. His influence can be detected in the protracted correspondence which followed, during which the Board of Trade pointed with some justification to the wide difference between the Admiralty's relations with the Navy (they 'are the owners, designers and generally the builders of the Ships of the Nation') and their own position with respect to the Mercantile Marine. ('This difference appears to have been under-rated, if not entirely overlooked by the President and Council of the Royal Society'). They reasonably stated that they did not wish to introduce legislation which would interfere unduly with the affairs of ship-owners; they made much of the differences of opinion over compass correction, which they considered 'peculiarly unfit for legislative or administrative interference' and they declined absolutely to adopt any of the proposals put forward.[61]

Magnetic charts of the world

Among the many achievements for which Evans is justly remembered is the production of the first magnetic variation chart of the world to be published by the Admiralty. Edmund Halley's original variation charts of 1701 and 1702 had been followed by many later versions, mainly the work of private individuals. In England charts were produced by Dodson and Mountaine in 1744 and 1756, Samuel Dunn in 1775, John Churchman in 1794, Thomas Yeates in 1817 and Peter Barlow in 1833. In Europe there were many more.

Charts of the other two elements, inclination (dip) and magnetic force, did not appear until the nineteenth century. In 1819 the Norwegian geophysicist Christoph Hansteen published maps showing the changes in variation and inclination throughout the seventeenth and eighteenth centuries[62] while in the late 1840s Edward Sabine, who had been appointed by the Royal Society to reduce and publish the results of a general magnetic survey of the globe being undertaken at the direction of the Admiralty, for the first time produced charts of all three elements for the mean epoch of 1842–45.[63] Small, updated versions of these charts were included in the second and subsequent editions of the *Admiralty Manual of the Deviations of the Compass.*

By this time magnetic observatories had been established widely, both at home and abroad, the voyages of Captain James Ross had added greatly to the knowledge of magnetism in the Southern Ocean, officers in charge of surveys were forwarding regular observations and there was a broad exchange of information at international level. This steady flow of data was co-ordinated by Colonel Sabine in co-operation with Admiral Beaufort, whose great hope had been to see it published by the Admiralty. Sadly he died before this could be achieved, and the task of reducing the vast quantity of information to a common epoch and preparing it for publication was worthily undertaken by Evans.

The first Admiralty variation chart appeared in 1858 and was a considerable advance on any previous work. Information was given on the rate of change of variation on a worldwide basis and updated editions were published at regular intervals. The Compass Department thus took on a further continuing commitment which was to have an important bearing on its future half a century later (see p. 165). In 1907 three new Admiralty charts were added, giving the values of the magnetic inclination and magnetic force (vertical and horizontal). These had been prepared by the Superintendent and his Assistant (Commanders Chetwynd and Creagh-Osborne) but when, five years later, the department ceased to be under the Hydrographer, the task of co-ordinating all geomagnetic data was taken over by the Astronomer Royal.

Routine Work Continues

While the pioneering work of Evans and Smith was progressing smoothly towards a complete understanding of the theory of ship magnetism, the routine work of the Compass Department went steadily on. The correspondence registers which, with a few unexplained gaps, were still conscientiously kept, show that Evans was at pains to maintain Johnson's high standard of service to the Fleet. He made regular visits to the dockyards to examine their stock of compasses,[64] to check on the storage and testing procedures (Johnson's deflecting apparatus was still in use), to assist in placing the Standard Compasses and to oversee the swinging arrangements. At the south coast ports and at Sheerness swinging was now undertaken regularly by the Masters of the flagships, with Evans and occasionally Mr Brunton covering the River Thames. Checking deviation cards was still essential, as was clearly shown by a hurried despatch sent to the *Urgent* which had sailed for Constantinople with a deviation table in which all the signs were reversed.[65]

It will be recalled that in 1848 cuts in naval expenditure had led to the cancellation of all orders for new compasses, including the Admiralty Standard. The annual estimates for the department remained constant at £1118 (£383 of which was the salary of the Superintendent) until in 1854, Johnson having died, they fell to £547, the lowest figure ever reached. Fortunately during hostilities estimates were quickly set aside. The outbreak of the Crimean War saw a huge increase in expenditure on compasses and, for the first time for six years, orders for new Standard Compasses were again placed with Mr Barrow. Three years later the return of peace and the immediate run down of the Navy left large surpluses of compasses available for the new ironclads that were about to be built. A brief increase in demand occurred in 1857 due to the Indian Mutiny but by the following year the Estimates for the Compass Department were down to £716 (the naval pay of the new Superintendent now appearing on another vote) and, despite the flurry of ship-building in the 1860s, they remained almost constant at this level for the next eleven years. At the Observatory the reduction in activity was also reflected in the number of compasses tested which fell from 2505 in the years 1855 and 1856 to only 1483 in the two years which follows.[66]

As wooden walls gave way to ironclads so gradually commercial firms began to take over the traditional role of the dockyards as the builders of Her Majesty's ships. For many years, however, the fitting out and arming of these ships was still undertaken in the Navy's own yards, the ship being delivered by a steaming party from the contractor as soon as she was ready to go to sea. Evans was greatly worried by this procedure. Although he visited each ship during building to ascertain her magnetic state, the compass arrangements used on passage were often temporary and the contractors were seldom aware of the hazards of navigating these highly magnetic ironclads in which the deviation was liable to undergo marked change during the first few days at sea. Eventually he suggested to Their Lordships that they 'might, under the circumstances, deem the Certificate of the Superintendent of Compasses as to the efficiency of the Compass arrangements a requisite preliminary to the vessels quitting the original port'.[67] Thereafter all compass equipment was installed and the ship swung before making her first passage.

Compasses during the 1860s

In contrast with the spectacular advances made in developing the theory of ship magnetism, little effort appears to have been expended on the design of the compasses themselves. The Admiralty Pattern 1 was still an excellent Standard Compass, and Evans clearly considered that the binnacle compasses then in use were adequate. In addition to the liquid compass supplied for use in the binnacle in rough weather, all ships now carried liquid boats compasses although a proportion of common (dry) boats compasses was still supplied as these could be more easily repaired on board. After 1860 the lead in boats compasses passed from Dent[68] to West who in that year took out a patent for a new liquid boats compass with a corregated metal diaphragm and expansion chamber.[69] Evans took a particular interest in this compass and arranged special trials for it in two HM ships. It was a compass that could also be used in the binnacle where in some screw-ships severe vibration was making the use of a liquid compass increasingly necessary.

During this period an event occurred which might well have altered the history of compasses in the Royal Navy. In November 1862 the Superintendent of the Naval Observatory in Washington, Captain M. Gillis, wrote to the President of the Royal Society for information about English books on compass matters. The letter was passed to Evans who sent him the *Admiralty Manual*, the reports of the Liverpool Compass Committee and a number of other recent papers. At the time the United States Navy was actively considering the introduction of a liquid compass made by the firm of E. S. Ritchie and Son of Boston. Ritchie had been invited to design a remote reading compass for the USS *Monitor*[70] and had been appalled at the standard of the compasses then in service. Having obtained a contract for making liquid boats compasses based on an English pattern, he soon developed his own 'improved, floating compass' with a buoyant card of reduced diameter, as in Crow's compass of 1813 (see p. 8). From this he developed a Standard Compass, which he placed high above the deck ('above the line at which the ship's magnetism is sensible', Gillis wrote to Evans) and linked to a lower compass by means of a thin rod. When, in 1863, responsibility for compasses in the US Navy was transferred to the Bureau of Navigation, Ritchie's liquid compass was adopted as standard.

Hoping that he might also interest the Royal Navy in his new compass, Ritchie sent a sample to Evans, who unfortunately took little interest in it. In a rather condescending acknowledgement[71] he told Ritchie of the excellence of English compasses (mentioning West's new compass). He dwelt on the problems of iron ships, dismissing the value of 'elevated compasses' in the presence of iron masts, and he explained heeling error – which was irrelevant in the context. At no time, however, did he comment on the new features, merits or performance of the American compass, possibly consider-ing that this was outside his mandate.[72] Ritchie, who had originally intended to visit England to demonstrate his new compass, was discouraged and cancelled his visit. In any case he probably had enough to occupy him. The introduction into the US Navy of his compass, which was basically an improvement on an original British design, was completed in the early 1870s, putting the US Navy well ahead of the Royal Navy in compass matters for the next forty years. Another excellent opportunity had been missed.

Reorganization

In 1863 Captain George Henry Richards succeeded Washington as Hydrographer. He was an old shipmate of Evans, having been second in command of the *Acheron*, of which Evans was the Master, from 1847 to 1851. Together they had been involved in an arduous survey of New Zealand and subsequently in compiling the New Zealand Pilot.

Evans was five years the senior in age and Richards under-standably found his surveying experience very useful. When, in 1865, the Chief Naval Assistant to the Hydrographer, Rear Admiral Becher, was due to retire Richards proposed that Evans should be offered the post whilst still retaining overall responsibility for magnetic matters. Evans, who had recently been promoted to Staff Commander and already conducted much of the Compass Department business from the Hydrographic Office, was ideally qualified for the appointment. In his report to Their Lordships[73] Richards stressed the enormous importance of the study of ship magnetism in the modern navy 'each one of our ponderous iron-clad vessels has been found in herself almost a distinct problem'. He went on to explain 'the serious inconvenience (to use no stronger term) which would result, should the Admiralty, under the existing limited acquaintance which obtains on this very important science, be deprived through any unforeseen circumstances of the services of the present Superintendent.' In order to convey some idea of 'the labour and of the intricate nature of the mathematical investigation which each particular ship requires', also to emphasize the load now falling on Evans, Richards continued:

> The duties performed by the Superintendent at present are multifarious – he has charge of the Compass Observatory at Woolwich where all Magnetic experiments connected with Surveying and other branches of the Navy are carried out. He attends at the Hydrographic Office for three days in the week to investigate the deviation returns from every ship afloat and to perform his portion of the duty in connexion with the Charts – and he visits every Iron Ship of War which is constructed in the United Kingdom before she is permitted to leave her port of building, – settles by actual experiment the positions for her standard and other Compasses, often a very perplexing question, frequently having to correct them by artificial means; – superintends her first Swinging and pronounces her safe to leave her port. This process has generally to be repeated two or three times at different ports before she finally proceeds to Sea. I do not think that these various duties can continue to be advantageously performed by any one person, and I feel that the time has fully arrived when a re-organization of the Compass Department should take place.

Richards then demonstrated how, by changing Evans's appointment as proposed and bringing in a new officer, to be called the Superintendent of Compasses, the load on Evans could be reduced while the additional cost to the Navy vote would be negligible. He did, however, add 'that the time may not be many years distant when it will be desirable that the services of two officers shall be exclusively devoted th the Compass Department'.

By an Admiralty Order in Council dated 29 June 1865 a new post was established under the Hydrographer with the designation 'Chief Naval Assistant and in charge of the Magnetic Department'.[74] Staff Commander Evans was appointed with a salary of £500 a year in addition to his half pay. His successor as Superintendent of Compasses was Mr William Mayes, the Master of the ironclad battleship *Defence*. Responsibility for compass matters was thus totally integrated into the Hydrographic Department where it was to remain for almost half a century.

NOTES

CHAPTER 2

[1] The Hydrographer also had problems in his own department. Only four days before Johnson's death he had sent a circular to all officers in charge of surveys informing them of a £10,000 cut in the estimates for the Hydrographic Office (Hydrographer's Letter Book, No. 19, p. 153). Savings of any kind would therefore be welcome.

[2] ADM 235, M/3 (Out), p. 52.

[3] Hydrographer's Minute Book, No. 8, p. 443.

[4] ADM 235, M/1, p. 365. Only the cost of buying or repairing the Standard Compass was borne by the Compass Department, expenditure on all other compasses falling to the Storekeeper-General.

[5] National Maritime Museum, Magnetic Compass Collection, Pamphlet P1 (17–19).

[6] Hydrographer's Minute Book, No. 8, pp. 232, 441.

[7] Hydrographer's Minute Book, No. 9, p. 233.

[8] *Phil. Trans. Royal Society*, 1841, 1844, 1845.

[9] Two further supplements to the *Practical Rules* were also issued, both describing methods of graphical projection of the deviation. The first, by Mr R. J. Napier of Glasgow, gave a simple method of obtaining a table of probable deviations from a limited number of scattered observations and of converting courses or bearings from compass to magnetic, or vice versa (National Maritime Museum, Magnetic Compass Collection, Pamphlets P6 (16) and 7/6 (9)). The second, by Captain A. P. Ryder RN, was similar in principle but 'simplified for seamen'.

[10] "Report of the British Association meeting, 1854 (Liverpool)', *Athenaeum*, No. 1406, (7 October 1854), pp. 1205–6.

11 *Athenaeum*, 28 October 1854, 9 and 16 December 1855, 3 February, 10 and 17 March 1856. See also Charles H. Cotter, "The Airy-Scoresby controversy', *Annals of Science*, 34 (1977), pp. 589–99.

12 *Phil. Trans. Royal Society*, 1856, pp. 1–53.

13 Archives of the Royal Greenwich Observatory, Vol. 1262, Section 26.

14 Gray's binnacle is described, with illustrations in *The English Cyclopedia*, Vol. 2, London, 1860, p. 106.

15 National Maritime Museum, Magnetic Compass Collection, Item R4.

16 ADM 235, M/7, p. 48.

17 ADM 235, M/2, p. 106.

18 National Maritime Museum, Magnetic Compass Collection, Item R4.

19 This practice was, of course, contrary to Admiralty instructions which stated that a ship was always to be navigated by her Standard Compass.

20 ADM 235, M/5, p. 143.

21 ADM 235, M/2, p. 173.

22 National Maritime Museum, Collection of Swings, 1859.

23 John Towson, 'Deviation of the compass on board of iron ships', *Athenaeum*, No. 1406.

24 *First Report of the Liverpool Compass Committee to the Board of Trade; 1855*, HMSO, 1857, p. 9.

25 An account of this voyage is given in W. Scoresby, *Journal of a Voyage to Australia and round the World for Magnetical Research*, London, 1859. Scoresby, who was 66 years old when he undertook this arduous task, died before his account was published. It was edited by Archibald Smith, who wrote a fifty-page introduction which included much criticism of Airy's methods. Airy again felt bound to reply, which he did in a further article in the *Athenaeum*, No. 1672 (12 November 1859).

26 *First, Second and Third Reports of the Liverpool Compass Committee to the Board of Trade*, HMSO, 1857 and 1861, National Maritime Museum, Magnetic Compass Collection, Item 9/18.

27 The bar was later named the Flinders bar by Sir William Thomson. Commander Walker, the Queen's Harbour Master at Plymouth, had tried two vertical bars, in the fore-and-aft and athwartship planes, during the 1840s, but the idea was never pursued.

28 *Reports of the Liverpool Compass Committee*, p. 1.

29 *Journal of the Royal United Services Institute*, Vol. 3, (1859), p. 91.

30 *Phil. Trans. Royal Society*, 1860, p. 337.

31 Following experiments in the *Garryowen* in 1835, Johnson had suggested that the permanent magnetism of a ship could be determined from the direction in which it had lain on the building-slip, but this idea had never been actively pursued. With the huge increase in permanent magnetism it now assumed far greater importance. Evans showed that the north point of the needle was generally drawn towards that part of the vessel which was furthest from north when on the building-slip.

32 During this period the *Great Eastern* rode out a particularly violent gale at

Holyhead, which was responsible for the wreck of 133 vessels including the *Royal Charter* (see Alexander McKee, *The Golden Wreck*, London, Souvenir Press 1961).

33 Professor Christie had read a paper on this subject to the Royal Society as long ago as 1828, to which he drew Airy's attention at the time of the *Rainbow* experiments, while pointing out flaws in the theory of Barlow's plate. Archives of the Royal Greenwich Observatory, Vol. 1258.

34 *Phil. Trans. Royal Society*, 1862, Part 2.

35 See page 7. The arrangement of needles recommended by Smith was as follows: two needles should be placed with their ends at 30° from the centre line of the card. Four needles should be placed with their ends at 15° and 45° from the centre line. These arrangements produce a magnetic resultant equivalent to a very short needle at the centre of the magnet system.

36 Johnson had shown that two Admiralty Standard Compasses placed 2 feet apart produced a negative quadrantal error in each other of approximately 8° (*Deviations of the Compass*, 2nd edn, 1852, p. 52). This led to the rule that compasses should never to closer to each other than 4½ feet.

37 Evans was an associate of the jury dealing with ship's tackle and rigging at the Exhibition and wrote a very interesting report on this section (National Maritime Museum, Magnetic Compass Collection, Item 9/7).

38 *Athenaeum*, No. 1748, 27 April 1861.

39 Hydrographer's Minute Book, No. 11, p. 198.

40 *Transactions of the Institute of Naval Architects*, Vol. 2 (1861).

41 Evans quoted from the Liverpool Compass Committee's report on the *Great Britain*: 'This extraordinary ship has been stranded and strained and altered; has traversed both hemispheres and been very many years on active service; yet her lines of no deviation are now much the same as Dr Scoresby would indicate them to have been when upon the stocks.'

42 *Transactions of the Institute of Naval Architects*, Vol. 3 (1862).

43 It is also of interest to note that Evans's talk was followed by one by Rundell in which he urged the fitting of a vertical soft-iron bar, forward of the compass, as recommended by the Liverpool Compass Committee. This was not, in fact, generally done until Sir William Thomson introduced a Flinder's bar in his second binnacle, in 1879.

44 Printed by J. D. Potter, 1862. National Maritime Museum, Magnetic Compass Collection, Item 7/7.

45 Hydrographer's Minute Book, No. 11, p. 339.

46 'Report of the British Association meeting', 1862.

47 ADM 235, M/2, p. 164.

48 National Maritime Museum, Magnetic Compass Collection, Item 10/1 (1).

49 An account of the change of title from Master to Navigating Lieutenant and later to Lieutenant (N) is given in Vice-Admiral B. B. Schofield's *The Story of HMS Dryad*, Kenneth Mason, Emsworth, 1977, p. 15.

50 *Phil. Trans. Royal Society*, 1865, p. 263.

51 Lieutenant Alexander, who served in the Compass Department from 1907 to 1929, recalled seeing the magnets removed from the deck of *Minotaur* when the steering-compass was being changed to one designed by Sir William Thomson.

52 ADM 235, M/2, p. 288.

53 This represented the number of degrees of Compass error for each degree of heel and could be as high as 3°.

54 William Mayes, the Master of *Defence*, who was responsible for these and other observations, received the approbation of Their Lordships and was subsequently to succeed Evans as Superintendent of the Compass Branch.

55 In *Minotaur*, where the armour plate extended the full length of the ship, (i.e. there were no armoured transverse bulkheads, as in *Warrior*), the quadrantal deviation was consequently small.

56 *Journal of the Royal United Services Institute*, Vol. 9 (1865), p. 277.

57 ADM 235, M/2, p. 329.

58 21 October 1865. National Maritime Museum, Magnetic Compass Collection, Item 9/7 (18).

59 Now CD Pamphlet 11.

60 This was a tall order. W. W. Rundell, commenting on the suggestion that Evans should be responsible for compass matters in both the Royal and Mercantile navies, said: 'Able and persevering as that gentleman is, he would have occasion to say "Save me from any friends!" when he found what an enormous responsibility was placed upon him'.

61 National Maritime Museum, Magnetic Compass Collection, Item P10 (3) and (4). An interesting commentary by W. W. Rundell on this correspondence appears in the same collection, Item P6 (3); also in the *Transactions of the Institute of Naval Architects*, Vol. 7 (1866).

62 C. Hansteen, *Magnetismus der Erde*, Christiania, 1819. Reviewed by Edward Sabine in *Proceedings of the British Association*, 1835. (National Maritime Museum, Magnetic Compass Collection, Item 8/5 (16)).

63 *Proceedings of the Royal Society*, 1868–76.

64 In 1857 we find him suggesting the sale of obsolete Barlow's correcting plates, still held in store but little used in the previous twenty years.

65 Hydrographer's Minute Book, No. 9, p. 430.

66 ADM 235, M/2, p. 164.

67 ADM 235, M/2, p. 265.

68 Dent himself died in 1860 but his firm was still making compasses for the Navy at the end of the century.

69 This compass also received a special mention at the International Exhibition of 1862.

70 USS *Monitor* was a heavily armoured 'raft', carrying a single gun turret, which was built to counter the southern warship *Virginia*. The two ships fought an inconclusive battle in Hampton Roads on 8 March 1862.

71 ADM 235, M/3, p. 87.

72 Evans did tell Ritchie that the compass had been sent to the Observatory for testing. Although the test records for the period are still in existence they do not mention this compass and it seems probable that no comparative tests were ever carried out. The compass is still held by the National Maritime Museum.

73 Hydrographer's Minute Book, No. 12, p. 404.

74 Admiralty Order in Council, 29 June 1865, entitled 'Hydrographical department' (Naval Historical Library).

In the doldrums, 1865-74

'It is an historical fact that the British Navy stubbornly resists change.' (Admiral of the Fleet Lord Fisher, *Records*, Hodder and Stoughton, 1919, p. 177)

The years 1855–65 had seen great changes both in the Navy and in the activities and prestige of its Compass Department. The pioneering work of Evans and the mathematical genius of Archibald Smith had led to immense progress in understanding and tackling the many essentially new problems that arose from the use of steel and armour plate. The safe navigation of Her Majesty's latest ships had been established on sure foundations. But seamen in general are cautious about accepting bold changes in outlook. Just as sixty years after Trafalgar competition between the crews of the new steam vessels continued to centre primarily around their skill at rapid sail-changing, so in the compass field there was still reluctance to break with tradition and accept the advantages offered by liquid compasses and accurate compass correction.

The time was now ripe for a fundamental reappraisal of policy to meet the needs of a fleet capable of greater speed and mobility than ever before, yet whose compasses were plagued with the problems associated with vibration, heavy gunfire and large deviations. The change in the organization of the Compass Department had brought in a new Superintendent, fresh from the job of navigating one of the latest ironclads. This offered an ideal opportunity for taking a fresh look at the compass requirements of the new navy.

William Mayes had had an interesting if unusual career since passing for Master in 1849. In March of that year he had sailed in the schooner *Lark* for West Africa, under Commander Charles Hall,[1] serving in various ships on that coast before spending three and a half years in the *Espiegle* on the American and West Indies station. On returning to England he passed for Master of battleships and obtained a first class certificate in steam at the Royal Naval College before joining the paddle sloop *Cyclops* in May 1857. In this ship he attended on the *Agamemnon* when laying the first trans-Atlantic cable and subsequently surveyed the route for the Red Sea cable from Suez to Aden, with which Their Lordships' expressed satisfaction. For the next two years, whilst 'on leave' from the Navy, Mayes worked with the India Electric Telegraph Company laying a cable from Aden to India before being appointed, in 1861, as Master of the new ironclad battleship *Defence*. It was while serving in this ship that he caught the eye of the Superintendent of Compasses for the good work he did in arranging for three ships to be swung when heeled (see p. 69), after which Evans often found him useful for carrying out magnetic experiments.[2] When, in June 1865, it was decided that compasses could no longer be managed by one man, Mayes was appointed to assist. Sadly it was not a happy choice.

Evans was by nature a traditionalist and had tended to oppose any technical change. Unfortunately over the next nineteen years he continued to keep a tight control over all major compass matters himself, although he was generally too busy in his new post to consider the changes in compass policy that were so urgently needed. Mayes, on the other hand, appears to have been completely dominated by his chief and to have been content simply to confine himself to the routine running of the Observatory and to his work on board ships. Neither man seemed capable of realizing that the methods which had been satisfactory during the 1840s and 1850s were now in need of revision. As a result the Compass Department gradually drifted into a period of stagnation and for many years progress of any sort was virtually at a standstill.

In September 1869 Vice Admiral Sir Thomas Symonds, commanding the Channel Squadron, wrote to Their Lordships complaining that 'Our present compasses are utterly useless when firing heavy charges or going at full speed, whilst the water compasses used in the Cunard packets and in yachts are trustworthy and would be uninfluenced by concussion of guns or vibration caused by the screw. Even the boats compasses (being liquid) answer better than the ships.'[3]

It will be recalled that for many years it had been the practice to provide every ship with a liquid compass for use under these extreme conditions yet it appears that on this occasion they had not been used. Thus the Admiralty had simply to draw attention to the regulations while at the same time pointing out that the liquid compasses supplied by HM ships were 'as good if not better' than those supplied to the Cunard. It was unnecessary to mention that no attempt had been made to improve the design of compasses since the days of Captain Johnson.

Six months later Admiral Symonds wrote again, enclosing detailed reports from the captains and navigating officers of his squadron voicing their dissatisfaction with many aspects of the compass arrangements. A lengthy reply,[4] signed by both Evans and Mayes, set out the Admiralty's policy on the use of dry or liquid compasses, quoting Captain Johnson's experiments of twenty years before when he compared the different types of compass during gunfire and in heavy weather, and drawing attention to a recent Admiralty order which stated that when necessary a liquid compass should be kept permanently in one of the binnacles. In answer to the squadron's request for liquid Standard Compasses it announced that these had in fact been supplied to the two latest ships, *Monarch* and *Captain*, and that this change would be extended to other ships if found necessary. This does not appear ever to have been done. Many other points were answered in detail. It was a clever and well-reasoned reply and required no further action from the Compass Department.

Seven years had passed since Ritchie had tried to interest the Royal Navy in his liquid compass for general use. Now a further opportunity for reconsideration had come and gone. Despite a final assurance in the Admiralty's letter that 'at all times the Compass Department has been ready to receive suggestions, and to test and receive, but with extreme caution, apparent improvements', the status quo was maintained.

Bridge compasses

For centuries sailing-ships had been navigated from aft and all chartwork was carried out in the cabin of the captain or the master. The introduction of steam led, in time, to the development of a forebridge, normally with a small 'pilot house', but the steering arrangements and the binnacle compasses remained aft. The Standard Compass still took its chance, generally being sited after the ship was built, in a position where the deviation would be as small as possible. Although the 'Rules to be attended to in the construction of iron ships' laid down that 'a place is to be prepared for the Standard Compass, and to be shown on the plans', no firm requirement had yet been stated that this should be in the position best suited to the navigation. Whilst in some ships (e.g. *Warrior*) it had been found possible to place the Standard Compass at the after-end of the forebridge, in others the siting was often very inconvenient and led to many complaints. (e.g. 'The Officer of the Watch now has to come down and walk 50 feet before he can tell whether the ship's head is the right way', 'I do not remember seeing a Standard in a more inconvenient spot either for Navigating or Observing'). Some ships wrote to the Admiralty requesting the provision of a bridge compass; in others the ship's officers made their own arrangements without any authority, but these were seldom satisfactory due to the proximity of telescopic funnels, ventilator cowls or other moveable iron. When, in 1865, the need for a charthouse near the bridge was at last recognized it became the habit, in those ships where the Standard Compass was a long way from the bridge, to fit an additional compass in or near the charthouse for the convenience of fixing the ship's position.

In December 1869 Rear Admiral Ryder, who until recently, had been second in command of the Channel squadron, suggested to the Admiralty that every ship should have a compass on her bridge.[6] Here was a perfect opportunity for the Compass Department to put pressure on the constructors to provide a magnetically suitable site for the Standard Compass in the position where it was most needed. Unfortunately Evans, whose time at sea had been spent mainly in small ships, objected to the suggestion as unnecessary and Mayes who, from his service in *Defence*, must have understood the position far more clearly, acquiesced. It was said with justification that a multiplicity of compasses[7] in a ship was a nuisance because of their varying errors, but there is no doubt that another excellent opportunity to improve the navigation arrangements of the Fleet had been missed.

Bright ideas

Evans had had his fair share of gentlemen with bright ideas, most of which were aimed at preventing the ship's magnetism affecting the compass and were therefore easily dismissed. One man, however, took matters a stage further. In 1866 Mr Evan Hopkins read a paper to the United Services Institution entitled 'Terrestrial magnetism with reference to the compasses of iron ships, their deviations and remedies'.[8] After condemning as inaccurate both the Merchant Navy practice of complete compensation and the naval habit of using a table of deviations, he went on to explain how much better it would be to demagnetize the whole ship, so saving all the trouble and expense of swinging. He, Mr Hopkins, could achieve this with the aid of a powerful electric battery and he had already patented such a scheme.

This claim was received with much scepticism. Not only had Mr Hopkins ignored the inconvenient effect of magnetic induction in soft iron but he had not yet attempted to put his claim into practice. Evans, through the Hydrographer, strongly opposed the idea. It appears, however, that Mr Hopkins had influential friends for, after publishing a series of advertisements and newspaper articles, he managed to get a question asked in parliament about the cost and time taken in swinging HM ships. Evans was required to prepare a paper in reply.[9] At the same time the Admiralty, bowing to pressure, decided to allow Mr Hopkins to experiment on the new 6621 ton iron screw-ship *Northumberland*, the largest and most heavily armoured ship in the Navy. After two very ineffective attempts he boldly claimed that he had completely destroyed her magnetism in a few hours, but Evans was easily able to demonstrate that no change whatever, either in the deviation or in the vertical and horizontal forces, was perceptible. He then spent a fortnight at Sheerness in January 1867, under extremely adverse weather conditions, working on the ship with the help of his son. This time, however, they operated not only on the hull, as had been agreed, but also on the iron beams in the vicinity of the poop and steering compasses, thereby introducing localized magnetic poles which inevitably had an effect on the deviation. Eventually the father became ill and the attempt had to be abandonned. The Master of *Northumberland*, Thomas Batt, kept Mayes fully informed of the (lack of) progress in a series of most amusing letters.[10]

In May of that year the son, the Reverend E. Hopkins, read a further paper to the Royal United Service Institute[11] on behalf of his father, who still maintained that his method had been proved, only his illness preventing a completely satisfactory conclusion. He complained of lack of assistance from the Admiralty and, rather strangely, of the fact that some of the beams were sheathed in wood which had had to be removed. Nevertheless he announced that he was now prepared to demagnetize all the iron ships in the Fleet and to train naval officers to carry out his system.

Although a subsequent swing of the *Northumberland* by Mayes revealed small reductions in the deviation of the poop and steering compasses, there was no permanent effect. Rather, the deviations had become much less stable and were therefore more dangerous. By the end of the year most of the change had disappeared. Evans reported the whole episode to the Royal Society in a paper entitled 'On the amount and changes of the polar magnetism at certain positions in Her Majesty's iron-built and armour-plated ship *Northumberland*',[12] in which he stressed the dangers of such treatment and how transient was any apparent benefit. Nevertheless, when in the following year Mr Hopkins died, his daughter appealed to the Admiralty for a pension in recognition of her father's contribution to the advancement of Science'.[13] Ten years later the Reverend E. Hopkins took out a further patent on his father's method but he does not appear to have tried to sell his services to the Admiralty.

The patent books of this period contain many new ideas for improving the magnetic compass, notable amongst which is Paget's design of 1868 (Patent No. 843) which in some of its features pre-empted Sir William Thomson's compass of the next decade. Later it was to feature in one of his many court cases. It does not, however, appear to have been tried by the Compass Department. Two other less successful designs must also be mentioned. Commander Arthur's 'self-registering' compass was a beautifully made instrument designed to record the ship's head every two and a half minutes. It was examined at the Observatory and tried at sea in the *Fox* but in view of the highly skilled maintenance it would require and the fact that its deviation would inevitably differ from that of the Standard (navigating) Compass, it was not pursued.[14] A less successful compass was that invented by the Earl of Caithness, which was reported on in glowing terms, in conjunction with Nunn's improved overhead binnacle light, in the *Journal of the Royal United Services Institute*.[15] By attaching the compass bowl to a ball-and-socket joint from which hung a heavy weight to keep it level, it was hoped to prevent the card from oscillating in bad weather. The eminence of the inventor caused the First Sea Lord, Sir Alexander Milne, to take a personal interest in the outcome of the sea trials but the consistently poor reports of its performance at sea caused the Hydrographer much embarrassment.

Another attempt to neutralize the effects of magnetism was made by Navigating Lieutenant Chapple of the iron turret-ship *Prince*

Albert (2537 tons). Completed in 1866, this vessel was employed on gunnery duties at Devonport and thus did more than the normal amount of firing. Her Standard Compass was originally fitted above the pilot house on a light bridge between the two foremost turrets, where it must have suffered severely from concussion. In 1867 the bridge was strengthened and extended to form a hurricane deck over the two turrets. On 31 July of that year Lieutenant Chapple noted that coefficient B had changed by 13° since the ship had been swung only twenty-five days earlier and this he believed to have been caused by recent firing. (Although he had never previously reported the fact, he then claimed that firing *always* changed the deviation.) Evans thought it more probable that the compass had been affected by some disturbing force and sent Mayes to investigate, but without result. It was over a year later that Chapple himself discovered that the opening and closing of a large iron hatch only 14 feet from the compass could change the deviation by 'many degrees'. That this had been overlooked by Mayes during his investigation reflected little credit on the department.

Meanwhile Chapple had been carefully observing the deviation before and after firing and on several occasions had noted changes of 6° or 7°, although it appeared to return to normal after a few days in harbour. He also noted that a second Standard Compass fitted on the quarter-deck was unaffected, showing that it was the magnetism of the flimsy hurricane deck and not the hull that was being altered. An attempt was made to neutralize the effect by firing half the rounds on one heading and half on the reciprocal and this seems to have achieved some measure of success. His conclusions were submitted to the Admiralty in a paper entitled 'On the alteration of the magnetism of iron ships from concussion and other causes',[16] which was passed to the magnetic department for comment. It was unfortunate that its author's understanding of the theory of ship magnetism did not match the energy with which he conducted his trials, as his paper contained some truly remarkable statements, of which just one example must suffice. Referring to the differences noted at the two Standard Compasses, one on the bridge and one aft, he writes 'the difference . . . between the two compasses is owing to their position in the ship; the after one being at the extremity, only one end of the magnet may be said to act; in the fore, both ends act and consequently we may expect a much greater change.'

Chapple asked that his paper should be published with the sanction of Their Lordships but this would imply approval and endorsement of his opinions and could obviously not be allowed. Evans was also concerned lest its appearance should cause alarm in the Fleet, and he and Mayes went to considerable trouble to point out its errors and to explain the accepted theory. Chapple however, appears to have resented this and after an acrimonious correspondence in which he cast considerable doubt on the competence of the Compass Department, a minute in the Hydrographer's own handwriting reads:

> This officer . . . has written numerous papers to the Admiralty on the subject but unfortunately he has never written them in the spirit in which an officer should write who desires to convey information. On the contrary they have always been written in a spirit of self-sufficiency and of opposition to the Department from which he has learnt all that he really does know of the subject.[17]

This was an unsatisfactory outcome to what should have been an informative trial. There is no doubt that the changes observed by Chapple were genuine, if transient, and they were later confirmed by other ships,[18] but they were generally not serious and navigators soon learnt to guard against errors after firing by frequent observation of deviation. Chapple's pamphlet was later published privately. It eloquently underlined the importance of constantly observing the deviation, particularly when the ship was subjected to concussion, but this was probably its only merit.

The move to Deptford

At the end of 1869 the swinging buoys at Greenhithe were relinquished and turned over to the Thames Conservancy. They had been of great value to the Admiralty, particularly during the 1840s and again during the Russian War and the Indian Mutiny, but the Navy was now making little use of the London river and in the final year only nine swings are recorded. The Admiralty retained the right to use the buoys if required but this was seldom asserted.

In the following year, when Woolwich Dockyard was finally sold after 350 years of building ships for the Royal Navy, the Compass

Department was moved from the house in Maryan Road, Charlton, where it had been for some 26 years, to the yard at Deptford. An additional office for the Superintendent was also established in Somerset House as part of the Hydrographer's organization. The original wooden observatory was moved, exactly as it stood, and re-established on the Green in Deptford Yard and four rooms were provided in an adjacent building to serve the department as office, receiving and examination rooms, and museum. The following extract from a minute by the Hydrographer, written during the planning stage, shows that this was no plush accommodation:

> at present the place allotted is a store, adapted alone for the reception of casks and rough cooperage articles. It is necessarily inefficiently lighted, ventilated and without fireplaces or security from damp and much would have to be done to render the requisite offices and storerooms efficient and habitable . . . to secure the efficient preservation of the compasses of the Fleet[19]

The necessary improvements were apparently satisfactorily effected at a cost of £400. Mr Brunton, who had enjoyed free accommodation at Maryan Road since 1844 and had kept the garden 'in perfect order', was allowed to remain in residence for a further year until the property was relet, after which he was granted a lodging allowance.

With this simple move the Compass Department settled quickly and easily into its second home. Here it was to remain until the extension of London's electric tramways and the need for more space to build workshops and test facilities for aircraft and gyro-compasses eventually forced a further removal some forty-seven years later, in 1917.

Staff matters

Mayes was promoted to Staff Commander in August 1867 on achieving the necessary seniority as a Navigating Lieutenant. Later in that year the Hydrographer decided that the increase in ship-building now warranted an addition to the strength of the Compass Department, as foreshadowed in his report of 1865. In a minute to Their Lordships dated 24 March 1867 he wrote, 'owing to the greatly increased number of ships which require personal attention and supervision it is positively necessary that another Naval Officer should be attached to the Hydrographic Department'. He went on to explain that the many wooden ships building with iron ribs and beams (the composite system) required as much attention as the largest ironclads and that the number requiring investigation would rise from 25 in 1867 to 55 in 1868.[20] On 2 March 1868 Navigating Lieutenant Ettrick William Creak was appointed as Assistant Superintendent of Compasses.[21]

As was the habit for those entering the navigation specialization, Creak had joined the Navy as a Master's Assistant in 1849, at the age of fourteen. In 1863, having already spent much of his time abroad, he was promoted Master and sailed in the *Esk* for the Australian station where he made a number of surveys, including one of Nyola Bay in the Fiji Islands. From the start he seems to have taken a special interest in compass matters and, while serving in *Esk*, submitted a paper to the Admiralty on the effects of large changes in latitude. This was subsequently published by the Board of Trade. He also reported on the strange case of the chartered iron troopship *Trevelyn* whose captain had left England with a defective azimuth compass and, having lost confidence in his deviation table, decided to ignore it without attempting to prepare a replacement. Making land thus became an 'anxious task'. Creak found that the steering compass was also useless, as it still had the corrector magnet that had been applied before leaving England and no soft-iron correctors. Once again the Admiralty felt it necessary to draw the attention of the Board of Trade to the woeful lack of understanding of compass matters by so many Merchant Navy captains at sea.[22]

Having earlier attracted the attention of his future chief, Creak joined the Compass Department at a time when its reputation was fast declining. He went on to serve it with great distinction for the next thirty-three years and was personally responsible for raising it once more to a position of influence and respect.

Evans had been promoted to Staff Captain in December 1867 'for his services to Nautical Science'.[23] Under the terms of the Admiralty Order in Council of 1865 his appointment and that of Mayes had both been for a period of five years only, but in June of 1870 they were extended for a similar period.[24] (Mayes' appointment was subsequently renewed on three further occasions until he finally retired in 1887.) Evans was placed on the retired list with the rank of Captain in 1872 but he retained his post and in February 1874, on the retirement of Rear Admiral George Henry Richards, Evans succeeded him as Hydrographer, a post which he held for the next ten years. In 1873 he was created a Companion of the Bath. No further appointment was made to the post of 'head of the magnetic department', the new Hydrographer continuing to exercise a significant measure of control over its activities himself.

In the meanwhile Evans had continued his excellent work with papers and publications, many of which were produced in co-operation with Archibald Smith. A third edition of the *Admiralty Manual*[25] which appeared in 1869, had a considerably extended section on the 'Application of theory to practice' and a new part 4 of nine pages on compass correction, replacing the former two-page appendix. Correction was now allowed at the Standard Compass as well as the steering-compass but was still only intended to reduce the deviation as a matter of convenience and in order to equalize the directive force on all headings. No attempt was to be made at close correction. In the Royal Navy semicircular deviation was still corrected by a single horizontal magnet set at an angle, although other methods, including Airy's, were described. Two methods were given for correcting quadrantal deviation with soft iron, of which that headed 'Without calculation' is so straight forward that it is surprising to find the remark 'quadrantal deviation is not often corrected mechanically but is generally left for tabular correction'. (In the new ironclads coefficient D sometimes amounted to 7° or 8°, even at the Standard Compass.) It is probable that Evans had not tried it in practice since the *Trident* trials of 1856. His two concerns were always the difficulty of obtaining unmagnetized soft iron and the inconvenience of observing bearings when spheres were fitted. The 'Captain Evans's two compasses' method was described at some length and for the first time there was a practical description of the correction of heeling error. The appendix on mathematical theory was largely rewritten and extended. A fourth edition of the *Admiralty Manual* which appeared in 1874 was simply a corrected version of the third.

Ever since the correspondence with the Board of trade in 1865 Evans had realized the need for a simple publication to complement the *Admiralty Manual*, much of which was beyond the grasp of the average officer at sea.[26] His *Elementary Manual for the Deviation of the Compass in Iron Ships* appeared in 1870 and was written in the form of questions and answers. It was a comprehensive and valuable book covering all aspects of compass work, their design and positioning, obtaining and applying deviation and the magnetic characters of ships, and it gave details of all the mathematical calculations that might be required of a seaman. Correction was covered in detail on the lines given in the *Admiralty Manual*. Airy's method of observing the errors directly and correcting with two magnets is described as the 'tentative method' but it seems extraordinary that fifteen years after the appearance of Gray's binnacle this should still be done by drawing chalk lines on the deck. No reference is made to binnacles with adjustable magnets. With regard to soft iron, Evans advised that the Navy did not correct quadrantal deviation and, despite the recommendations of the Liverpool Compass Committee, he considered the use of what we now call a Flinders bar as 'too complicated'. Nevertheless this was an extremely useful book which gave the Hydrographer the opportunity to tell the Board of Evans's international reputation and of the extent to which other countries were indebted to the Compass Department for so many published works. A second edition came out in 1873, containing many new footnotes, with a third edition in 1875 which was reprinted as the fourth and fifth editions in 1879 and 1883.[27]

In 1870 Evans was invited by the Board of Trade to comment on the Compass aspects of a syllabus prepared by J. T. Towson, of the Liverpool Marine Board, for the examination of Masters and Mates. This matter had been under consideration ever since Airy had originally suggested it in 1857, when commenting on the second report of the Liverpool Compass Committee, and in the intervening years it had been raised by many competent authorities, including the Royal Society. Initially the examination was introduced as a voluntary subject, successful candidates receiving a special endorsement to their certificates, but in March 1872 it was established as a firm requirement for all officers sitting for Master or Mate.[28] A further twenty years were to pass, however, before commercial compass-adjusters were required to obtain similar certificates of competence, a matter which had first been suggested by Captain Johnson as early as 1847.

In 1872 Evans again addressed the Royal United Services Institute *'On the present state of our knowledge respecting the magnetism of iron ships and the treatment of their compasses'*,[29] bringing up to date his papers of 1859 and 1865. His report explained the Admiralty's gradual and cautious acceptance of the need for reducing the deviations of compasses, contrasting it with the wide and often ill-informed use of correction in the Merchant Navy, and gave details of the method used, normally employing only a single magnet along the lines set out in the latest edition of the *Admiralty Manual*. It also stated that experiments with Evans's twin compasses were still in progress, although no record of these has been discovered. In conclusion it was far more generous in its attitude to Airy's contributions than any of Evans's earlier works.

Due to ill health Archibald Smith was unable to be present when this paper was read and he died later in the same year. Of his contributions to the science of magnetism it would be impossible to speak too highly. The following brief extract from a long and penetrating obituary notice written by Sir William Thomson for the Royal Society encapsulates the essentials of his outstanding work: 'The constancy to the Compass problem in which Smith persevered with a rare extreme of disinterestedness, from the time (1841) when Sabine first asked him to work at practical methods from Poisson's mathematical theory, until his health broke down two years before his death, was characteristic of the man.'[30]

Only six months before Smith died the government had requested his acceptance of a gift of £2,000 as a mark of its appreciation of 'the long and valuable services which he had gratuitously rendered to the Naval Service in connection with the magnetism of iron ships and the Deviation of their Compasses . . . which has so far conduced to the safe navigation of iron ships, not only of the Royal and Mercantile Navies of this country, but of all nations'.[31]

Evans's paper to the Royal United Services Institute appears to have been his last writing of importance on the matter of compasses, although in the same year he also addressed the Royal Society on the subject of the 'Changes in variation on the coasts of Great Britain'[32] and was responsible for drawing up instructions for the magnetic observations to be made by Captain Nares during his celebrated voyage around the world in HMS *Challenger* (1872–76).[33]

Time for change

When, in 1874, Captain Evans took over the post of Hydrographer, he had already been in charge of the Compass Department for nineteen years, a period of tremendous change in the Navy which had seen the gradual transition from wood to iron, from sail to steam, and from paddles to screw. By 1874 the revolutionary ironclads of the early 1860s, with their broad-sided gun ports had already been rendered obsolescent by the invention of the revolving turret (albeit still with muzzle-loading guns). New classes of warships, including armoured cruisers and heavy coast-defence battleships, were appearing and the first torpedoes were already at sea. In 1870 the shattering loss of the *Captain*, which capsized in the Bay of Biscay with the loss of 473 lives, finally convinced the Admiralty of the folly of mixing sail and steam and 1873 saw the launch of the *Devastation*, the first warship without a full set of masts and rigging.

Evolution in the Navy had naturally demanded changes in the activities of its Compass Department which, despite its cautious approach, had successfully ensured that no HM ship had been lost through the inadequacy of its compasses. The complex theoretical problems concerned with ship magnetism had been brilliantly solved, and deviations were normally contained within reasonable limits. British publications, compasses and methods were taken as a model by many maritime nations. Yet it is clear that the Navy was not entirely satisfied with its compass arrangements, and for good reason. Deviations, which were still on occasions substantial, are awkward to handle and can lead to mistakes, yet Evans remained firmly against close correction, fearing that this might lead officers to ignore deviation altogether. His method was still to reduce the errors by immoveable magnets and any suggestion of flexibility, as had been offered by Gray's binnacle of 1856, was anathema to him. He was opposed to the correction of quadrantal deviation by Airy's method of soft iron and he never adopted the Flinders bar, as proposed by the Liverpool Compass Committee in 1860.

Compasses, too, were being criticized at sea. The Admiralty Standard Compass, which had served the Navy so well since 1840, was often unsatisfactory under the severe conditions of vibration now becoming the norm and the regulations required that it should be unshipped when firing heavy guns. It is true that liquid compasses were provided for use in the binnacle under these conditions (and occasionally to replace the Standard) but replacing compasses was, of itself, a nuisance, and although the liquid compasses were an improvement, those supplied for the Navy still had their limitations. The opportunity offered ten years earlier to adopt the superior American type of liquid compass had been missed and the idea does not appear ever to have been re-examined. The Standard Compass was often very inconveniently sited, while the provision of a suitable compass near the position in the ship most convenient for navigation was by no means always achieved. All in all the compass arrangements in the Fleet still left much to be desired.

During the 1840s Captain Johnson had had to learn his trade from scratch, but he had constantly striven for improvement and was receptive to new ideas. His successors were sound and conscientious in carrying out their task but, despite the undoubted advances achieved, they had lacked the progressive outlook and breadth of vision to move with the times and to take advantage of the opportunities offered. There was a marked tendency to defend the status quo, without any serious effort to investigate or improve matters. For the ten years from 1865 the Compass Department had really stood still. Routine work, and there was plenty of that, had continued but all research and development or forward thinking had virtually ceased. It was small wonder the Navy was dissatisfied. The stage was thus perfectly set for the entry of Sir William Thomson.

NOTES

CHAPTER 3

1 Three years earlier Evans had married Commander Hall's sister Elizabeth; one can speculate (but no more) on whether this had any bearing on subsequent events.

2 Hydrographer's Minute Book, No. 12, p. 377.

3 ADM/235, M/10, p. 222.

4 Hydrographer's Minute Book, No. 15, p. 507.

5 ADM/235, M/10, pp. 208, 211.

6 ADM 12/826.

7 It is interesting to note that the provision of an uncorrected telltale compass in the captain's cabin still persisted into the era of armoured ships. It can have been of very little use.

8 *Journal of the Royal United Services Institute* (RUSI), Vol. 10, (1866), p. 85. This paper was repeated at the meeting of the British Association in Nottingham, see *Athenaeum*, 8 September 1866.

9 Parliamentary Paper, No. 244 (1866), entitled 'Tabular statement showing the means adopted for correcting or ascertaining the deviation of the compasses during the past three years, in

each of Her Majesty's ships *Achilles, Bellerophon, Black Prince, Lord Warden, Minotaur, Prince Albert, Prince Consort, Research, Resistance, Scorpion, Royal Oak, Warrior, Wivern* and *Zealous*, showing also, under the name of each ship, the dates on which the ship was swung for deviation, or on which compensating magnets were applied or on which the position of the magnets was altered; and showing, further, the time occupied by the operation on each occasion, and the computed cost of each verification or adjustment'.

10 ADM/235, M/10, pp. 183–86, 189.

11 *Journal of the RUSI*, Vol. 2 (1867), p. 260.

12 *Phil. Trans. Royal Society*, 1868, p. 487.

13 Hydrographer's Minute Book, No. 14, p. 114.

14 ADM/235, M/2, p. 337.

15 *Journal of the RUSI*, Vol. 12 (1868).

16 National Maritime Museum, Magnetic Compass Collection, Item 9/4 (11).

17 Hydrographer's Minute Book, No. 17, p. 324.

18 Ibid., No. 20, pp. 82, 256.

19 Ibid., No. 15, p. 75.

20 Ibid., No. 14, p. 283.

21 His appointment does not, however, appear in the Navy List under the staff of the Hydrographic Office until 1884, only three years before he relieved Mayes in the post of Superintendent.

22 ADM 235, M/2, p. 350.

23 H. S. Dawson, *Memoirs of Hydrography*, 1885, p. 181, reprinted Cornmarket Press 1969.

24 Hydrographer's Minute Book, No. 16, p. 21.

25 National Maritime Museum, Magnetic Compass Collection, Item 7/10.

26 Captain Lecky in his *Wrinkles in Practical Navigation* (George Philip 22nd edn. 1937) says of the *Manual* 'the reading is altogether too stiff for any but learned professors'. p. 631.

27 National Maritime Museum, Magnetic Compass Collection, Items 7/16 to 7/18.

28 Board of Trade, Circular No. 414 (May 1870), No. 517 (December 1871).

29 *Journal of the RUSI*, Vol. 16 (1872).

30 *Proceedings of the Royal Society*, No. 150 (1874), p. xvi.

31 Admiralty letter, 1 July 1872 (ibid. p. xvi).

32 National Maritime Museum, Magnetic Compass Collection, Item 9/8 (4).

33 Ibid., Item 9/8 (5).

Sir William Thomson

4

> Our Authorities are exceedingly heavy to move in any way which involves the introduction of new ideas . . . I have had two years struggle with the Compass Department of our Hydrographic Office to induce them to take up some suggestions I have brought before them for the correction of the compass in iron ships . . . I now see that if anything is to be done in the matter, the whole business of it will fall upon myself. (Letter from Sir William Thomson to Professor Peirce of Harvard University[1])

For the last quarter of the nineteenth century the affairs of the Compass Department were largely dominated by the figure of Sir William Thomson. Various suggestions have been made as to why Sir William, already a renowned scientist, should have turned his attention to compasses comparatively late in life. Always interested in the sea (he had in 1856 become actively involved in the practical problems of laying the trans-Atlantic cable, for which he was later knighted), in 1870 he purchased his own yacht, the *Lalla Rookh*, and the problems of the seamen became his own. Thereafter his contributions to navigation were to continue as a major factor in his work for the rest of his life. It was not therefore surprising that when, in 1871, the Reverend Norman Macleod invited him to contribute an article to his newly founded magazine *Good Words*, he should have chosen as his subject 'The mariner's compass'.

Other factors may have contributed. Some years later (1885) when giving evidence in a patents case, (*Thomson* v. *Moore*) Sir William stated that it was the necessity of writing an obituary notice on Archibald Smith for the Royal Society which had first turned his attention to compasses, while in his book *Records* Admiral Fisher suggests that it was being confined to his yacht with a broken thigh which led him to invent 'his marvellous compass and sounding machine'.

Whatever it was, having chosen to write on what he believed to be a comparatively simple subject, he quickly realized that he knew very little about it. At the same time his early studies soon convinced him that there was much to criticize in the compasses then in use. The first part of his article did not therefore appear until 1874, with Part 2 following a full five years later. In the event they were concerned mainly with the history of the subject and with terrestrial magnetism, and barely touched on his own inventions.

Sir William appreciated the need for an accurate (i.e. closely corrected) compass and set about designing a binnacle which would enable this to be achieved, following Airy's principles. It was when he was designing the compass to go with it that he became convinced of the need for a very light card with the shortest possible needles. In 1873 he wrote to Evans asking about the Admiralty Standard Compass and about the sizes of the compasses used in the *Great Eastern* and in 'our grand modern merchant ships'. He explained that he was thinking of a tiny instrument with two half-inch needles and a fine glass pointer suspended by a fibre of silk, but with no card.[2] This, he felt, could be corrected very accurately but although he demonstrated such an instrument to the Royal Society of Edinburgh in 1874 he did not explain how it would be used at sea.

Evans's reply to Sir William has not been preserved but it evidently gave him little encouragement for he wrote shortly afterwards to Froude complaining 'how people in all departments of the Admiralty . . . are averse to and, if they could, they would be impregnable against, all suggestions from without'.[3]

In the same year Thomson addressed the British Association in Belfast 'On the perturbations of the compass produced by the rolling of the ship'.[4] The paper contained a mathematical discussion of the errors due to rolling, as distinct from the effects of heeling error, and showed that with a compass of short period these could be very large. They could, however, be avoided by making the period of the compass long in comparison with the period of roll of the ship. After a year and a half of experimenting, both ashore and in his yacht, Sir William took out his first patent for a compass and binnacle (No. 1339, 29 March 1876), introducing the famous Thomson dry-card compass which has made him renowned among mariners ever since.

The essential features of this equipment, as set out in the final specification, dated 27 September 1876, were as follows:

The compass: a very light paper card with a thin aluminium rim connected to a central boss by silk threads. In this way the weight was thrown to the outside, giving a long period of oscillation. Cards were provided in sizes from 4 to 12 inches, with 2 or 4 (later 8) small magnetic needles. Being extremely light, there was very little friction on the pivot. (The weight of a 9-inch card was 104 grains as against 1500 grains for the 7 1/2-inch card of the Admiralty Standard Compass.) The gimbals were supported on knife edges and a chamber in the base of bowl, into which hung a disc, was filled with caster oil to give some damping.

The binnacle: a conventional wooden 'pillar' of wide diameter which carried two sets of scissor magnets, fore-and-aft and athwartship or, as an alternative, a single magnet which could be slewed. Quadrantal deviation was corrected by soft-iron spheres carried in wooden troughs secured to the binnacle and heeling error by an adjustable vertical magnet fitted in a clamp.

Ancillaries: the patent also covered a new type of azimuth circle, the forerunner of that still associated with the name of Thomson, but with a mirror in place of the 60° prism now in use (introduced by Patent No. 5676 of 1883). This enabled bearings to be taken over the spheres, so overcoming one of Evans's objections to quadrantal correctors. A second azimuth instrument in the form of a 'sun-compass' was also provided for determining compass errors when adjusting.

In a later patent (No. 4876) in the same year the scissor magnets were removed and the fore-and-aft and athwartship magnets fitted in slides. The spheres could also be slewed to correct a coefficient E. This patent covered modifications to the azimuth circle, including a second mirror to enable simultaneous bearings to be taken of two objects 180° apart. It introduced the Thomson deflector (see p. 110) and a torsion dip needle, the first example of a true heeling-error instrument (see p. 147) as we now know it. The complete specification also included a dwarf binnacle, intended for use as a steering-compass, with separate magnet racks for fitting on a bench alongside it.

It was Sir William's intention that once the compass had been closely adjusted the correctors should be altered by the ship's officers as frequently as was necessary to keep it accurate. There would thus be no deviation (which might be applied the wrong way) and no deviation table need be kept. It was a bold if somewhat unrealistic concept and went against every principle of the Admiralty's prudent policy. Nevertheless it was welcomed by great numbers of seamen for whom applying deviation was fraught with apprehension.

Having designed his compass and binnacle, Sir William appears to have set about 'selling' it with the aim, not unreasonably, of achieving the maximum commercial reward. Between 1876 and 1880 presentations on the subject were made to the RUSI and to other influential bodies, including four papers to the British Association. Hoping to interest Airy and to enlist his support, he sent him an early prototype which, unfortunately, was delivered before his letter of explanation.[5] The elderly astronomer is said to have examined it intently for some time before saying simply, 'It won't do.' Sir William's comment on this verdict was similarly terse: 'So much for the Astronomer Royal's opinion!' He was right.

He next persuaded a number of owners to fit his equipment in their ships, making all the initial compass adjustments himself. Enjoying the benefit of a (temporarily) accurate compass for the first time and dazzled by the glory of not having to allow for deviation, shipmasters were unanimously enthusiastic. It was in many ways an ideal compass for merchant ships and its use spread rapidly. Over a century later the Kelvin dry-card compass could still occasionally be found at sea.

Unofficial trials in the Navy

In January 1877 a model was obtained for the Compass Observatory but Mayes appears to have taken little interest in it. Certainly no comparative trials were arranged. However, realizing that this approach was unlikely to advance his ambitions Sir William quickly resorted to less orthodox methods. He arranged privately for his compass to be tried in the *Minotaur* (Captain Lord Walter Kerr, the flagship of Vice-Admiral Beauchamp Seymour, commanding the Channel Squadron), also in the turret-ship *Thunderer* (Captain J. C. Wilson) and later in the gunnery firing-ship *Gorgon*. He claimed, among its merits, that the compass would remain steady during gunfire or when steaming at high speed. As these trials had no official sanction the captains sent their reports direct to Sir William and thus enabled him to remedy a number of early defects and shortcomings.

Comparison was, of course, being made between a closely corrected Thomson compass and a partially corrected Admiralty Standard and it is not surprising that reports favoured the Thomson. On 9 August 1877, following a summer cruise to Vigo, Lord Walter Kerr, supported by his admiral, suggested to Their Lordships that this compass should at once be adopted for all HM ships chiefly, it appears, on the grounds that 'it had no deviation'. Certainly the binnacle provided for the first time a simple means of adjustment to meet the inevitable *changes* in deviation, but it had been tried on one voyage only and over a very limited range of latitude, so that little change would have been apparent. Also, as Mayes was quick to point out, no new principles were involved, and close correction could equally well have been applied to the Admiralty Standard had it been the policy to do so. Lord Kerr's report said nothing about the relative merits of the compasses themselves, and no trials had been made to test the effects of gunfire or high-speed steaming. On these points Sir William's claims appear to have been accepted on trust.

At this point the Compass Department was inevitably drawn into the discussion. Evans, who was now Hydrographer, called for a report from the Superintendent on the equipment he had acquired nine months earlier. Mayes' reply was unenthusiastic. He saw no merit in the new design of compass, which he believed would be too easily damaged. He rightly pointed out that the advantages of having 'practically no deviation' could be achieved with any compass and was not the invention of Sir William Thomson, but he omitted to mention the convenient way that correction was provided for in the Thomson binnacle. He stated that he could not 'without a much more exhaustive trial . . . admit the superiority claimed by the inventor . . . or recommend its introduction in the Navy'.[6]

Evans concurred in this report.[7] Probably he foresaw a threat to the Admiralty Standard Compass and was determined to quash it. He emphasized to Their Lordships the complexities of compass theory and practice, which could not be grasped without considerable study, and he rather condescendingly stated that Sir William's lack of understanding of the requirements of the Fleet were no reflection on the great man. He did, however, reluctantly agree that the equipment in *Minotaur* should be purchased for trial, both in that ship and later in some smaller ship, but he added, 'I cannot recommend, even as a matter of trial, that Sir William Thomson's compass should be looked upon as at all likely to supersede the Admiralty Standard Compass.' In concluding paragraphs, he added:

> Finally on the subject I would remark if the character of an organisation is stamped by its successful working, then no one knows better than Sir William Thomson the value of the Admiralty Compass System for, in his Presidential Address to the British Association for The Advancement of Science in 1871, he paid marked testimony thereunto in these words: 'I firmly believe that it is to the thoroughly scientific method thus adopted by the Admiralty that no Iron ship of Her Majesty's Navy has been lost through error of compass.'

In the light of later events it would appear that the department was already whistling to keep up its spirits.

In addition to publicizing his new compass, Sir William was endeavouring to interest the Admiralty in his new sounding-machine,[8] one of which had also been supplied unofficially for trial in the *Minotaur*. He was, of course, known personally to members of the Board, not only as an eminent scientist but as a member of the committee established in 1871 to report on designs of warships, following the loss of the *Captain* which had capsized during a gale in 1870 with the loss of 473 lives. It was therefore clear that despite the remarks of the Hydrographer and the unorthodox approach of Sir William, his inventions had to be given their serious attention. Both equipments were therefore purchased and Their Lordships called for further reports. The price quoted was £80 for the pair (compass and sounding-machine).

A month later Evans drew Their Lordships' attention to the fact that a Thomson compass was also fitted in the *Thunderer* whose captain now requested that it should be purchased and supplied officially. On being asked why he had obtained no authority for fitting this equipment Captain Wilson gave the remarkable reply that it 'was lent by a mutual friend for private purposes and, of course, no authority being required, none was asked for!' He went on to state, 'It is the only compass we have hitherto had on board on which we could rely', and gave as his opinion, 'No reliance is to be placed on compasses supplied by the service.'[9]

Evans was justifiably furious at this implied attack on the Compass Department. Further, it was clear that, contrary to regulations, both the *Thunderer* and *Minotaur* had been navigated by the Thomson compass rather than the Admiralty Standard. He drew Their Lordships' attention to the grave and dangerous departure from normal service custom regarding the introduction of equipment upon which the safety and efficiency of the ships depended, and he recommended that *Thunderer* should not be permitted to retain the compass.[10]

Although Evans received the support of the Board on this occasion, he was already fighting a rearguard action. In April 1878 Sir William wrote to the First Lord, the Right Honourable W. H. Smith MP, asking him to consider introducing both the compass and the sounding-machine into the Royal Navy.[11] He pointed out that the compass was already at sea in sixty ships, that it had been tried by the Imperial German Navy (which had ordered another) and by the navies of Russia, Italy and Brazil, and he suggested more extensive trials, both as an azimuth compass and in other positions. Evans proposed awaiting the result of the *Minotaur* trials, and pointed out the great expense that would be involved, at £60 a time. A suitably noncommittal reply was sent to Sir William, but two more compasses were purchased for trial in the *Neptune* (later transferred to *Glatton*) and the *Boadicea* (later changed to *Euryalus*) all being adjusted by the inventor. At the same time the First Sea Lord ruled that, pending a decision, the purchase of normal service compasses should cease.

Support for Sir William

Reports from ships fitted with the new compasses, although generally favourable, were not wholly uncritical, and appropriate extracts were passed to Sir William. He thus continued to benefit from trials conducted at the Navy's expense, a procedure not unknown to manufacturers today! In 1879, having made a number of improvements to the original design, he took out his third compass patent (No. 679) covering new equipment which has virtually provided the prototype for most standard binnacles ever since. The horizontal magnets were placed in numbered holes at different levels, the vertical magnets were placed in a bucket whose height could be adjusted by a chain, the spheres were mounted on brackets, and for the first time a Flinders bar was fitted on the binnacle instead of being built into the ship, as suggested by the Liverpool Compass Committee. The method of threading the compass needles was improved and a new method of suspension was introduced, consisting of a sprung-wire grommet from which the compass bowl was hung by short chains. The aim of this suspension was to provide the compass with greater protection against the effects of gunfire (which Sir William had claimed would not disturb it). As far as the Navy was concerned it was the grommet which really saved it.

Apart from the claimed absence of deviation, the advantages of the Thomson compass that immediately commended it were its sensitivity, which was better than any of the normal Admiralty compasses, and its large card, which made it easier to read and to steer by. It was also generally better under conditions of vibration than the Admiralty Standard, even when the latter was fitted with the India-rubber suspension that had been introduced in 1876. However, despite repeated requests, the Compass Department was unable to obtain reports from sea on its performance during gunfire when compared with that of the service liquid compass especially provided for such occasions. Changing compasses was a nuisance and was often ignored. In any case it appeared that ships were determined to have the Thomson. Not until March 1882 does a clear statement comparing the behaviour of these compasses appear in the Admiralty files. This came from the battleship *Superb* and was welcomed by Evans as 'a record of fact rather than opinion'. With its grommet protection the Thomson had stood the concussion better than the liquid compass, although the latter more quickly returned to rest.[12] By this time, however, the battle was virtually lost.

On the matter of deviation Sir William, like Airy, believed that despite the inevitable changes due to ship magnetism or to geographical position, the compass could be kept accurate by frequently adjusting the correctors. This was a most dangerous assumption. A cardinal rule in the Admiralty's policy had always been that the compass must never be considered correct, and to suggest otherwise would be to encourage neglect in the constant observation of deviation that was so central to the Admiralty system. Yet with the Thomson compass no table of residual deviations was maintained and the *Practical Rules* were ignored at every turn. Further, each time the correctors were moved all previous data was destroyed and it was no longer possible to analyse the changes that were occurring in the magnetic state of the ship.

Yet, while the Hydrographer and the Compass Department could scarcely believe what was happening, the reasons were all too plain. The operational requirements of the Fleet in 1880 were very different from those of 1860. Unfortunately with Evans's caution and Mayes's inertia the department had failed to move with the times and had lost the confidence of those at sea. Even the compasses themselves, although conscientiously cared for and tested at the Observatory, were out of date. It is a recorded fact[13] that practically no new compasses had been purchased for the Fleet since 1860, while the design of the majority was a decade or two earlier. To many officers at sea it must have appeared that the Thomson compass provided exactly what the Navy needed.

Meanwhile Sir William continued to press for the wider introduction of his equipment by every means at his disposal and the official files of the period contain many of his letters, making suggestions or drawing attention to favourable reports he had received. His correspondence with the Admiralty was often accompanied by a private letter to the minister to ensure that action was taken. Above all he worked on the captains of Her Majesty's ships and, as his biographer records, 'As Sir William on his summer cruises in his yacht made the acquaintance of influential Naval Officers, there arose a gradual movement within the Navy for the adoption of the Compass.'[14]

In October 1879 Captain J. A. Fisher was appointed to command the new 10,000 ton turret-ship *Northampton*. Having been impressed by the Thomson compass he had seen in the *Thunderer* he immediately arranged that the *Northampton* should be fitted with one of the latest type, which Sir William had agreed to lend the Admiralty free of charge. His glowing report,[15] rendered after only a month's trial and just one target practice, was detailed and direct. The compass 'did not move one degree' when firing 'electric broadsides' or at speed, and in his view, 'this one fact alone should be sufficient to lead to the supply of one of Sir W. T.'s compasses to every one of HM Ships, because now in action we are practically without a compass.' He did not believe that the liquid compass was the answer, although it is doubtful whether he had ever tried one. He also made the valid point that 'the same arrangements for conning the ship should be employed in action as at any other time'. Subsequently he requested and obtained a second Thomson compass for the conning tower. Fisher appreciated (apparently unlike Sir William

himself) that the correct way to use the new compass was with a
table of deviations and he stressed the simplicity of reducing its
errors should they grow too large. He compared this with the
inconvenience of the Admiralty system which involved having to
redrill the pillar of the Admiralty Standard to reposition the magnet,
a laborious process which still only produced an approximate correction. He commented on the sluggishness of the Admiralty compasses
and, in summarizing the advantages of the Thomson, he made
particular mention of the correction of quadrantal error, which
Evans had always opposed. Finally, he made the point that 'Educated
Officers who are fit to be entrusted with the Command and Navigation of HM Ships are enabled to correct their compasses if desirable,
whereas the present adjustments of the Admiralty Compass are
unknown to most officers.'

In fact the Admiralty system of correction was sound but it
was ponderous, inflexible and difficult to apply. The results were
intentially only approximate. Against this, the Thomson system
purported to be simple, effective, accurate and easy to understand
and use. Further, Sir William had prepared a set of plain straightforward guidelines for correcting his compass which were in marked
contrast with the Admiralty instructions, even as given in the
Elementary Manual.

A last stand

With Sir William Thomson's unrelenting pressure and Captain
Fisher's strong support the cautious approach which the Compass
Department had adopted for so many years was in danger of being
swept aside. The pendulum would then inevitably swing too far.
The Hydrographer decided to put up a spirited defence. In his
comments to the Board dated 12 February 1880[16] Evans started by
saying,

> From the tone adopted in these reports [by Captain Fisher] and
> from the general tenor of the remarks . . . it would appear that
> the compasses of the Fleet rather than Sir William Thomson's
> were under trial in HMS *Northampton*, and that the Compass
> Department of the Admiralty was on its defence for the inferiority
> of its compasses and system as contrasted with that of Sir William
> Thomson.

He then set out the merits of the current Admiralty system and organization, stressing the need for caution and the very special technical knowledge required of a subject which 'without being actually obtuse . . . is very complicated and, to the ordinary run of minds, I should think especially unattractive'. The knowledge of naval officers on this subject was 'extremely limited', hence the requirement for trained experts in the Compass Department.

After giving an account of the origin and progress of this organization since 1837, of the introduction and application of the *Practical rules* and of the invaluable work of the Compass Observatory in maintaining the standard of the compasses in the Fleet, he outlined the problems that had had to be solved during 'the transition states of the Navy . . . from sailing to steam ships, from wood-built to iron-built ships and finally to armour-plated ships', and he pointed to the excellent record of the department over the previous forty years.

Turning to 'certain reported merits' of Sir William Thomson's compass, Evans admitted the theoretical advantage of the light card with short needles but considered that this 'large and fragile card . . . will require to be severely tried as to its endurance'. The card had, by this time, been in use in some ships for over three years! On the matter of correction, which he pointed out could equally be applied to the Admiralty Standard Compass, he made much of the fact that shortly after its adjustment by Sir William the compass in *Northumberland* was found to have an error of $3\frac{3}{4}°$. He stressed the difficulty of obtaining pure soft iron for the spheres, one of the reasons why he was opposed to quadrantal correction in the Navy. Regarding the use of permanent magnet correctors, his view was still that 'considering the inexperience of our officers' he was most strongly against 'entrusting them with the manipulation of these correctors' (in the Admiralty system the correctors were, of course, intentionally made difficult to manipulate).

Evans stressed the fact that as the Admiralty Standard Compass was 'intended *solely* for Navigational purposes' it must be carefully safeguarded and 'should be replaced by a liquid compass during the temporary and exceptional occasions of heavy gun firing'. Somewhat surprisingly he went on to mention the general use in the US Navy of the improved liquid compass which he had turned down in 1863. Finally, although he believed that the Thomson compass might have advantages for use in conning towers, he considered that its reliability for navigational purposes had yet to be proved.

The report concluded with a number of appendices giving details of the number, value and maintenance costs of the compasses in the Navy. A total of 5188 compasses of all descriptions was currently valued at £24,650 and the supply to the fleet was maintained almost entirely by repair, the annual cost of which was £375 for standards and £2400 for the remainder. The only new compasses purchased since the end of the Russian war a quarter of a century earlier had been 5 standards (for the Indian troopships) bringing the total ever made to 316, 25 boats compasses (in 1860) and 142 liquid compasses to augment those required for use when firing (in 1877). The department could not be accused of being extravagant.

To replace these compasses by those of Sir William Thompson would be extremely expensive. The price quoted for his standard compass and binnacle with correctors was £45 but to this would be added £5 for the azimuth circle and £10 each for two accessories which Sir William considered essential, the heeling-error instrument and the deflector.[17]

This very comprehensive report had been drafted by Staff Commander Creak (he had been promoted in 1873) and its original, which is held in the Hydrographic Department,[18] contains very few amendments by Evans. One addition, however, in the Hydrographer's own hand, is of particular significance as it shows clearly that he did not expect his opinions to be questioned: 'I assume that their Lordships are fully aware that in making these remarks I do so as an acknowledged authority, not only in this country but in Europe and America, and that it would be an affection of modesty on my part were I not to claim this position.'

Requests for Thomson compasses

Meanwhile the *Northampton* had sailed for the West Indies, having been instructed to keep a record of the deviations of her two Thomson compasses whenever the ship was swung.[19] This was faithfully performed. A comprehensive report rendered a year later showed that perfect correction was seldom achieved and that errors in the conning-tower compass once reached $23\frac{1}{2}°$. Nevertheless it was clear that under severe vibration or shock of gunfire the

Thomson compass, with its grommet suspension, was greatly superior to either the Admiralty Standard or the other steering compasses
in use which did not, of course, enjoy such protection. Regrettably
no mention was made of the service liquid compasses. Although
Evans commented in April 1881, 'I am not surprised at the failure
in the Northampton to keep these compasses accurately pointing,'
he went on to recommend that, while the Admiralty Standard 'and
every point of its organisation' should remain, it was advisable 'to
place in our iron clads and ships of exceptional character from
excessive steam power, one or more Thomson Compasses as auxiliary to the Standard.'[20]

Applications for fitting Thomson compasses, mainly for steering
with the 'steam-wheel' on the bridge, were soon on the increase.
Some were soundly based, others offered the flimsiest of excuses.[21]
Approval was normally given wherever vibration was excessive and
a particularly severe case occurred in the 8710 ton screw-ship *Superb*
in which, when at full power, some compasses simply spun round
and round.[22] In November 1881, after testing a number of compasses
in this ship Creak conducted comparative trials with a Thomson
compass and an Admiralty Standard which had been specially fitted
with half-weight needles. Both compasses proved equally steady.
On the other hand, the Admiralty 'J card', originally designed for
use under severe conditions, was one of those which simply spun
round. The erronious belief that heavy cards were best in rough
weather had originated during the trials of the Admiralty Standard
in 1840 (see p. 7) and the mistake had never been corrected.

Requests came from all classes of ship, and amongst those to
apply successfully were the battleship *Thunderer* (to replace the out-
of-date compass lent in 1877 and never returned), the armoured
cruiser *Nelson* and the gunboat *Firm*. Although at the start of 1881
only a handful of Thomson compasses had been fitted, from then
on the number grew rapidly. In March of that year Captain Fisher
was appointed to the new 11,880 ton turret-battleship *Inflexible*[23]
and immediately asked that Thomson compasses should be provided
for all steering positions in the ship, a total of six. The Hydrographer
agreed, as a special case,[24] the positions were confirmed by the
Superintendent and the compasses were adjusted by Sir William
himself, who also greatly enjoyed a week's cruising in the Channel
as guest of the captain. He records that one of the steering-compasses
provided had a 15 inch card and 20 inch spheres, the largest ever

fitted. In January 1882, the First Sea Lord personally directed that all the Channel squadron should be fitted with Thomson compasses 'for the training of officers', and the Storekeeper-General expressed great anxiety about the 'fancy prices' being charged.[25]

The bombardment of Alexandria

In the same month, following the breakdown of negotiations with the Mahdi in Egypt, ships of the British Mediterranean Fleet under Admiral Sir Beauchamp Seymour carried out a close-range bombardment of the forts at Alexandria. Three of the battleships engaged carried Thomson compasses and all reported on their satisfactory performance. An extract from the account of the action by Captain J. A. Fisher of H.M.S. *Inflexible* reads as follows:

> All Sir W.T.'s compasses were in position. They were unaffected by the firing. Without them it would not have been practicable on account of the shoals to take up our position so close to the batteries as the Standard Compass cannot be kept shipped when heavy guns are fired. It seems essential that every vessel should be supplied with one Sir W. T. Compass which is unaffected even by the continuous firing of the eighty ton guns.[26]

The Captain went on to remark that the great superiority of the Thomson compass had led to its adoption for all ships of the French navy. It may be noted, however, that the battleships *Sultan* and *Penelope* which also took part in the action and were not fitted with Thomson compasses, both remarked on the very satisfactory performance of their service liquid compasses, but little notice appears to have been taken.

Introduction of Thomson compasses for all steering positions

Further reports favourable to Sir William continued to reach the Admiralty and matters came to a head in the spring of 1883, curiously as a result of a very unfavourable report on the service compasses by Captain St John of the *Iron Duke* which was later shown to have been quite without foundation.[27] Nevertheless, the First Sea Lord, Admiral Sir Astley Cooper Key, decided that the time had come to accede to the widely held wishes of the Fleet. His minute read, 'There is a growing opinion among Officers in Command and Navigating Officers that the Thomson Compass is, for all service requirements, superior to the service compasses. In this I concur'. After discussion with the Hydrographer he ruled that the Thomson compass should be provided at all steering positions, ie. on the bridge, in the conning tower and for the binnacle compasses. No change was, however, to be made in the Standard Compass, the Hydrographer having stated in a final plea, 'fearing, as I do, that such a change could not be made without risk and would further entail an entire revision of our compass legislation and the practical education of our officers to meet the change, I am unwilling to incur the responsibility of making a recommendation which would appear to countenance such a measure'.[28]

The Navy was thus committed to the Thomson compass for all steering positions, but the Admiralty Standard had had a reprieve. It proved to be only a temporary stay of execution. Meanwhile the Compass Department had a busy time ahead. The Superintendent, accompanied by Sir William's agent, visited each dockyard in turn to determine for every ship the number and position of the compasses required. Hitherto the initial adjustment of Thomson compasses had been done by either Sir William himself or his agent, with an occasional swing by a member of the Compass Department. It was now necessary to train the Queen's Harbour Masters and Staff Commanders of the flagships in the appropriate techniques and they were accordingly invited to attend and watch all swings conducted in their area.[29] Although the Standard Compass was now regularly adjusted with magnets and, occasionally, also by soft-iron spheres, it was still the policy that correction should only be approximate. Regular observations of deviation were as important as ever. Similarly it was now accepted that the Thomson steering-compasses were no longer to be regarded as having 'no deviation'. After the initial euphoria a sense of realism was at last returning.

Compasses in torpedo-boats

One class of vessel for which the Thomson compass proved quite unsuitable was the torpedo-boat. First introduced in the early 1870s, several of these craft were built for foreign navies by the British firms of Yarrow and Thorneycroft, and in 1877 HMS *Lightning* was commissioned for the Royal Navy (built, surprisingly, by the French firm of Forges et Chantiers). At first the build-up was slow, four boats by 1880, eight by 1885. Thereafter numbers increased rapidly, large orders in 1886 and 1888 quickly bringing the total up to 60. By the end of the decade torpedo-boats had been ordered by no less than eighteen of the world's navies.[30] They initially proved so difficult to combat that the Admiralty seriously wondered whether the supremacy of the battleship might be threatened.

British boats were at first provided with a normal Admiralty steering compass and a liquid boats compass but these became increasingly inadequate as craft advanced in speed and sea-keeping capability. The Compass Department was aware of the problem and for some time Staff Commander Creak had been working on an improved liquid compass, fitted with a float to take the weight of the card off the pivot (as in Crow's liquid compass of 1813 and Ritchie's of 1862). In October 1881 a prototype of this compass was tried in a torpedo-boat alongside two specially prepared Thomson compasses, during a very lively sea trial at which Sir William himself was present. It proved to be in every way superior, bing 'perfectly steady under severe trial', where 'Sir William Thomson's was quite unserviceable'.[31] When fully developed this compass became the Admiralty Pattern 24 liquid compass and was fitted in large numbers.

By 1884, however, Sir William had perfected a new compass which he believed would work well in torpedo-boats. Although the few craft then in service appeared to be content with their liquid compasses, further comparative trials were arranged at his request, but the result was precisely the same. The Hydrographer again reported to the Board that the liquid compass 'stands the lively movements of the boat in a seaway when Sir William Thomson's fails under the same conditions'.[32] It was a small but pleasing triumph for the department.

Litigation and loyalties

From 1884 to 1888, while the Fleet was being equipped with Thomson steering compasses, Sir William was occupied with a wide range of other activities. He was also much involved in litigation against compass manufacturers who, he alleged, had infringed his patents. The details of these cases have been admirably summarized by Commander W. E. May[33] and, except where they bear on the activities of the Compass Department, are outside the scope of this narrative. Sadly their study does little for the image of either Sir William or British justice. Although the ideas patented by Sir William were sound and their application excellent, when taken individually it is doubtful whether most justified their patents, the majority (e.g. light card, heavy rim, detachable caps or pivots) having been tried and documented in former years.

Throughout the many hearings, Sir William's position appears to have ensured that his statements on compass matters and those of his witnesses would be accepted without question. Sometimes as many as six witnesses were called to testify to the excellence of his compasses, (which was not normally in question) including Captain J. A. Fisher and Rear Admiral Hotham, who had commanded the battleships *Inflexible* and *Alexandra* respectively during the bombardment of the forts at Alexandria in 1882. The latter's replies show that he really knew very little about compasses but he did on one occasion let drop the interesting remark that throughout the bombardment his ship had been steered not by its Thomson compass but by a liquid compass which had answered well.[34] Mayes and Creak were generally called as witnesses for the defence and, while the evidence of the latter was always sound and frequently showed that Sir William's claims to originality were unfounded, it carried little weight against such eminent opposition. Mayes made it clear that as the Admiralty Standard Compass had been selected by the Board nearly fifty years before, it was not his place to suggest a change. At times the Compass Department did not show up well and Sir William's council made the most of it.

The Thomson compass becomes the Standard for the Navy

When, towards the end of 1887, Staff Commander Creak succeeded Mayes as Superintendent of Compasses, it was already apparent that opinions in the Navy regarding the merits of the Thomson compass were by no means unanimously favourable. Ships were getting faster and guns heavier. At high speed, even in calm weather, the compass sometimes oscillated as much as $2\frac{1}{2}$ points and similar behaviour could result from gunfire. In a number of cases compasses were severely damaged. In a memorandum to the Hydrographer dated 5 March 1889[35] Creak said:

The very high degree of excellence which has been claimed for Sir W. Thomson's compass under all conditions, and the large sum of money which has been spent in providing it for HM Ships render it desirable to enquire for the good of the Service whether such claim is substantiated by the results of experience.

After outlining its early history, including the introduction of the grommet suspension 'which practically saved it from extinction', Creak went on to enumerate some of the problems experienced, particularly in conning towers (one of the positions for which it had been specially introduced). He enclosed no less than twenty-four recent (1885–88) adverse reports which showed that, despite its claims to withstand vibration and gunfire, the Thomson compass frequently broke down under both. Several of the ships concerned had already received Creak's new liquid compass for trial and these all reported on its excellent performance, stating that under similar circumstances it was steadier and more reliable. Many officers also disliked the Thomson azimuth circle and it was for this reason that the battleship *Anson* even asked that the Thomson compass on her bridge should be changed for an Admiralty Standard.

Creak had long been convinced that liquid compasses were the right answer. His memorandum therefore went on to suggest the following detailed compass policy for the Fleet:

1. The continued use of the Admiralty Standard Compass, fitted with the new lightweight needles; the improved liquid compass to be substituted when conditions made this necessary.

2. For conning towers, where the Thomson was proving particularly troublesome, the new liquid compass fitted with quadrantal correctors.

3. In torpedo gun vessels and torpedo-boats, where the Thomson had proved quite inadequate, the new liquid compasses should continue.

4. The Thomson compass to continue to be used at all other steering positions, in accordance with existing Admiralty policy.

The Hydrographer, Captain W. J. L. Wharton FRS, who had relieved Evans in July 1884, wholeheartedly supported these proposals and suggested to the Board that they should be implemented at once.[36] He expressed warm appreciation of the work Creak had done since taking over as superintendent, in particular the development of his improved liquid compass which was already proving superior to the Thomson pattern under the difficult conditions found in modern warships. He suggested a committee to look at the evidence and decide on the future.

Their Lordships were now faced with something of a dilemma for they were all firmly committed to Sir William Thomson. It was soon apparent that his earlier work in cultivating the acquaintance of influential naval officers was about to be put to the test. What followed is a sorry tale.

The four naval members of the Board each wrote a minute eulogizing the Thomson compass and condemning the adoption of the new liquid compass (which none of them had seen at sea) without further trial. They also called for reports from the Channel Squadron and the Mediterranean station. Six months later, with the question still unresolved, we find Lord Walter Kerr, who was about to hoist his flag in the battleship *Trafalgar*, asking for a Thomson compass to be fitted on the Admiral's bridge in place of the Admiralty Standard.[37] Whilst agreeing to the fitting of an additional Thomson compass for the Admiral's use, Creak pointed out that this request raised far wider issues. The excellent reports on the performance of his improved liquid compass had so far all been based on the small torpedo-boat version as, due to delays by the makers, the Standard version was only then becoming available. Creak accordingly proposed that a series of comparative trials between his compass and the Thomson should be conducted in a selection of ships of different classes. In order that the trial should be in every way fair to Sir William, Creak proposed to let him know all he could of the defects in his compasses which militated against satisfactory performance in HM ships and suggested that he should be invited to superintend the fitting and adjustment of his compasses himself. In forwarding these proposals the Hydrographer again suggested that a special committee should be formed to consider the reports and to decide on future action.[38]

Meanwhile the improved liquid compasses had not, of course, been seen by the Channel Squadron or Mediterranean Fleet so that when responding to the Board's request these ships were comparing a corrected Thomson compass with the old, partially corrected Admiralty types. Their reports, when received, were not surprisingly favourable to the Thomson. As the Hydrographer was the official adviser to the Board on all navigational matters he naturally felt it necessary to point out this anomaly again, and commented:

I have no shadow of doubt that the Thomson compass is superior to the Admiralty Compass as fitted in these ships. The point remains, is it as suitable for standard purposes, under all circumstances, as the improved liquid compass when corrected for quadrantal error, a compass which none of these officers has seen. It is to decide this that I have recently asked for a committee, after both compasses have been duly tried as Standards.[39]

Alas the Hydrographer was unable to impress his views on the Board. His proposal was brusquely swept aside by Rear Admiral Hotham with the comment,

Sir William Thomson's compasses ought to have been introduced as Standard some years ago and I see no reason for waiting until trials are made. [Had not Their Lordships themselves suggested further trial?] We need a reliable compass at once. We have individually no opinion of a liquid compass compared with Sir W. T.

When the naval members of the Board met again to discuss the problem, they had before them a précis of fifty-one reports favourable to the Thomson which had been received in the early days, between 1877 and 1883. These had been unearthed by the Secretary to the Board from office records and were intended to offset the twenty-four more recent unfavourable reports forwarded by Creak.[40] The Board came to the unanimous opinion:

a. That the Hydrographer, in his submission, condemns the Admiralty Compass. [This was a very strange interpretation of the Hydrographer's words!]
b. That there is a remarkable unanimity in the reports from 1877 to 1883, 51 being favourable to the Thomson and unfavourable to the Admiralty Compass. [These reports were 6–12 years old but were apparently preferred to the more recent reports, unfavourable to the Thomson, which were not referred to.]
c. That the majority of the leading Mercantile Lines use the Thomson as Standard. [This was true but quite irrelevant as their circumstances were entirely different.]
d. That until it is proved by practical experience that the new liquid Hydrographic Department compass is superior to the

Thomson, the latter should be the Service Compass – and be in all cases fitted under the supervision of Sir W. Thomson or his representative.[41]

Capitulation to Sir William was total and unconditional. As an afterthought the Controller proposed that 'As Captain Wharton [the Hydrographer] is the Head of the Department which deals with compasses, I think it is only fair that he should be given an opportunity of expressing his views *viva voce* on the proposed substitution of the Thomson for the present Standard.' On 19 November 1889, following a further meeeting at which the Hydrographer was present, the Board ruled:

> 1. That the Thomson Compass should be adopted as the Service *Standard* Compass.
> 2. That the Hydrographic Department Liquid compass should be tried in such ships as may be hereafter determined by the Board.

In case there should be any question about their unswerving loyalty to Sir William, the final paragraph by the Permanent Secretary read as follows: 'The Board further desire that the new liquid compass shall be styled 'Improved liquid compass' and the word 'Admiralty' not to be used.'[42]

Four days later Sir William was invited to the Admiralty to be informed of the decision. It is interesting to note that it was with Captain Fisher that he stayed while in London.[43] Later it was rumoured that once his compass had been adopted Lord Kelvin, as he shortly afterwards became, used to visit the store at Deptford, generally unannounced, to examine the stock of compasses. He would then send one of his friends on the Board a list of orders to be sent to his firm.[44] The ultimate insult came when he placed his own portrait on the cards for the Standard Compasses supplied to the Navy in the position which for nearly half a century had been occupied by the naval crown.

A final assessment

The die was now cast and the Navy was committed to Sir William Thomson's compasses for all major applications. In view of the fact that Creak's liquid compass had already shown considerable promise which was later amply confirmed, this was a most retrograde step for which the Admiralty was to pay dearly both in trouble and money for the next two decades. Equally certainly, the Compass Department, through its lack of enterprise and its failure to move with the times, was largely to blame for the situation with which it was now faced. Having missed the chance in 1862 and again in 1870 to introduce liquid compasses on the American pattern, the Navy, whose ships were yearly getting larger and more powerful, had been left with an excellent but old-fashioned Standard Compass and a number of serviceable though obsolete subsidiary types. The door had thus stood open for Sir William Thomson and he had seized his opportunity.

Even then, had serious efforts been made at once to arrange truly comparative trials between the Thomson compass and the Admiralty Standard, particularly with its new lightweight needles, the situation might have developed very differently. The Admiralty Standard could certainly have been closely corrected and under a less cautious regime this would probably have been done in the early 1860s. Had it also been mounted in a grommet-type suspension, which was far more effective than the India-rubber suspension then in use, there is little doubt that it would have been as steady as the Thomson since its period was well over 20 seconds.[45] Unshipping the card in action was mainly official solicitude for a valuable instrument. Had it been given an effective shockproof suspension it would probably have functioned perfectly. As however Sir William had claimed that his compass could withstand gunfire, it was generally assumed that it must be better and the fact that it, too, required the protection of its grommet suspension was conveniently overlooked. Before long even this was shown to be inadequate.

With hindsight there were undoubtedly faults on all sides. Evans had been responsible for compass matters for almost thirty years. His international reputation has been justly built up during the first half of this period when, with the help of Archibald Smith, many new and perplexing problems had been solved. Thereafter the pressures of his office prevented his personal involvement and, whilst he continued to use his position and reputation to support the cautious policies for which he had been responsible, he became increasingly out of touch and unaware of the need for change.

Above all he was apparently unable to appreciate the ineffectiveness and incompetence of his Superintendent of Compasses.

Mayes himself was probably capable enough in purely routine matters but was totally without imagination or initiative, and was completely dominated by Evans. He was also lazy and stubbornly resisted change. Despite the radical advances that were happening at sea, compass development had been at a standstill. When resolute action and comparative trials were needed to establish the true worth of Sir William's equipment, as opposed to his exaggerated claims, Mayes had done absolutely nothing. Finally, he had been quite unable to appreciate the potential merit of the liquid compass being developed by Creak and gave him no backing whatsoever.

Neither can Their Lordships escape censure. It was true that the Thomson compass had shown many advantages over the current Admiralty equipment then at sea, but no attempt was made either by the Compass Department or the ships at sea to compare like with like. Senior officers preferred to rely entirely on 'trials' sponsored by the inventor and all too readily swallowed the glib assertions of Sir William about the superiority of his equipment, whilst yielding to his pressure and persuasion. It is possible they may have been not a little embarrassed by the poor showing of their own compass 'experts'. When, therefore, in 1889 a new Hydrographer and a new Superintendent of Compasses were at last able to show not only that the Thomson compass had its limitations but that they had a better and cheaper solution to hand, it was too late. Their Lordships were by then totally committed to Sir William, with whom some were on the friendliest of terms. It would have been embarrassing to retract.

Finally there was Sir William himself, the brilliant scientist and practical inventor, who undoubtedly had the needs of seamen at heart. With his binnacle, which had at last made accurate compass correction a practical proposition, he had produced a winner where prejudice and conservatism had for so long stifled progress. His compass, too, was excellent for many applications, but for the requirements of the Navy of the 1890s its introduction was a retrograde step.

NOTES

CHAPTER 4

1 Sylvanus P. Thompson, *The Life of Lord Kelvin*, London, 1910, p.659–60.

2 Ibid., p. 703.

3 Ibid., p. 705.

4 *Philosophical Magazine*, No. 48 (November 1874), pp. 363–69.

5 This letter contains the astonishing statement, repeated in other documents, that with compasses having long needles it was only possible to achieve full quadrantal correction with spheres weighing hundreds of tons! See Thompson, *Life of Lord Kelvin*, p. 709.

6 Hydrographer's Minute Book, No. 21, p. 291.

7 Ibid., p. 293 *et seq.*

8 This machine registered the amount of piano wire run out and was the first to enable soundings to be taken at speed. Depth was obtained from a table. Later chemically coated glass tubes were used which registered the depth directly. The Kelvin sounding-machine remained in service until the 1950s.

9 Hydrographer's Minute Book, No. 21, p. 351.

10 Ibid., p. 337.

11 Thompson, *Life of Lord Kelvin*, p. 711.

12 Hydrographer's Minute Book, No. 26, p. 144.

13 'Report by the Hydrographer', 12 February 1880, appendix D, Hydrographer's Minute Book, No. 23, p. 210.

14 Thompson, *Life of Lord Kelvin*, p. 713.

15 Letter from Captain J. A. Fisher to Admiral Ryder, 1 December 1879 (NS 4531/79).

16 Hydrographer's Minute Book, No. 23, p. 210.

17 This instrument enabled the compass to be corrected without the aid of sights, although no deviation table could be obtained. Sir William had demonstrated its use in the *Glatton* (Hydrographer's Minute Book, No. 22, p. 184) and in the *Northampton*. Although the instrument is still frequently used by commercial compass-adjusters, it has never found favour in naval circles.

18 Hydrographer's Minute Book, No. 23, p. 210.

19 Hydrographer's Minute Book, No. 23, p. 116.

20 Hydrographer's Minute Book, No. 24, p. 359.

21 In May 1883 the iron store-ship *Wye* attributed her grounding to the lack of a Thomson compass.

22 Creak wrote to the Hydrographer of this trial: 'I may also incidently remark that in the Captain's Cabin the excessive vibration caused the cruets to jump and revolve in their

stands . . . although the sea was calm at the time.'

23 The *Inflexible* was a remarkable vessel which epitomized the transitional stage of battleship design, having the heaviest armour (24 inches) and largest muzzle-loading guns (16 inches) ever employed in the Royal Navy. She still carried an extraordinary brig-type sailing rig yet was the first ship to be lit throughout by electricity.

24 Hydrographer's Minute Book, No. 24, p. 301.

25 Hydrographer's Minute Book, No. 26, p. 35.

26 Hydrographer's Minute Book, No. 27, p. 484.

27 Ibid., p. 264.

28 Ibid., p. 308.

29 Hydrographer's Minute Book, No. 29, p. 282.

30 Sleeman, *Torpedoes and Torpedo Warfare*, Vol. 2, p. 268. Griffin and Co., Portsmouth, 1889.

31 Hydrographer's Minute Book, No. 25, p. 368.

32 Hydrographer's Minute Book, No. 28, p. 284.

33 Commander W. E. May, 'Compass Department Memoirs,' p. 31 et seq., National Maritime Museum, Magnetic Compass Collection, Item R8 (2).

34 Minutes of proceedings *Thomson v. Batty*, p. 59, Naval History Library, Item Xc 77.

35 Hydrographer's Minute Book, No. 33 (Guard Book), p. 250.

36 Ibid.

37 National Maritime Museum, Magnetic Compass Collection, Envelope N1. (NS 3594/89).

38 Hydrographer's Minute Book, No. 33, p. 514.

39 Ibid., p. 539.

40 In a letter to her daughters, 23 November 1889, Sir William's sister, Mrs King refers to the fifty-one letters that had been 'hidden away in pigeon-holes in the Hydrographer's Office'. Her implied criticism of those in office at the time was quite unjustified and it is obvious that she had not been informed about the twenty-four more recent adverse reports. See Thompson, *Life of Lord Kelvin*, p. 889.

41 Secretary's minute, 15 November 1889, National Maritime Museum, Magnetic Compass Collection, Item R2 (4).

42 Permanent secretary's minutes, 19 and 26 November 1889, National Maritime Museum, Magnetic Compass Collection, Item R2 (4).

43 Thompson, *Life of Lord Kelvin*, p. 889.

44 May, 'Compass Department Memoirs,' p. 31.

45 In his evidence at the patent trial, *Thomson v. Batty* in 1888, (p.147) Creak confirmed that he had in fact tried the Admiralty Standard Compass in a Thomson binnacle with a grommet suspension and found it as steady and sensitive as the Thomson compass itself. No date is given for this experiment but it seems probable that it was conducted after he had succeeded Mayes as Superintendent in December 1887.

Still tied by tradition, 1874-87

5

'Will you walk a little faster,' said a Whiting to a Snail . . . (Lewis Carroll, *Alice's Adventures in Wonderland*)

In chapter 4 attention was concentrated mainly on the events which led to the introduction of Sir William Thomson's compasses into the Navy. We must now consider what other activities concerned the Compass Department during this very important period in naval development.

In the early 1870s, despite the general introduction of steam, the need for economy and increased range dictated that sail should still be the main mode of propulsion. This presented the constructors with a considerable problem as 'broadside' ironclads gradually gave way to armoured turret ships. The policy was seriously questioned, however, when the battleship *Captain* capsized in a gale in the Bay of Biscay on 6 September 1870, due to her top-hamper and at last, in 1873, the *Devastation* appeared as the first battleship to be completed without a full set of sails. She was followed shortly afterwards by the *Thunderer*, and despite periodic cutbacks in naval expenditure under successive Gladstone governments the next decade witnessed a considerable evolution in warship design. Steel became widely used for ship-building, with the *Comus* class of protected cruisers (1877) as the first all-steel ships in the Royal Navy. Gunboats, which had been introduced in the late 1860s, were built in increasing numbers. Breach-loading guns at last replaced the muzzle-loaders and the torpedo became a serious weapon of war. Although in the Royal Navy these were at first fired only from large ships, foreign navies were introducing small, fast torpedo-boats and 1877 saw the trials of the first British torpedo-boat, the *Lightning*. It was defence against these torpedo-boats which led to the development of the searchlight, first fitted in the battleships *Minotaur* and *Téméraire* in

1876, general electric lighting being introduced some five years later.[1] During the 1870s the naval dockyards, which had taken some years to make the changeover from wooden walls to iron, again began building the Queen's ships.

These innovations all had their impact on the Compass Department. As twin screws became the normal pattern and ships gradually lost their sails, increasing speed and manoeuvrability called for more convenient steering and conning arrangements. During the 1870s several ships had succeeded in getting a 'manoeuvring compass' fitted on the fore bridge, but for some time such innovations had to be asked for – and they were not always forthcoming – while there was as yet no clear policy on the matter. Occasionally a suitable position could be found on the bridge for the Standard Compass itself, but more often this was still sited an inconveniently long way away. When steam steering was introduced and a 'steam wheel' fitted on the bridge, the helmsman steered by the manoeuvring compass or by a separate steering compass which, as we have seen, from 1884 onwards was of the Thomson type. The helmsman was generally protected by a light structure called the conning tower (not to be confused with the armoured conning tower, introduced in the 1880s; see p. 137) which, in some cases, was combined with the charthouse. In action, however, large ships were still steered from a protected position on the main deck, under armour.

In December 1879 Captain Fisher of the *Northampton*, following his contention that the arrangements provided for conning the ship in action should also be employed at all other times, asked that his charthouse, which contained the 'steam-wheel and signalling arrangements', should be armoured to make it a war conning house, also that a second armoured conning tower should be provided aft. Although Evans may not have appreciated the significance of this suggestion, his comment on the value of charthouses was interesting: 'The Charthouse may almost be considered a luxurious convenience for ordinary use in the ease of navigation of the ship, but in action it would not be required'. The Controller added 'I should think the charthouse should be removed in action'.[2] This attitude persisted for some years and charthouses remained flimsy structures, sometimes even having a top that could be lowered to enable bearings to be taken from the Standard or manoeuvring compass. Not until 1888 do we read of the charthouse being built as a firm structure and the Standard Compass being fitted on top of it.[3]

The many new ships for which suitable compass positions had to be found imposed a considerable load on the Compass Department. In February 1881, in response to a query about the pay and allowances of the Superintendent and his Assistant,[4] Evans prepared a full statement of their separate duties which showed that Mayes was primarily responsible for the compasses of the fleet, their testing, fitting and adjusting, examining all returns and keeping abreast new inventions and developments. Creak assisted him with these duties in the field when necessary but was otherwise mainly imployed in the Hydrographic Office on such work as the variation charts, publications and progress in the science of theoretical magnetism. Evans clearly found him very useful. On the other hand any suggestions Creak may have made on material matters would have gone through his superior, Mayes, and often got no further (as, for example, the suggestion of doing away with the heavy 'J' card of the Standard Compass after the trials in *Superb*).[5] Even Creak's early work on liquid compasses appears to have received little encouragement. Nevertheless both men were clearly kept very busy visiting ships for, as Evans remarked at the end of his report, 'I would desire to add for Their Lordships' information that during the past fifteen years the number of ships to be visited for compass adjustment has increased from 34 to 139.' Later he reported that the average distance travelled by each officer was about 8000 miles per year. Occasionally other officers of the Hydrographic Office had to be called upon to assist.

Electricity

Dynamos for running searchlights were fitted in ships from 1876 but at first they were of limited power and were sufficiently far removed from the compasses to have no appreciable effect. Any danger lay principally in the use of the single-wire system (with an earth return) which, if run near the compass, could produce a considerable error. However, although ships occasionally reported unexplained deviations which they attributed to 'leakage of electricity', in most cases this was shown not to be the cause. In 1881 the Navy changed to a two-wire system and an order was given that wires in the vicinity of the compass must always be run close together. Thereafter it was the dynamo itself which constituted the principal cause of disturbance. Mayes conducted tests in the

troopship *Euphrates* in 1884 during which a disturbance was detected
as far away as 50 feet, but this was judged to be exceptional.
Nevertheless, from 1886 it was arranged that as a precaution all
drawings showing the positions of dynamos and searchlights should
be sent to the department for vetting.[6] Later, as dynamos increased
in output to 400 and then to 600 amperes, the matter became
more serious and sterner measures became necessary. These will be
discussed in the next chapter. In 1887, in spite of the department's
cautious insistence on the greater reliability of oil lamps, an order
was issued allowing navigation lights and steering compasses to be
lit by electricity.[7] However, it was to be another decade before this
was permitted at the Standard Compass.

Dramatis Personae

To return to the personalities involved. In March 1883 an enquiry
into the running and staffing of the Hydrographic Department[8]
recommended that Mr Brunton who, for almost forty years, had
faithfully examined and tested compasses at the Observatory, should
be retired and replaced by a naval pensioner. There is a story that,
when told of this decision, Mr Brunton, who was then over 80
years of age, protested most bitterly at the foolhardiness of giving
his most important post to a mere boy of 40. He had of course
done sterling work, particularly during the interregnum in the
1850s, when he had run the department singlehanded and refused
to allow the high standards set by Captain Johnson to be eroded.
His successor was Mr Thomas Foden, a retired Chief Quartermaster
on the staff of the Commander-in-Chief at Portsmouth, who had
been employed taking bearings from the magnetic hut for ships
swinging in Stokes Bay and was thus well used to dealing with
compasses. After some delay in obtaining a certificate from the Civil
Service Commissioners, he joined on 12 November 1883 and served
the department with great dedication until 1907. Mr Brunton retired
with a pension of £73 per annum plus £30 for his army service,
and despite many excellent testimonials Evans was unable to get it
increased. He was the first of many faithful servants of the Admiralty
Compass Observatory to have served through four decades.

Navigating Lieutenant[9] Creak was promoted to Staff Commander
on 23 February 1873 and from then on played an increasingly
important role in the activities of the department, rapidly making

his mark in the field of magnetic science. When not employed visiting ships, his duties kept him mainly in the Hydrographic Office and it was to him rather than to Mayes that many people, including the Hydrographer, increasingly turned for information. He was not, however, primarily concerned with material policy so that apart from the excellent report he prepared for Evans in 1880 (see p. 110) he played little part in the controversy over Sir William Thomson's compass until he took over as Superintendent in 1887. Creak himself had long been convinced that liquid compasses with floated cards could provide the best answer to the Navy's requirements and, despite the opportunities that had already been missed, he worked on his own design throughout the 1880s, achieving early success when in 1881 a prototype of his compass was shown to operate successfully in a torpedo-boat where Sir William's compass failed completely. Many of the ships to which later versions of this compass were sent for trial reported that at high speed they were far steadier than any other compass on board. With greater backing from his department and less pressure from Sir William, it is probable that this compass would later have been adopted as the Standard rather than the controversial Thomson.

In 1875 Creak prepared a paper 'On the effects of iron masts on compasses placed near them' which was presented to the Royal Society by Captain Evans and published in its proceedings.[10] When, in the following year, the *Challenger* returned from her voyage of circumnavigation with an immence amount of new data on geomagnetism, it was Creak who undertook its reduction. His analysis, which was not finally published until 1889 as part of the 'Report on the scientific results of the voyage of HMS *Challenger* during the years 1873–76'[11] contains charts of all the geomagnetic elements, updated to the epoch of 1880 and based very largely on the *Challenger* observations. Creak was also entrusted with the magnetic instructions for the Arctic expedition of 1875–6, under Captain George Nares, which reached what was then the furthest northerly point at 83°20'N, and his analysis of their results appeared in the *Proceedings of the Royal Society* for 1879.[12] Four years later his paper 'On the changes which take place in the deviations of the Standard Compass in the iron armour-plated, iron and composite built ships of the Royal Navy on a considerable change of magnetic latitude'[13] was also communicated to the society by Evans and was, in effect, a continuation of the report he had rendered some twenty years earlier, when Master of the *Esk* (see p. 92). In 1885 Creak was elected a Fellow of the Royal Society to which, as we shall see in later chapters, he continued to contribute original scientific works for another twenty years.

Captain Sir Frederick Evans retired from the post of Hydrographer in 1884 after ten very successful years, crowning his career by serving as one of the British delegates to the Washington Conference which gave final acceptance to the Greenwich meridian as the prime meridian of the world. His period as the second Superintendent of Compasses, from 1855 to 1865, had been one of intense activity in a new era of rapid naval development, and he had added enormously to the reputation of the department. When he died, little more than a year after his retirement, *The Times*[14] paid warm tribute to his achievements with these words:

> In 1855 he was appointed Superintendent of the Compass Department of the Admiralty, at a period when the science of terrestrial magnetism in relation to iron ships was in its infancy; he was at this time a mathematician of no mean repute, and sagaciously foreseeing the important part this abstruse science was destined to play in the Navy, now being revolutionized by the change from wood to iron, he devoted his whole energies to the study of the subject until he had made himself completely master of it. In conjunction with that accomplished mathematician, the late Mr. Archibald Smith, F.R.S., he published, in 1869, the 'Admiralty Manual for Ascertaining and Applying the Deviation of the Compass,' which was translated by all maritime nations, and has been the accepted text-book in our own and other navies up to the present time. In 1865 Captain Evans was appointed chief assistant to the hydrographer, retaining also his position as head of the magnetic department. In 1874, a vacancy occurring for the post of hydrographer, he was appointed to fill it; he had enjoyed the cordial friendship, esteem, and entire confidence of the three officers who had preceded him, and no more proper or worthy selection could have been made. He continued to perform the important duties of this office with great ability and conscientiousness until within little more than a year of his death. It should be added that Sir F. Evans was elected a Fellow of the Royal Society in 1862, and served for many years on its council, and

was more than once a vice-president. He was nominated a K.C.B. in 1881.

Long obituary notices also appeared in *Nature* and in the *Proceedings of the Royal Geographical Society*.[15]

Despite his conservative approach there can be no doubt that for the ten years from 1855, when he was Superintendent of Compasses, Evans, guided by Archibald Smith, had done a superb job during a crucial phase in naval history. His international reputation was second to none. However, as the onerous duties of his important office under the Hydrographer, and later as Hydrographer himself, took more of his time, he became increasingly out of touch with compass matters, for which, nevertheless, he retained responsibility. After Archibald Smith died in 1872 Evans failed to realize that further changes were still necessary. He opposed the introduction of Sir William Thomson's compass and binnacle, but for quite the wrong reasons. The binnacle was, in fact, a boon but its acceptance required a change in the Admiralty's policy towards compass correction which neither he nor the Compass Department could appreciate. During his last ten years in office his very presence had become a bar to progress while his stature and reputation served only to mask the complete ineffectiveness of his assistant, Mayes.

Captain Mayes completed his twenty-two years of totally undistinguished reign over the Compass Department on 13 December 1887. His appointment as Superintendent in 1865 was originally for a period of five years and it is difficult to understand why it was repeatedly renewed. During a period when the Navy was changing fast its Compass Department had remained almost static and its reputation, so painstakingly built up over a quarter of a century, was in tatters. Without doubt the conservatism of Evans had contributed, but Mayes seemed incapable of constructive thought and opposed all progress.[16] His character has been succinctly summed up by Lord Fisher in his book *Records*, in which he says, 'What most scandalised the dear old Fossil who then presided over the Admiralty Compass Department was that I wanted to do away with the points of the compass and mark it into three hundred and sixty degrees of the circle. (You might as well have asked them to do away with salt beef and rum!).'[17]

NOTES

CHAPTER 5

1 The first ship to be lit by electricity, the battleship *Inflexible* (see p. 123), had an 800 volt, single-wire (earth return) system but after a fatal accident the Navy quickly changed to an 80 volt system. By the mid-1880s all systems were two-wire.

2 Hydrographer's Minute Book, No. 23, p. 122.

3 Ibid., No. 24, p. 171, No. 32, p. 550, No. 33, p. 98.

4 As a result of this query it was arranged that for the future the maximum salary of the Superintendent was to be fixed at £750 and of his Assistant at £600 (Hydrographer's Minute Book, No. 24, p. 224).

5 Minutes of proceedings *Thomson* v. *Batty*, p. 149, Naval Historical Library, Item Xc 77.

6 Hydrographer's Minute Book, No. 31, p. 47.

7 Ibid., No. 32, p. 52.

8 Ibid., No. 27, p. 165.

9 This was the rank given to junior masters when that branch was finally discontinued in 1867.

10 *Proceedings of the Royal Society*, Vol. 23 (1875), pp. 582-88, National Maritime Museum, Magnetic Compass Collection, Item 8/8 (14).

11 'Report on the scientific results of the voyage of HMS *Challenger* during the years 1873-6', Part 6 Vol. 2, Royal Society, 1889.

12 *Proceedings of the Royal Society*, No. 196 (1879), pp. 29, 42.

13 *Phil. Trans. Royal Society*, Part 2 (1883), pp. 615-38.

14 *The Times*, 22 December 1885.

15 *Nature*, 14 January 1886. *Proceedings of the Royal Geographical Society*, Vol. 8 (February 1886).

16 Among the few relics left by Mayes in the Magnetic Compass Museum are two cards for the Admiralty Standard Compass on which the heavy needles have been hinged instead of being rigidly attached to the card. These are dated 1877 but no record can be found of their intended use or of any experiments done with them. Mayes died on 7 December 1904, three days before his seventy-ninth birthday.

17 Lord Fisher, *Records*, Hodder and Stoughten, 1919, p. 63.

The Department under Captain E.W. Creak F.R.S., scientist and practical seaman, 1887–1901

6

'Observe the deviation when possible, note it in a book, and learn its changes under every circumstance as you do the rate of a chronometer. Then on some thick, dirty night, the reward will come in the shape of a reasonable confidence that you can steer the required course without delay and detriment to the service upon which the ship may be ordered.' (Captain Creak, in an address to the Royal United Services Institute, 31 May 1889)

By 1884, following drastic economies introduced by successive Gladstone governments, it was apparent that the strength of the Navy had fallen dangerously low and was already behind that of France, which had been building fast. Questions in the House of Commons, and a series of articles in the *Pall Mall Gazette*, drew attention to the situation and led to something of an outcry in the country. Lord Northbrook, the First Lord, who seems to have been obsessed with economy, was forced to introduce an immediate construction programme, spearheaded by the battleships *Victoria* and *Sans Pareil* and including 12 new cruisers and 14 torpedo-boats. The Navy's total unpreparedness was further starkly highlighted the following year, when there was a serious risk of war breaking out with Russia. In 1886, after three further changes of government in fifteen months, Lord Salisbury succeeded Gladstone and appointed Lord George Hamilton and Admiral Sir Arthur Hood as the First Lord and First Sea Lord respectively (the last occasion on which naval appointments to the Board were made by the government in power). The choices were fortunate. Over the next three years plans were drawn up for a drastic reorganization of the Navy and its dockyards while a complete reappraisal was made of Lord Northbrook's hurried building programme. In 1887 the Colonial Conference added further urgency by publishing a devastating report which showed that adequate defence for British interests and commerce abroad hardly existed. At last, in the Navy Defence Act (1889), parliament reasserted its belief in the vital need to adhere to the two-power naval standard and a five-year programme of rebuilding was authorized, embracing 10 battleships, 42 cruisers and 18 torpedo gunboats.

The Compass Department thus faced the 1890s with the formidable task of catering for a huge increase in ship-building while also introducing the Thomson compass as Standard for all ships except torpedo-boats (and the Royal Yacht *Victoria and Albert*, as a Thomson compass would not fit into her ornate binnacle!) Fortunately, in Staff Commander Creak it had a superintendent of an entirely different calibre from his predecessor. When arranging his appointment in 1887 the Hydrographer, Captain Wharton, had written of him, 'No other such competent successor could be found.' His faith was to be fully justified. Three years later, when asking for Creak's reappointment on reaching the retirement age of 55, he wrote 'his qualifications of ability, practical experience and scientific knowledge are such as are not likely to be met with, I fear, again'.[1]

Creak was already a Fellow of the Royal Society, with a high reputation in scientific circles. Now freed from the frustrating and sterile influence of Mayes and the suffocating conservatism of Evans, he quickly showed that he was also an essentially practical man as he rapidly got down to implementing the many changes so urgently needed.

As his Assistant Superintendent Creak initially had the help of Staff Commander Charles Drake, an experienced Master and Navigating Officer with an excellent record, who had just completed a special five-month course in magnetic science at the Royal Naval College at Greenwich. Sadly his service in the department lasted only fifteen months before he died on 17 October 1888.[2] His successor was to be Staff Commander James Henderson, until recently the Squadron Navigating Officer at the Cape of Good Hope, but it was decided that he, too, should first do the five-month course at Greenwich. Staff Commander James Tully was therefore appointed temporarily to help with the growing number of day-to-day tasks of the department. When he was withdrawn only two months later to join the new battleship *Victoria*,[3] due to become flagship of the Mediterranean Fleet, his place was taken by Staff Commander Archibald Douglas,[4] late of the battleship *Audacious*, flagship of the China Station. Henderson finally took up his appointment on 29 April 1889, on completion of his course, and went on to relieve Creak as Superintendent in 1901.

On taking over as Superintendent on 14 December 1887 Creak faced a host of problems, great and small, which had long lain dormant. Of the latter, the swinging forms (S291) had been little changed since Captain Johnson's day and therefore made no provision for recording the position of the correctors. They were revised in 1888, and in 1890 became form S374a, the number they still have today. The rules for positioning compasses had not been updated since 1865, when the Standard Compass still took its chance for position after the ship was built. A new edition was published in January 1889. In some ships there was not even a communicating voice pipe from a remotely sited Standard Compass to the bridge. These and many other minor items were quickly put to rights.

Compass problems

Three years had elapsed since the Board had decided in 1884 to introduce Thomson compasses for all steering positions and these were now widely fitted. Meanwhile Creak's liquid compass had been developed to the stage where he had high hopes that it would soon be adopted as the Standard, in place of the Admiralty Pattern 1 compass which had served the Navy well for almost half a century. In the event, as we have seen, ignorance, prejudice and outside pressure ensured that it was given no chance. Despite the excellent reports it received, the Thomson lobby was too strong and in November 1889 the Board had decided 'that the Thomson compass should be adopted as the service Standard Compass'.

Creak clearly knew that he was right but he wasted no time with regrets. His task was now to coax good service from compasses which were in many instances unsuited to their task. He sent Sir William a long letter pointing out the many ways in which his compasses fell short of the service's requirements.[5] He drafted new regulations for the management of the Thomson compass as the

Standard and these were issued as an Admiralty order on 13 March 1890.[6] Since 1842 the name 'Standard Compass' had only been applied to the particular type of compass designed by the Admiralty Compass Committee. It was now necessary to distinguish the compass designated as Standard, and sited in the best magnetic position, from the large number of similar compasses carried for steering or conning. The order therefore emphasized that 'the principles governing the management of the Admiralty Compass heretofore supplied as the Standard are to be strictly maintained'. After being closely corrected, its magnets were only to be moved when it was shown that a permanent change had taken place, and then only by permission of the captain, the ship being immediately swung and a deviation return forwarded to the Admiralty. This was very different from the philosophy of 'frequent correction and no records' that had been generally applied to the other Thomson compasses. Although the navigation would often have to be conducted from a compass which was more conveniently placed, frequent comparison with the Standard was still essential. Creak had originally proposed that a plate bearing the words 'Standard Compass' should be affixed, but this did not appear in the published instructions.

A year later Creak prepared a further order dealing with the disposal of the redundant Admiralty Standard and steering compasses.[7] The former were to be designated 'landing-compasses' and used for surveying purposes or when swinging by reciprocal bearings, and in this capacity they enjoyed a further fifty years of useful life; the latter were to be used for dockyard craft and at the hand-steering positions of ships, where they would seldom be needed. The 'J' cards and the India-rubber suspension were both abolished. The pillars were to be held in store and, as it turned out, it was not to be long before good use was found for them. Creak also arranged for the disposal of the old hanging and bulkhead compasses, which could have been of little use for many years.

Introducing the Thomson compass as Standard meant the retrospective fitting of some 120 ships in addition to those in the new building programme. The 10 inch compass, with its wide binnacle and large spheres, took up a lot of room and sometimes required a rearrangement or even an extension of the compass positions. It was also an expensive programme for which finance had not initially been provided. The work had therefore to be spread over a number of years. Hitherto the supply of compasses had mainly come from the repair of existing stocks but, in view of the complete change in the types of compass now being ordered, past experience could no longer provide a guide to the requirements of the future. The Superintendent therefore took the opportunity, in conjunction with the Director of Stores, to revise the rules for provisioning and holding stocks of spares at the dockyards, at the same time restating the need for all compass items, except binnacles, to be sent first to the Observatory for testing.

Although in most ships the favoured position for the Standard Compass was still aft, in some cruisers it was now being sited on a platform above the forebridge which, while not necessarily the best magnetic position, was acceptable as it had many advantages. It was high enough above the armoured conning tower to be magnetically stable and it was, of course, far more convenient for navigation. On the bridge itself there was a need for a steering compass and an azimuth compass for use when manoeuvring. On occasions one compass could satisfy both requirements. It was in the conning towers, however, that the most intractable problems arose. The new battleships and large cruisers that were coming into service were designed to be fought from a heavily armoured conning tower, situated in the bridge structure and connected to a lower steering position (often called the lower conning tower) by an armoured tube. In case of action damage the whole arrangement was duplicated in the after part of the ship. The provision of useable, let alone accurate, compasses for these four positions presented an almost insuperable problem for the Compass Department. In some battleships the quadrantal deviation at the lower steering position could amount to $33°$ and the directive force to only 0.25 (the ratio which the mean directive force at the compass position bears to the horizontal component of the earth's magnetic force measured ashore). In the upper conning tower the figures were approximately $11°$ and 0.6. Space in the conning towers was very restricted and the fitting of large spheres was impracticable. With their light, weak needles the Thomson compasses gained little additional benefit from induction in their spheres and were almost uncorrectable.

In November 1889 Sir William suggested fitting 4 inch compasses in the conning towers which would enable the spheres to be placed much closer in and so provide greater correction, but these proved unsatisfactory and were, in any case, difficult for the helmsman to read. Six-inch compasses with stronger needles, introduced in 1891, were more successful and, where space could be found for fitting 12 inch spheres, a coefficient D of 11° could be corrected. In some cases however, the conning tower was too small even for these spheres. In the lower steering positions, where the compasses would still have had some 22° of uncorrected quadrantal deviation, the situation was impossible. On east and west courses the directive force dropped to almost nothing and the ship could hardly be steered.

The Peichl Corrector

In the year 1875 a Lieutenant Joseph Von Peichl of the Austro-Hungarian navy had invented a new and most ingenious type of correcting device which enabled the directive force to be equalized on all headings, thus also correcting the quadrantal deviation. The compass itself was surrounded by two rings, fitted one above the other and each carrying thirty-two soft iron rods, placed radially. These rods varied in length so that while their outer ends were arranged around a circle, their inner ends formed an ellipse. With the axes of the two ellipses set at right angles to one another and at 45° to the keel, the directive force at the compass was uniformly increased on all headings. By rotating the axes in opposite directions, it was possible to arrange that the directive force would be equalized on all headings, and the deviation so produced was sufficient to counteract a coefficient D of up to 15°. Permanent magnets were fitted to the bottom of the gimballed compass frame to correct the semicircular deviation and heeling error. Although the system introduced small octantal errors these were comparatively insignificant.

Von Peichl took out an English patent for his correctors in 1878 (No. 3928) and in the following year patented a special dipping-needle control compass (Patent No. 5045), the details of which need not concern us as, although one was purchased for the Admiralty in 1881, Mayes does not appear to have carried out any trials with it. The correcting system itself was adopted as standard by the Austro-Hungarian navy but the Royal Navy did not buy one as Mayes 'could see no point in it'.

Creak had no doubt watched these developments with interest for, within a year of succeeding to the post of Superintendent he had arranged for a Peichl system to be ordered for trial.[8] It was fitted in the conning tower of the battleship *Collingwood* and showed such promise that within six months Creak was writing to propose a more extensive trial, for which a further six equipments were approved. His report pointed out that these systems would now correct all the quadrantal deviation experienced, the range having presumably been increased since the earlier versions, also that they cost £40 and took up a space of only 20 inches. The Thomson compass, which could not of course be fully corrected, cost £48 and with its spheres took up a space between two and four times as great.[9]

It was at this point, in May 1889, that Creak read a paper to the Royal United Services Institute 'On the mariner's compass in modern vessels of war',[10] updating Captain Evans's last paper of 1872. Many new problems had arisen since the days of the early ironclads and Creak gave a wide-ranging analysis, mentioning in particular the acute vibration experienced in the fast cruisers and the violent motion of the torpedo-boats and pointing to the advantages of the liquid compass under these circumstances. Discussing compass behaviour generally, he emphasized that in modern ships the magnetic state of a compass position was now far more influenced by the magnetic condition of the adjacent iron than by the heading of the building-slip or fitting-out berth, a factor frequently misunderstood even in modern times. After explaining the difficulties experienced in conning towers, he described the Peichl system, in which he foresaw great potential. He touched on the experiments he was conducting with swinging a ship heeled (see p. 146), which were then just beginning, and he explained the hazards associated with the general introduction of electricity. Finally he foresaw the possibility that direction might one day be obtained from a gyro-compass, once a suitable motive power had been developed for the rotor.[11] It was a penetrating and comprehensive review.

The results of the subsequent trials of the Peichl system were unfortunately a grave disappointment. Due to protracted discussions between the Hydrographer and the Board over which ships should be fitted (in which the hand of Sir William Thomson is clearly discernable) matters were delayed for some eighteen months. Eventually approval was given for three systems to be supplied to the battleships *Nile* and *Camperdown* and to a cruiser of the *Galatea* class, whilst a further equipment was sent to the cruiser *Warspite*, where Rear Admiral Hotham, now Commander-in-Chief on the Pacific station, had requested a system for her steering-engine compartment. His letter also asked that the Standard Compass should be replaced by a Thomson which he requested should be fitted by Sir William himself or his deputy and on no account by an officer from the Compass Department!

Despite the promising trial in the *Collingwood* and the fact that quadrantal deviation could, in most cases, now be completely corrected, it appears that most navigating officers did not fully understand the Peichl system. The reports sent in were generally ambiguous and inconclusive. In the case of *Warspite* it seems unlikely that the compass in the steering-engine compartment was ever visited at sea. Certainly no mention was made of the fact that a coefficient D of 25° had been corrected, something that would have been impossible with the Thomson.

Creak nevertheless persevered for several years, arranging further trials in the cruisers *Hawke* and *Blake*, the latter reporting very favourably. He summarized the results in 1892 and again in 1894 when, rather optimistically, the Hydrographer wrote 'the Conning Tower difficulty may therefore be now considered as practically overcome'. However, although the instruments at sea continued to operate satisfactorily, for some reason no follow-up action appears to have been taken. Finally in March 1900 the Director of Stores suggested that as no reports had been received for several years, the trial should be closed.[12]

Meanwhile, Creak had also continued his work on the Thomson compasses themselves, even finding room for 15 inch spheres held in cradles which, with the induction from the stronger needles of the 6 inch compasses, could correct some 26° of quadrantal error. These were the largest spheres ever introduced officially into the service and must have been very inconvenient in the restricted space of the lower steering positions. In 1895, in a further attempt to solve the problem, Lord Kelvin himself proposed an ingenious corrector which was designed to be placed on top of the glass of the compass and turned for each alteration of course. This instrument had two horizontal magnets whose position could be adjusted against a semicircular scale when the ship was swung. The device was tried out at the Observatory but although theoretically sound it proved completely impracticable.[13]

Staff Captain Henderson took up the matter of the Peichl corrector once more in 1901–02, when he became Superintendent. He showed by experiment that in the conning tower it could increase the directive force by 25 per cent, five times better than the spheres of the Thomson, for an equivalent correction. As difficulties were still being experienced with the 6 inch Thomson compass he arranged for further trials to be carried out in seven capital ships of the Channel Squadron, two of which, the *Majestic* and *Hannibal*, were also given a Peichl liquid compass and corrector system and a Pattern 24 torpedo-boat compass for comparison.[14] Commander H. F. Oliver of the *Majestic* reported particularly favourably on the latter and recommended that it should be fitted in all ships of the squadron. Unfortunately, by placing the liquid compasses in an ordinary binnacle with fixed corrector magnets, instead of having them attached to the compass frame and gimballed with it, the Peichl corrector introduced serious oscillatory errors, and the trial itself was a failure. Henderson reported, however, that he did not think the Peichl system would be successful, even with its proper correctors, and so, after 12 years of endeavour, the trial was finally abandoned.[15]

What went wrong with the Peichl trial is not altogether clear as Creak had certainly done his best to get it launched. The correcting system was sound and had been shown to solve an otherwise apparently insuperable problem. It was a mechanical device but there is no indication that the moving parts gave any trouble. It was, however, a new concept and was probably not fully understood by many who had to deal with it. Perhaps the figure of Lord Kelvin, who still did not believe that any compass was better than his own, was still present in the background influencing Board decisions. Whatever the reason, it was a sad reflection on the way a scientific trial can go wrong if left to unqualified officers and not closely monitored – a lesson the Navy took many years to learn.

Before he retired Creak made one final attempt to solve the conning-tower problem by suggesting that the compass in the lower steering position might be viewed by means of a telescope from the upper conning tower, so enabling the upper compass to be dispensed with altogether, and saving considerable space. This system was further developed by his successor, Staff Captain Henderson, and worked surprisingly well despite the profusion of pipes and cables which largely filled the 40 foot armoured tube between the upper and lower positions.[16] Later, however, it was superseded by a projector system, designed by Captain Chetwynd in conjunction with Messrs Kelvin and White, which enabled the helmsman in the upper conning tower to view a projected image of the lower compass on a ground glass screen.

The improved liquid compass

When, in November 1889, the decision was taken to adopt the Thomson compass as Standard for the Navy, rather than the improved liquid compass, trials of the small torpedo-boat version (Pattern 24)[17] had already been in progress in other ships, particularly gunboats, for almost two years. When the larger standard-size version became available Their Lordships approved a limited issue for trial in the battleships *Anson*, *Monarch* and *Collingwood* and in the light cruiser *Active*. All reported in glowing terms. The following assessment, for example, came from the *Active*: 'On passage from Bermuda, when the ship rolled 35° and more, the card was steady. It was not affected by the firing of guns, either singly or in broadsides.'[18] All ships agreed that when subjected to the concussion of gunfire the new compass was at least as steady as the Thomson, even with its protective grommet, and all considered its azimuth circle greatly superior. The only adverse report received came from the fifth ship, *Warspite*, flying the flag of Rear Admiral Hotham, where the flag captain added, 'of the two, I prefer the Thomson'. This could surely have caused little surprise in the department!

At first the Board kept strict control over the number of ships to which the improved liquid compass was allocated but when it became clear that the supply of Thomson compasses could not keep pace with the demand, the Hydrographer was authorized to issue it in place of the old Admiralty liquid compass formerly provided to replace the Standard in bad weather.[19] The new compass proved particularly popular in the cruisers where, when steaming at high speed 'under forced draft', the vibration became so bad that Creak reported, 'Every other compass has failed.'[20] It had been his intention that gunboats, which could be nearly as active as torpedo-boats, should also have the improved liquid compass as standard, rather than the Thomson, but the Board declined to allow an exception.

In the very lively torpedo-boats the improved liquid compass had, from the start, proved itself the only compass which could operate efficiently under the very severe conditions experienced, Sir William Thomson's having failed on three separate trials, (1881,

1884 and 1888). In these craft the Standard Compass was normally sited well aft, mounted on a pillar previously provided for the old Admiralty Standard, but without an urn. These pillars were now drilled out to take corrector magnets and were fitted with spheres, but no Flinders bar.[21] The first class torpedo-boats could be steered from either forward or aft, with a light conning tower in each position. Space was very restricted and finding a suitable site for the steering compasses, (the Pattern 25 compass, graduated to quarter-points only), which were little more than glorified boats compasses, presented many problems. We even read of them being placed below, on the seamen's mess deck, or in the heads, and viewed through a suitable port. Because of the difficulty of communication between the only reliable compass, the Standard, and the forward position, it soon became the practice to handle and steer these boats exclusively from aft. Creak appears to have spent much time in helping to solve the torpedo-boats' problems, often going to sea with them and steering the boat himself. He must have been gratified to receive a letter from the Torpedo Officer of the battleship *Royal Sovereign* which carried two second-class torpedo-boats, assuring him, 'As regards your compasses in the torpedo-boats, they are excellent. We swear by them.'[22]

When the torpedo-boat destroyers (T.B.D.) appeared in the mid-1890s, it was expected that they, too, would be handled from aft. But these were larger ships and it was soon found essential for the captain to be forward, ahead of the funnels. A tiny bridge was therefore erected above the conning tower, often with little more protection than a canvas 'dodger' and the helmsman steered by a compass tucked in under the turtle deck. At first the Standard Compass remained aft, but this proved very inconvenient and it was later moved to a platform amidships, raised as high as circumstances would allow. However, when in 1904 an enquiry into a collision between two torpedo-boat destroyers showed that the officer of the watch in one of them had gone aft to check the course by the Standard Compass, leaving only the helmsman on the bridge, approval was finally given for the Standard to be moved forward and combined with the steering compass, the midship position being done away with. For ships that could steam at 30 knots these were primitive arrangements, but they were the best that could be managed and somehow they were made to work.

Despite the consistently good results obtained with the improved liquid compass wherever it was fitted, it seems unlikely that the decision to adopt the Thomson as Standard was ever seriously reconsidered by the Board. However, suddenly in 1895 disturbing reports began coming in of Thomson compasses being damaged by gunfire. The ships concerned were those with 9.2 inch guns and larger, and whilst it was the bridge compasses which were mainly at risk, even those in the conning towers were sometimes rendered unserviceable. In some ships it became the habit to unship the compass before firing and stow it below, a practice that could clearly not be followed in wartime.

The solution was simple. Each ship was provided with two small improved liquid compasses, with adapters to enable them to be fitted into the Thomson binnacle on the bridge and in the upper conning tower, in place of the Thomson compasses, whenever the heavy guns were fired. They appeared to work perfectly and the Hydrographer commented after a trial, 'It is evident that these compasses will withstand pretty nearly any concussion.'[23] He and Creak must have shared many a wry smile during this episode as it had, of course, always been the claim of Sir William Thomson that his compass need not be unshipped as it would withstand the shock of gunfire. This had been one of its chief selling points.

The adoption of the Thomson compass and the many problems which had followed in its wake had effectively brought to an end Creak's basic research into liquid compass problems. Consequently although his improved liquid compass continued to give good service whenever the Thomson appeared to fail, it was left to his successor, Captain Chetwynd, in 1906 to make the final, all-important breakthrough, that of making the compass card considerably smaller than the bowl, and it was this improvement that finally got it accepted by the Navy (see p. 169). The reduced diameter card had, of course, been a feature of several earlier compasses, including Crow's liquid compass of 1813.

Boats compasses

Despite the improvement in liquid compasses for ships, the boats compasses in service were still those designed by West in 1862, with some by Dent of an even earlier pattern. Accordingly, in 1890 four manufacturers, Lilley, Reynolds, Hughes and Dent, were invited to take part in a competition to design a new boat's compass, following Creak's latest principles. The specification asked for an instrument suitable for steamboats, which had considerable vibration, as well as for sailing- and pulling-boats.[24] Specimens were to be sent to Deptford for inspection and test before being filled with liquid, and were then to be tried in boats at HMS *Vernon* at Portsmouth. Lighting was important, with a preference for candles, which were easier to cope with than oil lamps and had already found favour in the torpedo-boats.[25]

The entry submitted by the firm of Dent, which had been making compasses for the Navy for over fifty years, proved the best on every count and was introduced as Boats Compass Pattern 20 in 1892. It was given a reduced-diameter card in 1907 (changing its pattern number from 20 to 182) and remained in service until the end of World War I.

It is interesting to note the remarkable extent to which the shadow of Sir William Thomson still influenced Their Lordships' thinking on compass matters. On being shown the results of this competition, the details of which had been approved by the Board, the Controller immediately asked whether Sir William had been invited to take part. Naturally he had not, as dry-card compasses had been considered unsuitable for use in boats since the 1850s. Nevertheless, at the Controller's insistence a letter was sent to Sir William setting out the Navy's requirements for torpedo-boat Standard and steering compasses and for boats compasses. He was invited to 'submit for trial any patterns that you have reason to think will give better results than those now in use, which are all liquid compasses of late type'. The Board apparently still 'had no opinion of liquid compasses'. The letter continued, 'Every facility will be given you to make any required trials and experiments at Portsmouth.' No such facilities had of course been offered to the other contestants.

Sir William replied that he hoped soon to have a compass ready for trial in a torpedo-boat and that he was making experimental compasses for use in other boats. After some months delay two further trials were made in torpedo-boats, almost exactly ten years after the original trials of 1881, and with identical results. The Thomson compass vibrated through 8 points while the liquid compass remained practically steady. Three months later Sir William wrote from Glasgow University, 'I do not think it necessary to have any further experiments with the torpedo-boat compass . . . it seems that the liquid compasses will be found more suitable in such vessels and in small boats.'[26] This ludicrous exercise had held up the introduction of the new boats compass for a whole year.

Heeling error

The correction of heeling error was a subject which had exercised the minds of the experts ever since Airy had made his experiments in compass correction in the *Rainbow* in 1838. It had first been seriously tackled by the Liverpool Compass Committee which, in the 1850s, had arranged to swing a number of ships heeled in order to adjust their vertical magnet. In the 1860s Archibald Smith had made a detailed mathematical investigation of the theory and had shown how, by measuring the vertical and horizontal forces at the compass position, the heeling-error coefficient could be calculated (see p. 69). Although a vertical magnet was occasionally used to reduce large values of heeling error, the main purpose of his formulae had been to calculate the deviation expected rather than to enable its correction. In the 1870s Sir William Thomson had, with his new vertical force instrument, provided the first simple means of adjusting the heeling-error magnets without inclining the ship and this had produced a good approximate correction.

Creak realized that in a modern, fast warship accurate steering was essential and that an oscillating compass could not be tolerated, yet there had never been a thorough investigation into all the contributory causes of heeling error. Accordingly, between 1890 and 1893 he was permitted to carry out a series of connected trials at Devonport in the cruisers *Orlando*, *Aurora* and *Thames* during which the ships were inclined 7° each way while coaling and were swung in each condition as well as when upright.[27]

The ships chosen offered some of the most difficult and varied conditions, with their Standard and bridge compasses fitted above the mass of iron of the conning tower and their lower compasses surrounded by armour. A total of six compass positions was investigated, including the steering engine flat, and careful measurements of the vertical and horizontal forces were made at each position on every occasion.

The initial trials in *Orlando*, which were attended by Sir William Thomson, showed that when applied to a modern warship, Archibald Smith's formulae were only approximately correct and for moderate angles of heel, as they did not take into account the effect of vertical induction in the horizontal soft iron as the ship rolled.[28] This aspect was thoroughly investigated during the second series of trials in *Aurora*, and Creak's subsequent report provided what is probably one of the most readable treatments of the subject ever prepared.[29] His final series of trials in the cruiser *Thames*, which were spread over eighteen months (1891–93) was designed to prove his theories and to provide the necessary data to enable correction to be made. The results were extremely satisfactory.[30] Creak's ultimate aim was, of course, to evolve a simple and accurate method of correcting heeling error with the ship upright and one that could be repeated at any time as the ship changed latitude. He developed a new form of 'heeling-error instrument' which worked on the method of balancing a magnetized needle by means of a sliding weight, the correct position of which could be determined for each compass position and for any geographical location by simple experiment and calculation.[31] As the instrument was designed to be placed in the position of the compass needles his original model was mounted in a conventional bowl but he very soon evolved the convenient flat instrument which has since been universally employed for almost a century. There can be little doubt that in this comprehensive investigation Creak made one of his most valuable contributions to the practice of compass adjustment, enabling the correction of an extremely complex error to become a simple routine.

To complete the accurate correction of the Fleet's compasses Creak looked again at the problem of determining the correct length for the Flinders bar, which had been the subject of his paper to the Royal Society in 1883 (see p. 129). Ever since Airy's original experiments it had been appreciated that part of the semicircular deviation, normally corrected by fore and aft permanent magnets, is in fact due to induction in vertical soft iron; also that the two parts of the error can only be separated by making observations in widely differing magnetic latitudes. Vertical-force instruments were therefore supplied to all ships proceeding to the southern hemisphere so that the appropriate observations could be made and the correct length of bar calculated.[32] An interesting and particularly valuable set of results was sent in by the cruiser *Royal Arthur*, which made observations at no less than seven separate locations between England and the Straits of Magellan.[33]

Increasing use of electricity

During the 1890s Creak became intimately involved in the problems arising from the wider use of electricity in the Navy. We have already seen in chapter 5 how its introduction, initially for searchlights and later for general lighting, began to have an impact on compasses early in the 1880s. Several cautionary articles appeared in the *Nautical Magazine*, highlighting the dangers, particularly in ships with single-wire systems. Although the Navy had changed to a two-wire system as early as 1881, the need to run the wires close together in the vicinity of the compass was not always observed and compass errors from this simple cause continued to occur right up to the end of the century. In the main, however, the problems to be tackled fell under the three headings of dynamos, searchlights and compass lighting.

In 1884, when conducting trials in the troopship *Euphrates*, Mayes had discovered that the compass could be disturbed by a dynamo at a distance of 50 feet, but this was apparently regarded as exceptional and in the following year a safe distance of 35 feet was inserted in the Dockyard Regulations. In February 1889 Creak conducted further trials in the cruiser *Northampton* which had reported serious errors. He recommended that the safe distance of each dynamo should be established by experiment, subject to a minimum of 35 feet; also that dynamos should be placed with their north and south poles equidistant from the Standard Compass and provided with efficient magnetic screening whenever circumstances compelled departure from these rules. It was all rather vague, but although ships continued to experience errors they were generally of manageable proportions.

The next shock occurred in 1892 when the cruiser *Orlando* reported from Australia that, following the fitting of a new dynamo some 31 feet from the Standard Compass, she was experiencing errors in excess of 20°. Clearly the recommended safe-distance tests had not been made. Creak was instructed to make a thorough investigation of the problem, in collaboration with the Assistant Constructor for Electrical Duties,[34] and in May 1893 trials were conducted in the new cruisers *Apollo* and *Blenheim*, both of which showed unexpectedly large compass errors. The *Apollo* carried two dynamos of 300 amperes each, the *Blenheim* one of 400 amperes. Experiments showed that the safe distances of these new machines were now 60 and 70 feet respectively, distances which, in many ships, it would be impossible to achieve.

It appeared that the main source of error experienced lay in the athwartship direction (i.e. a maximum with ship's head north or south), disturbances in the fore and aft direction being generally small. Accordingly, at Creak's suggestion, a correcting device in the form of an electromagnet was designed and fitted below the compass,[35] with an automatic switch to select whichever dynamo was running.[36] These arrangements proved very successful and with the cure to hand, all ships fitted with dynamos were instructed to swing, both with dynamos stopped and with each one running in turn, to ascertain their effect.[37] Twelve ships, all cruisers, out of the first batch of twenty-seven to be swung were found to have errors large enough to warrant correction and were fitted with the new electromagnet. The remainder were simply warned to take special care when their dynamos were running. Further ships were later added to the list, in particular the torpedo-boat destroyers in which the necessary safe separation could not be found.

The Hydrographer accepted the necessity for correcting the Standard Compass with an electrical device, but was greatly opposed to the principle. In 1895, when commenting on the siting of the 600 ampere 'daylight' dynamo in the new 15,000 ton battleship *Majestic* he wrote, 'It cannot be considered satisfactory if these enormous ships are to be navigated by a compass which will depend on electrical correctors for its accuracy. These correctors are very ingenious but it is quite a different thing to [the dynamo] being outside the limits of any possible influence.' He had been assured by Lord Kelvin that it was possible to construct large dynamos with small external magnetic fields, and he consistently pressed for their introduction. The new dynamo under discussion for the *Majestic* certainly represented an improvement. It was provided with a 4 inch belt of armour round the pole pieces which, in spite of its huge output, kept the safe distance down to 60 feet, the same as the older machines of only half the capacity.[38]

Gradually, by screening and by fitting dynamos as far from the compass as possible, the problems were overcome and matters improved. Although corrector coils continued to be fitted for several years they had a comparatively short life and are not mentioned in the *Torpedo Manual* after 1900. (Responsibility for all electrical work in HM ships remained with the torpedo branch, based on HMS *Vernon* at Portsmouth, until World War II.)

Since 1886 it had been the practice for plans showing the arrangements for fitting dynamos and searchlights to be passed to the Compass Department for vetting. However, no official safe distance for the latter appears to have been laid down, and this often led to argument between departments. When, therefore, in 1890, a new pattern of 'electric-light projector' was to be introduced, Creak decided to carry out formal safe-distance trials at Portsmouth,[39] and this important procedure has been continued for all new electrical equipment ever since.

On the matter of lighting, we saw in the last chapter how the natural prudence of the department was overruled in 1887 and authority given for steering compasses to be lit by electricity, the light being placed in the hood or suspended over the compass from a tripod. When, in 1891, a demand arose for the Standard Compass to be similarly lighted there were considerable doubts about the wisdom of such a move. Fears were voiced that leaking currents might magnetize the spheres and Flinders bar or that the lamp itself might disturb the compass. Creak decided to consult Sir William Thomson on the subject and received a helpful and reassuring reply, minimizing the dangers and suggesting that he should try placing the lamp 8 inches *below* the compass card. In December 1891 Creak and Mr Richards, the Assistant Constructor, again collaborated in a series of trials in the cruisers *Melampus* and *Royal Arthur*, from which they concluded that, subject to strict safeguards, it would be safe to proceed.[40] Two 16 candle power lamps were placed below the compass, as suggested by Sir William, and the insides of the binnacle and hood were painted white to improve illumination. The wires to the lamps were to be led vertically up from the bottom of the binnacle and clipped close together.

This system was fitted in the Channel Squadron for trial but although generally welcomed, many found the glare too strong and some found difficulty in taking bearings at all. Further experiments were needed and a number of officers sent in their own ideas, including Lieutenant Creagh-Osborne of the *Dido*, a future Superintendent. Finally it was decided to adopt a screened light, fitted *above* the compass on a special gibbet or, as an alternative, fitted in the hood in place of one of the oil lamps. After initial tests in the *Royal Sovereign*, which showed that a 4 c.p. lamp was adequate and prevented the metal screen becoming too hot, the system was widely fitted for operational trials. Favourable reports were received from all stations, both at home and abroad, the Channel Squadron reporting in December 1896 that it was a 'complete success'.[41] An alarm occured in 1897 when the cruiser *Endymion* observed a sudden change in the deviation of her Standard Compass, which the ship's officers attributed to the spheres becoming magnetized by electricity.[42] However, Creak showed this to be unfounded and the error was traced to the fact that during repairs the binnacle had been rewired with widely separated leads. An order was therefore issued that Admiralty approval must be obtained before making any change to the wiring in the vicinity of the compass and this remained in the *Queen's (or King's) Regulations* for many years. At last, in January 1898, the scheme for lighting the Standard Compass by electricity was approved by the Board.[43]

It has never been simple to arrange satisfactory compass lighting and new problems tend to arise as circumstances change. In 1906 approval was given for a small lamp to be attached to the Kelvin azimuth circle but a few years later Captain Chetwynd, when designing his new patent liquid compass (see p. 169), decided to revert to lighting the compass below, the use of frosted glass in the bottom of the bowl and translucent mica cards making this a very satisfactory solution. And so, as operational requirements have changed over the years, the story has continued.

Other tasks

The volume of work undertaken by Creak and Henderson during the last decade of the century was prodigious. Then, as now, the staff of the Compass Department was required to check and approve all the appropriate plans of new ships, to carry out inspections during building and finally to do the initial compass adjustment. There were also many problems to be solved in the ships already at sea. As the building programme, begun in the late 1880s, gathered momentum and the number of ships increased, the bound volumes containing the 'Records of observations for deviations' (i.e. swinging reports), which were referred to the Compass Department, got bulkier each year. Two volumes were needed annually from 1891, three from 1896 and for many years to follow. As each new ship normally required three visits and many were being built in northern ports, the staff was constantly on the move.

At the same time work at the Compass Observatory at Deptford required regular supervision and the instruments had constantly to be checked. The introduction of the Thomson compass had greatly increased the load on Mr Foden, the number of items to be tested having virtually doubled in the seven years to 1891. It was to double again before the end of the century. Meanwhile Creak's considerable experimental work also had to be fitted in. In 1895 the original wooden observatory structure, which was over fifty years old, was falling apart and had to be largely rebuilt.

The revision of Admiralty publications provided yet another continuing task in which Creak's conscientious work was to serve his successors well for many years. In 1870 he had assisted Captain Evans with the preparation of the *Elementary Manual of the Deviations of the Compass*, and in 1887, the year he became Superintendent, he had revised the sixth edition. In 1897, following his heeling-error experiments, he produced an enlarged ninth edition containing a full discussion of the subject and for the first time providing tables to assist in placing the spheres and Flinders bar. After his retirement in 1901, when almost 66 years old, Creak completely rewrote the *Elementary Manual*, discarding the original question-and-answer format and providing a most readable compass primer. This excellent volume was published in 1903, with further editions in 1908 and 1912. It was reprinted without amendment in 1918.

The *Admiralty Manual of the Deviations of the Compass* by Evans and Smith naturally claimed Creak's early attention. In 1882, during the reign of Mayes, he had revised the fifth edition and this was further updated in 1893 and 1901, with the sixth and seventh editions. In 1912, when seventy-seven, he assisted Chetwynd with a further revision, which was reprinted without amendment in 1920. For many years, both these Admiralty manuals were also in regular use in the United States Navy.

The *Practical Rules*, which had not been out of print since 1842, was also periodically revised, the last edition appearing in 1899 in hardback and costing tuppence. Another popular pamphlet, *Compass Questions and Answers for Acting Sub-Lieutenants*, was first published in 1885 when Creak was appointed to examine these officers at the Royal Naval College at Portsmouth. This, too, was reprinted at intervals up to 1914.

Outside the naval service Creak published a wide range of books and articles on magnetic matters, of which his entry on compasses in the tenth edition of the *Encyclopaedia Britannica* deserves special mention. He also contributed the article on terrestrial magnetism in the fifth edition (1886) of the *Admiralty Manual of Scientific Inquiry* and in 1903, as President of the Geographical Section of the British Association, gave as his address 'The progress of our knowledge of magnetism both afloat and ashore'. This splendid review appeared in the Association's *Proceedings* and was reprinted in periodicals in both Britain and America.[44]

Terrestrial magnetism was always one of Creak's special interests. During the 1870s he had undertaken the enormous task of analysing the magnetic results of the voyage of the *Challenger* and had also reported to the Royal Society on Captain Nares's expedition to the Arctic with *Alert* and *Discovery* (see p. 129). In 1895 he contributed a further paper to the Society 'On the magnetic results of the voyage of HMS *Penguin* 1890–93',[45] which covered her surveys in Australasia, and in 1904 he reported on her subsequent voyage across the Pacific (1899–1900) under the command of Captain A. M. Field, who was later to relieve Wharton as Hydrographer.[46] These papers both dealt extensively with reports of magnetic anomalies, yet another subject of which he had made a special study. From 1898 to 1900 he served on the Council of the Royal Society.

During Creak's final year as Superintendent he became actively involved in the preparations for the British Antarctic expedition under Captain Robert Falcon Scott. He personally drew up the magnetic instructions and was responsible for the fitting of a magnetic observatory aboard the *Discovery* and for arranging the loan, from Admiralty sources, of the necessary compasses and other instruments. Amongst the latter was a Lloyd–Creak dip circle, another invention for which he was partially responsible, and a considerable improvement on the old *Fox* dip circle which had been used by Ross more than half a century earlier.[47]

In 1890, on reaching the age of 55, Creak had been automatically placed on the retired list, but had been allowed to continue as Superintendent of Compasses. Having joined the department at an early age, he had insufficient seatime to qualify him for promotion to Captain on retirement, in accordance with the regulations, but this rank was eventually granted him in 1892 by special Order in Council,[48] in recognition of his services to the Compass Department.

He was made a Companion of the Bath in 1901, and on 1 April of that year was succeeded as Superintendent by Staff Captain James Henderson who had been his able assistant for the past twelve years. As the new Assistant Superintendent the Admiralty appointed Lieutenant the Honourable Louis Wentworth Chetwynd who had entered the Navy in 1880 at the age of 13, through HMS *Britannia*, and had had ten years experience as a Navigating Officer. After completing the special six-month compass course at the Royal Naval College at Greenwich, Chetwynd joined the department on 1 April 1901, and was promoted Commander at the end of the year.

Creak's thirteen years as Superintendent had been a period of intense activity during which he had succeeded in re-establishing the reputation and authority of the Compass Department despite much interference from Lord Kelvin who still exercised considerable influence through his direct access to the Board. He had been intensely loyal to the service and, had done his best to implement Admiralty policy. Only after he retired did he write to the Hydrographer, by then Rear Admiral Sir William Wharton, saying, 'When the Thomson Compass was first introduced as Standard Compass on board I felt it my duty to try and make it a success. It was, however, in many respects the bête noire of my existance.'

Through ignorance and prejudice the Navy had allowed itself to take a wrong turning. However, with his improved liquid compass, Creak had put them on the right track once more and his successors would shortly reap the benefit. At a time when the Navy was becoming increasingly mobile he had done all in his power to smooth its path. Indeed, as the Hydrographer had written of him in 1897, there was 'no other man who so entirely combined the scientific and practical knowledge necessary for superintending the compass arrangements in modern vessels of war'.[49]

In his retirement Creak continued to take an active interest in magnetic matters and there is a record of his having visited the Compass Department in 1916 at the age of 81, when he had a discussion on aircraft compasses and terrestrial magnetism with the Director, Captain Creagh-Osborne and again in 1919 with the International Hydrographic Conference. He died on 3 April 1920, in his eighty-fifth year, being honoured by a long obituary notice in the *Proceedings of the Royal Society*, contributed by Admiral Sir Mostyn Field KCB, FRS.[50]

NOTES

CHAPTER 6

1 Hydrographer's Minute Book, No. 34, p. 252.

2 Ibid., No. 33, p. 42; W. E. May, 'Compass Department Memoires', National Maritime Museum, Magnetic Compass Collection, Item R.8 (2).

3 Tully was fortunate to leave the *Victoria* three months before she was sunk in collision with the *Camperdown* in June 1893. Lieutenant G. H. Alexander, who was later to relieve Mr Foden as compass-examiner, was a survivor from the *Victoria*.

4 'Compass Department Memoires'.

5 Hydrographer's Minute Book, No. 33, p. 533.

6 National Maritime Museum, Magnetic Compass Collection, Item R2/4b (Admiralty reference NS 303/90/2222).

7 Ibid., Item R2/4c (Admiralty reference NS 1384/90/985); Hydrographer's Minute Book, No. 37, p. 22.

8 The system supplied to the Royal Navy had a liquid compass but it is interesting to note that before deciding on this the Austrian-Hungarian navy had done trials with a number of compasses, including the Thomson, which they had rejected at an early stage. The soft-iron correctors of the RN system had been modified from the original of 1878 by introducing irregularities into the ellipses to eliminate the octantal error.

9 A full description of the Peichl corrector, with copies of the correspondence between Staff Commander Creak and Lieutenant Von Peichl is contained in the National Maritime Museum, Magnetic Compass Collection, Item R6 and Envelope N 10.

10 *Journal of the Royal United Services Institute*, Vol. 23 (1892), pp. 949–75.

11 Lord Kelvin had discussed this possibility in a paper to the British Association in 1884 but he had not developed the idea (*Report of the 54th Meeting of the British Association*, 1885, pp. 625–28).

12 Reports of the trials of the Peichl corrector are in the National Maritime Museum, Magnetic Compass Collection, Envelope N 10. (Admiralty reference NS 1840/1900).

13 A letter from Lord Kelvin describing this instrument is held with the Magnetic Compass Collection at the National Maritime Museum. (Envelope N1).

14 Hydrographer's Minute Book, No. 54, p. 314.

15 Ibid., No. 57, p. 40; National Maritime Museum, Magnetic Compass Collection, Item R6.

16 Hydrographer's Minute Book, No. 51, p. 205, No. 56, p. 245.

17 Initially this compass was fitted with a central stile or shadow pin for taking bearings. Later, when it was fitted with an azimuth circle, the compass became Pattern 24A.

18 Hydrographer's Minute Book, No. 35, p. 375.

[19] Ibid., No. 35, p. 26.

[20] *Journal of the Royal United Services Institute*, Vol. 23 (1892).

[21] Surplus pillars released when the Thomson compasses were fitted as standard were quickly turned to good account, both for torpedo-boats and for the torpedo-boat destroyers, which followed in the mid-1890s.

[22] Private letter in National Maritime Museum, Magnetic Compass Collection, Envelope N5.

[23] Hydrographer's Minute Book, No. 39, p. 220, No. 40, p. 99, No. 41, p.307, No. 47, p. 231.

[24] Ibid.,

[25] Ibid., No. 34, p. 145.

[26] Ibid., No. 35, pp. 25, 145.

[27] Ibid., No. 33, p. 560.

[28] These trials also showed up a serious flaw in the design of the Kelvin suspension. As the ship rolled the compass swung to and fro on its chains, transferring laterally across the vertical magnets. This 'motion of translation' introduced serious errors in the conning-tower compasses, where the stronger needles had greatly reduced the period of oscillation.

[29] 'Report on trials in *Aurora*', National Maritime Museum, Magnetic Compass Collection, Envelope N 12.

[30] Hydrographer's Minute Book, No. 35, p. 441.

[31] In Sir William Thomson's original vertical-force instrument, which was based on Archibald Smith's formulae, the vertical magnetic force was counter-balanced by torsion.

[32] The calculation required is known as 'separating P and c' (P = the effect of the permanent fore and aft magnetism of the ship, c = the effect of the magnetism induced in the vertical soft iron, acting in the fore and aft direction).

[33] Hydrographer's Minute Book, No. 37, p. 168.

[34] National Maritime Museum, Magnetic Compass Collection, Envelope N 8. (Admiralty letter, NS 557/93).

[35] Ibid., (Admiralty letter, S 6794/93) and Hydrographer's Minute Book, No. 37, p. 85.

[36] Ibid., No. 38, p. 142.

[37] Ibid., No. 38, p. 187.

[38] Memorandum to Hydrographer by Superintendent of Compasses, 11 October 1895. National Maritime Museum, Magnetic Compass Collection, Envelope N 8.

[39] Hydrographer's Minute Book, No. 34, p. 101.

[40] Ibid., No. 35, p. 285; National Maritime Museum, Magnetic Compass Collection, Envelope N 8. (Admiralty letter, NS 4502/91).

[41] Hydrographer's Minute Book, No. 40, p. 94.

[42] Letter to Hydrographer from the Captain, *HMS Endymion*, 27 May 1897, National Maritime Museum, Magnetic Compass Collection, Envelope N 8.

[43] Hydrographer's Minute Book, No. 42, p. 60.

[44] Report of the 72nd meeting of the British Association, 1903.

[45] *Phil. Trans. Royal Society*, 1895.

[46] Ibid., 1904.

[47] An account of the Lloyd-Creak dip circle appears in *Terrestrial Magnetism and Atmospheric Electricity*, October 1901, pp. 119–20.

[48] Admiralty Order in Council, 6 October 1892.

[49] Hydrographer's Minute Book, No. 42, p. 337.

[50] *Proceedings of the Royal Society*, Vol. 97, 1920.

A new century brings new challenges, 1901-14

7

'Fear God and Dread-Nought' (From the grave of Admiral of the Fleet Lord Fisher at Kilverstone Hall, Norfolk)

'It is astounding to me, perfectly astounding, how the very best amongst us fail to realise the vast impending revolution in Naval Warfare and Naval Strategy that the submarine will accomplish.' (Admiral Sir John Fisher, 1904)

The twentieth century dawned with war in South Africa and the Victorian era drawing to its close. Following the Naval Defence Act (1889), successive construction programmes had done much to build up Britain's naval strength while more efficient guns, better control arrangements, the gradual introduction of water-tube boilers and the beginning of oil fuel were all adding to its effectiveness. In 1898 an experimental torpedo-boat destroyer, the *Viper*, achieved a speed of 36 knots on trials and the Navy ordered its first 30 knot destroyers, powered by steam turbines. At the Fleet Review of 1897, staged to mark the Queen's diamond jubilee, the Admiralty amassed a total of 165 ships without recalling any from abroad. It was an impressive display of Britain's naval might which included 22 battleships, 40 cruisers and 20 torpedo boats, although many were past their prime.

Germany became greatly alarmed at this show of strength and, under successive German navy laws, plans were drawn up which represented a real challenge to Britain's naval supremacy. Once again it was apparent that the two-power standard was being seriously threatened and the arms race in Europe entered a more urgent phase.

The year 1904 saw the signing of the entente cordiale and the appointment of Admiral Fisher as First Sea Lord. Sweeping changes could now be expected. To concentrate greater strength in European waters the various fleets were reorganized and redistributed, whilst over a hundred obsolete vessels were scrapped to save manpower. During the next few years large numbers of cruisers and destroyers were laid down and the building of submarines, which had only begun in 1901, several years after the French, Americans and Japanese, was greatly accelerated. Above all the first dreadnought, a new type of warship, faster, more powerful and better protected than any battleship hitherto designed, was laid down in October 1905 and completed in the incredibly short time of twelve months. It was followed a year later by another new type of capital ship, the battle-cruiser, with lighter armour but with a speed of 25 knots and it was these two classes which were to form Britain's new battle fleet. Under the Cowdor programme, passed in 1905, parliament agreed that four dreadnoughts (later super-dreadnoughts, with 13.5 inch in place of 12 inch guns) or battle-cruisers should be laid down each year. Whilst it was inevitable, despite the efforts of the First Sea Lord and the strong feeling in the country (expressed in the music-hall ditty 'We want eight and we won't wait'), that cutbacks in this programme would take place, nevertheless by 1912 the remarkable total of twenty-two new capital ships had been completed.

When the century was just three months old, Staff Captain James Henderson[1] relieved Captain Creak as Superintendent of Compasses, taking over a department whose reputation and authority had been considerably restored. Whilst the evolution of the Navy had already had a profound effect on the activities of the Compass Department, still greater and more radical changes now lay just ahead. Although Henderson himself was to serve a mere three and a half years as Superintendent before handing over to Commander Chetwynd, the problems posed by wireless telegraphy and the submarine were both to concern him. By the end of the first decade the far-reaching impact of aircraft and the gyro-compass was also beginning to affect the small department.

Wireless telegraphy

It is common knowledge that in 1896 Marconi brought to Britain his new invention for employing radio waves (known at the time as Hertzian waves) for communication, setting up his commercial company in the following year. It may be less well known that a naval captain, Henry Jackson (later Admiral of the Fleet and First Sea Lord, see p. 216) had successfully conducted similar experiments in HMS *Defiance* at Devonport which probably predated Marconi's by several months. By 1900 wireless equipment (including sets designed by Jackson) was being sent to sea for trials in the Fleet and it was not long before reports were coming in of compasses being seriously disturbed. Experiments in the cruiser *Jaseur* at Portsmouth late in 1901 showed that the safe distance from the Standard Compass of a large Marconi inductor coil was in excess of 30 feet (20 feet being acceptable for a steering compass),[2] and this was soon confirmed during trials in the Channel Squadron. As a result a number of wireless telegraphy offices, which had already been fitted too close to compass positions, had to be moved. Thereafter tests were always carried out before new equipment was introduced and the Compass Department was kept informed of all wireless fitting plans. Nevertheless the normal struggle to maintain the safe distances, particularly as more powerful sets appeared, required constant vigilance by the department for many years.

Submarines

In October 1900, after a skilful and determined campaign by the First Lord of the Admiralty, George Goschen, the Board reluctantly agreed to the purchase of five Holland-type submarine-boats from the Electric Boat Company of America. Despite strong opposition from the Controller of the Navy, Rear Admiral Sir Arthur Wilson VC (who secured a place in history by referring to the submarine as that 'damned un-English weapon') and from the Director of Naval Construction, the order went through and the boats were successfully built under licence by the firm of Vickers at Barrow-in-Furness. Thanks largely to the vision of Sir John Fisher, a further 70 boats were built during the next 10 years, gradually increasing in size up to 700 tons, and many more were to follow as Britain prepared for war.

The importance of an efficient compass in a submarine, particularly when navigating 'blind', needs no emphasis, yet no magnetic compass could operate satisfactorily inside an enclosed steel vessel. It was therefore necessary to place it in a watertight binnacle *outside*

the pressure hull and to arrange for all material within a 7 foot radius
of the compass needles to be non-magnetic. This is the arrangement
still employed today whenever a magnetic compass is fitted in a
submarine.

Realizing that special compasses would be required, Henderson
immediately applied for a grant of £100 to cover the necessary
experiments, and this was probably the first example in the department's history of a specially funded development project.[3] The
compass used was a modification of the well-established torpedo-
boat compass (Pattern 24B) in which the underside of the card was
illuminated and graduated in degrees from 0° to 180°, the eastern
half being painted green and the western half red. The upper surface
of the card was marked in the conventional manner and the binnacle
was fitted with a glass window at the top so that the compass could
be read from the casing when on the surface. The lower half of the
binnacle, which was not watertight, contained the normal permanent
magnet correctors, which were encased in brass to prevent them
rusting. Spheres were fitted but no Flinders bar.

The problem of viewing the compass from inside the hull was
solved by fitting a telescope binnacle, designed by the firm of E. J.
Dent which also made the compasses. A tube, containing a rather
crude telescopic system, passed through a watertight gland and
enabled the helmsman to read the compass from below. It was an
awkward arrangement, which must have given him considerable
eye strain and it was superseded in 1908 by the first of a series of
projector binnacles in which an image of the lubber's point and a
sector of the card was projected down a watertight trunk onto a
ground glass screen in the control room. Variations on this type of
binnacle remained in service for some fifty years until a suitable
transmitting magnetic compass for submarines eventually went to
sea in 1960.

Although more effective than the telescope binnacle, early versions of the projector had the great disadvantage that if the light
failed it could not be replaced with the submarine submerged. In
1918 the raising and lowering (RL) type of binnacle was introduced
and this went through a large number of variations and improvements (RL VIIs were still found at sea in the *Odin*-class submarines
at the beginning of World War II). As these binnacles were 'hull
fittings' their design was undertaken by the Director of Naval
Construction,[4] with the Compass Department merely providing the

compass. However, in 1936 the Admiralty Compass Observatory assumed responsibility for the projector system and a series of ACO projector binnacles followed, in which the illuminating lamp was fitted inside the hull, the same lens system serving to take the light up the tube and to bring it down again. The raising and lowering mechanism was therefore no longer needed and a much better image could be obtained. Among other improvements introduced were the provision of a window to allow the compass card to be viewed directly when steering from the bridge and the blooming of all lens surfaces to avoid flare, the first known use of this process in the naval service. Many variations of the ACO projector binnacle appeared over the next ten years to meet particular requirements, including those of the X-craft, but these will be discussed further in chapter 10.[5]

To enable submarines to navigate accurately on the surface, a small portable compass and binnacle was introduced in 1909, for use on the bridge. It could be closely corrected and became affectionately known as 'Faithful Freddie', the talisman of several generations of submariners who were reluctant to go to sea without it. Although no longer officially allowed, it is still (1984) occasionally issued.

Staffing and organization of the Compass Department

The great increase in ship-building during the early years of the century, which had included the introduction of submarines, placed a heavy load on the two compass officers who found themselves constantly travelling, while the growing complexity of ships and the many new problems to be solved added greatly to the load. In November 1903 the Hydrographer made a successful application for a third officer for the department and three months later, following a short course at the Royal Naval College at Greenwich, Commander H. M. K. Betty was appointed as a Naval Assistant.[6]

The year 1904 saw the retirement, on 1 October, of the Superintendent, Staff Captain Henderson, after only three and a half years in the post, and the appointment of Commander the Honourable L. W. P. Chetwynd as his successor. When Chetwynd was originally appointed to the branch in 1900 the regulations had allowed him to serve for an indefinite period while remaining on the active list. However, in December of that year the Admiralty had ruled that an officer who had held a shore appointment for five years must elect either to go back to sea or else to accept retirement, continuing to serve on the retired list.[7] This new regulation placed Chetwynd at a disadvantage. In view of his frequent and close touch with ships' officers his position would be easier if he were himself on the active list. At the same time the duty of Superintendent was a complex one which would be much impaired if the holder changed every five years. The Hydrographer therefore immediately asked that Chetwynd should be retained on the active list as a special case, but this was refused. Consequently, in October 1905, when he had completed five years ashore, he was required to decide whether to retire or to return to sea. It was indeed fortunate for the branch that he elected to be placed on the retired list and to remain in charge.

Meanwhile, as Assistant Superintendent, the Admiralty appointed Commander Frank Osborne Creagh-Osborne, an experienced Navigating Officer who had recently been promoted whilst in the twin-screw battleship *Mars*. He had already seen action in the cruiser *Diana* during the China War, for which he wore the campaign medal. He was also a keen yachtsman and had had the unusual honour of being elected an honorary member of the Royal Yacht squadron. Before joining the department he was required to do the statutory six months course at Greenwich so it was not until 1 January 1905 that he finally took up his appointment.

In November 1905 a committee appointed to enquire into the working of the Hydrographic Department had, as one of its terms of reference, 'The Transfer of the department of the Superintendent of Compasses to the Controller's Department'. The committee was chaired by Rear Admiral C. H. Adair and consisted of the Hydrographer, Captain A. M. Field, the Captain of the Navigation School, Captain H. F. Oliver, and two other members. When asked whether it would be practicable to maintain the present relationship between the Superintendent of Compasses and the Hydrographer on all questions connected with terrestrial magnetism and at the same time bring the Superintendent into sufficiently close touch with the Controller as regards the work of his department, Chetwynd replied:

Yes I believe it would. If the Superintendent of Compasses were in the Controller's Department the details of the compass work, which entail frequent communication with the Director of Naval

Construction, Director of Stores and Director of Contracts would be more easily arranged, as would also the carrying out of decisions as regards compass headings in ships under construction. The terrestrial magnetism does not entail personal communication with anyone in the Admiralty except the Hydrographer, and I am of the opinion that this part of the work could be equally well carried out if the Superintendent of Compasses were in the Controller's Department, but in direct communication with the Hydrographer for the purposes of terrestrial magnetism.

This was a well-reasoned reply. However, the Assistant Hydrographer, Captain T. H. Tizard, was of the opposite view. He told the committee,

With respect to the transfer of the Compass Department, I am of the opinion it would be a mistake. Most of the main magnetic work is absolutely bound up with Hydrography and now that all Navigating Officers can correct their own compasses, the principal work of the Compass Department, as far as ships is concerned, is to select a proper place, as free as possible from local influence, for the Standard Compass in all newly built ships and also to advise how far disturbing influences such as motors, etc. should be kept from the compasses . . . This can as easily be done under the Hydrographer's superintendence as without it . . .

This statement showed a somewhat superficial understanding of the breadth and depth of the Compass Department's work. Nevertheless the committee recommended that the compass organization should remain part of the Hydrographic Department, as otherwise there was some risk that its important work with terrestrial magnetism would be neglected. However, when compass staff visited ships they should be considered as representing the Controller.[8]

The committee made several suggestions regarding the staffing of the branch. First, the appointment of the Superintendent should be a permanent one, but that of the Assistant should be for three years, unless he should volunteer to remain permanently and there was difficulty in finding a replacement. Second, as a result of a recent Admiralty decision only to repair naval ships in HM dockyards, the amount of travelling had been greatly reduced and the third officer was no longer needed (he left the department in April 1906). On the other hand there was much outstanding computing to be done and the committee recommended the addition of a computer and a clerk. In the event, only the clerk was appointed. Third, when Mr Foden, the compass Examiner, retired he was to be replaced by a boatswain or gunner on the active list, there being a surplus of these ranks in the Navy. Mr Foden was due to retire in January 1906, on reaching the age of 65, but was allowed to continue until March 1907 to enable Mr George H. Alexander, boatswain and second-class surveyor, then serving in the *Skylark* on the East Indies station, to return to England and take over his duties. He was to serve the department with great distinction, both on the active and retired lists, until 1929, becoming Chief Compass Examiner when the task multiplied many times during World War I.

When Mr Foden had joined the branch in 1883 he had been paid a salary of £70 in addition to his naval pension of £41, and the Treasury had laid down that his employment should not earn any increase. As we have seen, in view of the enormous expansion in the scope of his job, his salary was raised to £100 in 1887 and to £120 five years later. A request for a third increase in 1900 was turned down on the grounds that he would retire in the following year at the age of 60, and although he stayed to the age of 66 the matter does not appear to have been reconsidered. In 1907 the Hydrographer endeavoured to get him an increase in pension on the grounds that the job had radically changed and that he had probably saved the Admiralty quite £100 a year by doing small repair jobs himself instead of sending defective compasses back to the makers. The Treasury allowed him a gratuity of £100 instead of the £52 to which he was entitled, but otherwise had no sympathy for his many years of loyal service, adding simply that he had been lucky to have been allowed to remain to the age of 66![9]

The Navy accepts liquid compasses

It will be recalled that in 1902, when investigating the performance of the 6 inch Kelvin[10] compasses in the conning towers of the capital ships of the Channel Squadron, Henderson had also arranged a final trial of the Peichl liquid compass and corrector system in the battleships *Majestic* and *Hannibal* (see p. 141). The two ships were also issued with Pattern 24 liquid compasses for comparison and these had been very favourably reported on by Commander H. F.

Oliver. Although Henderson must have been aware of Creak's views on liquid compasses, it seems possible that he may have had little previous opportunity to observe their behaviour at sea as he appears to have been particularly impressed on this occasion. He therefore lost no time in arranging for the Channel squadron to carry out further trials in order to compare their performance in the conning tower with that of the 6 inch Kelvin dry-card compasses already fitted.

Trials made during the spring cruise of 1903 showed clearly that the Pattern 24 was far less disturbed by the training and firing of the forward barbette guns than the Kelvin and that it came to rest much more quickly, so making accurate steering easier. Because of the induction in the spheres by the more powerful needles of the liquid compasses it was also possible fully to correct the large coefficient D. (It was accepted that as a consequence the spheres would need adjusting with change of latitude.) The Board therefore approved that all battleships in commission should be provided with a torpedo-boat liquid compass and that the Kelvin binnacles fitted in their upper conning towers should be modified to receive them.[11]

Although the 10 inch Kelvin compass was still retained in the lower conning tower and was still the official compass for use in both the Standard and steering positions, it was rapidly losing favour at sea. For several years ships with heavy guns had had to replace it with a liquid compass during firings; now it was about to disappear altogether from the upper conning towers of capital ships. In October 1903 approval was given for the Pattern 24A to be issued to gunboats [12] and, as greater speeds brought increased vibration, other ships soon began requesting liquid compasses to replace their Kelvins in much the same way as twenty years earlier they had asked for the Thomson compass to replace the old Admiralty varieties. By 1904 Lord Kelvin was seriously worried, particularly as the Mercantile Marine were also experiencing difficulties. In November of that year he wrote to Admiral Fisher, now First Sea Lord, asking if the Navy would try out a compass fitted with a new sprung suspension (Patent No. 22031 of 1902) which he thought would be a great improvement over the grommet.[13] This compass was also lit from below (Patent No. 22034 of 1902). It was tried in the cruiser *Topaze*, which suffered particularly badly from vibration, but although an oscillation of three points (54°) was reduced to one, it could only be considered a partial success.[14]

Meanwhile Lord Kelvin was working on a radically new design of compass with a two-tier bowl, which became known as the pontoon compass (Patent No. 22695 of 1904). In the lower compartment was a controlling liquid compass, which did not have a card, whilst the upper, visible compartment contained a conventional Thomson dry card on which the polarity of the needles was reversed so that it would follow the lower compass. To the uninitiated the instrument still gave the appearance of being a normal Kelvin dry-card compass and, as there was no card on the liquid compass, swirl error was largely eliminated.

Not for the first time Lord Kelvin arranged to have his invention tested privately in one of His Majesty's ships. It was fitted in the cruiser *Caernarvon*, building on the Clyde, and in September 1905 her captain, Sir George Warrender, reported to the Admiralty that it showed promise. This time the Admiralty immediately agreed to buy the compass and to make the trial official.[15] A compass by Dobbie McInnes of Glasgow, which also had a new sprung antivibration mount, was fitted at the same time, for comparative trials, but was not a success.[16]

Meanwhile it transpired that a second unofficial trial of the pontoon compass was being conducted in the gunboat *Plucky*, tender to HMS *Mercury*, the Navigation School, where its performance so impressed Commander Chetwynd, the new superintendent of compasses, that a further six were ordered for trial. They were fitted in the battleships *Caesar* and *King Edward VII*, in three cruisers and a scout, while a seventh compass was later ordered for the *Topaze* in a further attempt to solve her acute vibration problem.[17] It seems, however, that none of these compasses gave very much satisfaction and after two years they were withdrawn as the solution appeared to lie in a different direction altogether.[18]

This was the last serious attempt by Lord Kelvin to influence naval compass design, although his correspondence with the department continued until 1906. He died in the following year at the age of 83. So much of the work of this brilliant man had been of benefit to mariners. His binnacle had revolutionized compass correction whilst the compass, for which he is best remembered, continued to be popular with the Mercantile Marine for many years. For the Navy's problems, alas, it produced only a temporary solution and in the long run its introduction, against the advice of the Compass Department, held up the development of effective liquid compasses for almost a quarter of a century.

The Chetwynd Patent Liquid Compass

It will be remembered that Captain Creak's experiments with liquid compasses had been halted in 1889 when the Thomson compass was adopted, and his efforts were thereafter largely devoted to making the Thomson work. The excellence of his improved liquid compass had, however, been demonstrated in torpedo boats and, through the efforts of Staff Captain Henderson, the same compass had been introduced for other vessels, including submarines. In 1901 J. C. Dobbie of Glasgow took out a patent (No. 8305 of 1901) for improvements to compasses, which included the suggestion that the diameter of the card should be reduced to improve its steadiness. He had realized that the greatest disturbance was caused by the liquid round the edges of the bowl but as he did not pursue the matter, the significance of his patent passed unnoticed.

In 1905, when complaints about the instability of the Kelvin compass were becoming increasingly frequent and trials were being conducted with the pontoon compass, Commander Chetwynd decided to resume work on the liquid compasses themselves. Very soon he, too, was experimenting with a card of reduced diameter. There is a story (probably apocryphal) that Chetwynd had ordered a bowl and card for experiment and was annoyed to find on delivery that the latter was a size smaller than the former. Rather irritably he was twisting the bowl about on the table when he noticed that the card was remaining remarkably steady. Whatever the truth of the matter, this was the breakthrough that was really needed. Chetwynd immediately realized the advantages of this arrangement and in March 1906, six compasses with reduced-diameter cards were sent for sea trials, one of them to the *Dreadnought*.

On 12 November 1906, the Hydrographer reported on the new compass as follows: 'The reports from the various ships are unanimous in its favour and its behaviour under the severe test of the gun trials of *Dreadnought* shows that it is practically unaffected under the conditions when other compasses are quite unreliable.'[19]

He went on to recommend that it should be adopted for the Navy forthwith and fitted in all future vessels, as well as in existing ships where the present compasses were unreliable. This time Their Lordships raised no objection and the proposal was approved on 6 December 1906, with a first order for forty-four compasses. Six months later the compass was given a transparent bottom to the bowl, enabling it to be lit from below and obviating the inconvenience of the wandering leads still associated with the current Admiralty method of lighting (see p. 150).[20]

The six trial compasses and the first order of forty-four were known as Pattern 23A. The number was changed to 22A when the compass was lit from below, and this pattern has provided the prototype for most marine magnetic compasses ever since. The liquid compass had, at long last, triumphantly arrived.

Chetwynd's patents

On 16 November 1906 Chetwynd took out a provisional patent for a compass with a reduced-diameter card and a lubber's point consisting of a wire pointer projecting from the side of the bowl to reach it. Although this patent was at first opposed by Dobbie, it was eventually sealed on 31 December (as Patent No. 25965 of 1906), with the inclusion of a paragraph stating that the claimant was aware of Dobbie's patent of 1901 and claimed nothing which appeared therein.

The Hydrographer, Captain Field, gave his full support to the case. He appreciated the very wide implications of this patent, both to the Navy and the Mercantile Marine as well as to the navies of foreign nations, and he saw no reason why Chetwynd should not benefit from his invention and his initiative. Foreseeing the difficulties which might arise in the Navy he wrote to Their Lordships on 8 January 1907:

> It is undesirable that an officer upon whom devolves the duty of submitting proposals for the purchase of compasses for the Fleet should be directly interested (financially) from day to day in the number of purchases for that purpose. It would seem preferable on that account that any remuneration Their Lordships may grant should take the form of a gratuity.[21]

This minute also gave full credit to Captain Creak for having developed the liquid compass to the point at which Chetwynd was able to adapt it.

Meanwhile Dobbie appears to have been far from happy. He considered Chetwynd's compass an infringement of his patent and in October 1907 there was talk of a court case, which raised interesting legal questions since the Admiralty were reluctant to get involved with paying the costs of Chetwynd's defence. The Hydrographer, however, pointed out that the idea of an enlarged bowl had not really originated with either Dobbie or Chetwynd but with the firm of Chadburn & Sons, who had marketed such a compass thirty-five years before.[22] (He might also have added that it had been used ninety-four years before in Crow's liquid compass of 1813, Patent No. 3644.) It was Chetwynd, however, who had first realized its full implications. Eventually the matter appears to have been settled and after a considerable delay Chetwynd was given a gratuity of £2,700.[23]

Although this was his most important patent (No. 25965 of 1906), Chetwynd later had many others standing to his name, either alone or in conjunction with other contributors. A full list is given in appendix 6. Particular mention should be made of the binnacle he designed for use with his compass which was provided with a means of raising and lowering the corrector magnets on chains (Patent No. 1397 of 1907) and was extensively fitted in the Fleet. However his attempt to obtain additional remuneration for this item was unsuccessful.[24]

The introduction of new types of compass

From 1907 onwards, the task of modifying the various types of liquid compass in service went quickly ahead as torpedo-boat, submarine and boats compasses were all given reduced-diameter cards. Wherever it was fitted, the Chetwynd Patent Compass gave excellent results and it was not long before it was being demanded by individual ships. However, the Admiralty clearly did not wish to embark upon the expensive exercise of changing compasses throughout the Fleet, as had been done some twenty years earlier, and their policy was therefore to fit it only in new ships as they were built, and in others where the Kelvin had proved unreliable. Although approval was given in November 1908 for it to be supplied as the Standard Compass in all battleships and cruisers,[25] Kelvin Compasses continued in service for many years and were still to be found as the steering compasses in some of the older vessels at the end of World War I.

Meanwhile, as the provision of good compass positions became more difficult, the advantages that would be offered by some form of transmitting compass became more attractive. In 1902 the German firm of Siemens & Halske had patented such a compass which seemed to offer greater hope of success than any of the ingenious devices invented over the previous half-century. The transmission operated from a Wheatstone's bridge in which the resistances were varied according to temperature, which was itself regulated by the position of the master card. The Admiralty's attention was drawn to this compass when it was shown at the St Louis Exhibition of 1905, and one was eventually purchased, at a cost of £1,400, and fitted in the lower steering position of *Dreadnought*. Repeaters were placed in the conning tower and at the steering engine. Despite some sluggishness in the follow-up system the equipment appeared to show promise and in 1908 a second one was purchased for trial in the *Bellerephon*. However, this compass never appears to have been satisfactory and it was finally removed in 1913. A typical comment on it was that of the *Bellerephon*'s navigating officer, who complained that he had been 'sorely afflicted by that electrical compass'. By this time, however, the system for projecting the image of the compass in the lower steering position onto a ground-glass screen in the upper conning tower (see p. 141) had been greatly improved and appeared to provide the best solution for this particular problem, despite the considerable heat from the projector lamps.[26] The equipment, which was made by the firm of Kelvin & James White, had been widely fitted since 1908 and continued in service until after World War I. Although an improved version of the Siemens & Halske transmitting compass appeared in 1909 and was fitted in German submarines, the Compass Department declined to try it again.

An unusual requirement for a magnetic compass arose in 1908 in connection with fire control. In order to develop a plot of the enemy's movements the range and bearing had to be obtained simultaneously, and a special compass (designated Pattern 160) was therefore mounted in a bracket on the range-finder, with the lubber's point indicating the direction of the target. Small spheres, varying in size from one and a half to three-quarters of an inch, the smallest ever used in the Royal Navy, were attached to correct the quadrantal error and each range-finder was swung separately to adjust its compass.[27] After two prototype compasses had given good results on trials in the battleship *Revenge*, the gunnery firing-ship attached to HMS *Excellent*, they were widely fitted in the Fleet, and reports from twelve ships after a battle practice in 1910 show that they were very satisfactory.[28] The requirement, however, was short-lived and by 1913 they were being removed from many ships, possibly as by that time more accurate bearings could be obtained using the gyro-compass.

The Forebridge and the Standard Compass

In Chapter 6 it was noted that in some cruisers the Standard Compass had been moved, during the 1890s, from its traditional position aft to a platform above the forebridge. It was some years, however, before this arrangement became the general rule and in many ships the Standard remained aft, close to the alternative navigating position on the after bridge which was itself only finally abolished in 1906.[29]

The change in official thinking started in November 1903, when Admiral Fisher, then the Commander-in-Chief Mediterranean, sub-mitted three far-reaching recommendations for Their Lordships' consideration:[30] first that the Standard Compass should be moved to a platform above the conning tower, second that the forebridge should be abolished, and third that the conning tower should become the primary position for all conning and navigation, in keeping with his dictum of 1879 that 'the same arrangements for conning the ship should be employed in action as at any other time'.

The Hydrographer raised no objection to the Standard Compass being resited, provided it was placed as high as possible and at least 20 feet from the forward turret or barbette guns. However, abolishing the bridge implied that the conning-tower compass or, more usually, a projected image from the lower conning tower compass, would have to be relied on implicitly for such occasions as entering and leaving harbour, and at other times when very accurate navigation was essential, and this was quite unacceptable. If the bridge was to be done away with he considered that a compass and wheel should be provided *outside* the conning tower, at least 15 feet from the nearest gun and with a clear view ahead. Discussion on this subject continued for several years.

Siting the Standard Compass above the bridge proved very successful and the introduction of Hadfield non-magnetic steel in the vicinity greatly eased the problems of providing a 20 foot non-magnetic radius around it. With the coming of the Dreadnoughts in 1905 the Director of Naval Ordnance made one further attempt to abolish the bridge and, although he was unsuccessful, from then on the conning tower was enlarged and improved so that the ship could be handled from there at any time.[31]

In 1907, as a result of the greater boiler power of the new ships, a serious problem arose due to changes in the magnetism of the foremost funnel caused by the heat. During a full-power trial only a week after having her compasses adjusted, the battleship *Agamemnon* observed a deviation of 16° at her manoeuvring compass.[32] Although the problem was simply solved by moving the compass forward 12 feet, it was not long before other ships, including *Dreadnought*, were reporting similar troubles. The critical temperature was about 750°F, so that ships with Yarrow boilers, where the funnel temperature reached 800°F, were more affected than those with Babcock boilers, where it did not normally exceed 600°F. In some ships there was room for the compass to be moved forward clear of trouble, but in others the bridge had to be drastically altered.

Matters came to a head in January 1912 when, during a full-power trial in the battle-cruiser *Lion* (the first of the super-dreadnoughts) attended by Creagh-Osborne, the temperature of the funnel was 797°F whilst that of the funnel gasses was measured at 1032°F. A subsequent swing disclosed that her manoeuvring compass had acquired a coefficient B of -20°,[33] but in this ship the problem was far more serious. Her fighting top had been sited abaft the forward funnel, where it received the full force of the hot funnel gases, and her whole upper works had to be extensively rebuilt.

By 1913 the number of steering positions, and so the number of magnetic compasses required, had been considerably reduced from the eight or more provided at the turn of the century. The bridge had survived, and with it forebridge steering; there were also the Standard and manoeuvring compasses; there was a compass in the lower steering position, sometimes two, one of which could be projected to the upper conning tower and there was an emergency compass at the steering engine. Before long, however, the forebridge-steering position was done away with and even the Standard

Compass itself came under attack. In February 1914 the new super-intendent, Captain Creagh-Osborne, summed up the situation in a letter to the captains of the *King George V* class battleships as follows:

> I am writing to . . . the Captains of the *King George V* Class to prepare you for some queries regarding the suitability of the present Manoeuvring Compass for use as a Standard compass; it is the beginning of the third round with D.N.C.; the first ended by some hundreds of pounds being spent on *Agamemnon* and *Lord Nelson*, the second very many thousands of pounds in *Lion*, *Princess Royal* and other ships, and now they are at it again trying to cut down the 'safe distances' of the Compass from Funnel and Conning Tower, laid down as a result of the *Lion* fiasco.

Nevertheless, within a few years this change too had been accepted in many of the capital ships and cruisers. By then, however, the gyro-compass was playing an increasingly important role.

Gyro-compasses

When summarizing the development of the gyro-compass in 1919, Captain Creagh-Osborne wrote:

> The large variations in the magnetic character of Warships, especially after gunnery practice or after continuing for long periods on one course, made the construction of trustworthy deviation-tables for the magnetic compass a matter of great difficulty. The advent of the submarine, in which the interior of the hull is entirely shielded from the earth's magnetic field and in which there are very large disturbing forces due to the close proximity of powerful electrical machinery, rendered the need for some form of non-magnetic compass still more insistent.[34]

By far the most important event in the compass field during the early part of the century was therefore the invention of the gyro-compass. The possibility had been foreseen by Foucault in 1852, following his success in using a gyroscope to demonstrate the rotation of the earth, but although a number of inventions appeared over the next fifty years, none got beyond the laboratory stage. In

1884 Sir William Thomson described experiments he had conducted with a gyrostatic compass, but he did not pursue the matter.[35]

The first success went to Dr Herman Anschütz-Kaempfe, whose work began in 1901 with his interest in polar exploration. He believed that it might be possible for a submarine to penetrate to the North Pole under the ice, taking its heading from a directional gyroscope, and his early experiments, which included a trial in the German cruiser *Undine* in 1904, were directed towards this end. On this trial it was noted that while the instrument appeared to withstand the concussion of gunfire, it was seriously deflected by the rolling or pitching of the vessel. Early in 1905 the British Naval Attaché in Berlin informed the Admiralty about the new instrument and in September it was demonstrated to foreign representatives at Kiel, Commander Chetwynd attending on behalf of the Royal Navy. His report on this visit contains a very explicit description of the equipment which is reproduced as appendix 7. The price was £600. The demonstration, however, was not a success and in his report Chetwynd stated: 'I am of the opinion that the instrument is too delicate in construction to be sufficiently reliable for practical purposes.'[36]

By this time, however, Dr Anschütz-Kaempfe had appreciated the wider implications of his invention for navigation and had come to the conclusion that it might be possible to make his instrument north-seeking. He founded the firm of Anschütz & Co. in Kiel, and in March 1908 his first true gyro-compass was tried in the battleship *Deutschland*.

In January 1909 a translation of an article on the Anschütz gyro-compass, forwarded by the British Naval Attaché, excited considerable interest in the Admiralty, although both the Hydrographer and the Director of Naval Ordnance agreed that it was unlikely ever to supersede the magnetic compass. Nevertheless an equipment was purchased and a trial arranged in the cruiser *Grafton*, tender to the Gunnery School. The following extract from the report by Commander Creagh-Osborne, the Assistant Superintendent, bears out the prevailing view:

> From the results of these trials, which it must be noted took place under the most favourable circumstances for the gyro-compass, i.e. a smooth sea and absolutely no motion on the ship; it may be said that the gyro-compass fulfilled the claim of the inventors

in pointing True North within a possible error of 1°, but on the other hand the magnetic compasses came out of the trial almost equally well and there would appear to be no compensating advantage for the large expenditure which would be involved by installing these insruments, when looked at from a purely navigational point of view. If after further trials on board the Grafton at sea it appears to work satisfactorily under service conditions, it appears to be for consideration whether these instruments should be adopted for Steering Positions or other purposes at in between decks positions.[37]

The compass in *Grafton* had no method of transmission and had therefore been fitted on the starboard side of the forebridge for ease of comparison with the magnetic. However, a compass capable of driving repeaters was already undergoing trials in the battleship *Schleswig-Holstein*, and in March 1910, at the invitation of Anschütz-Kaempfe, Chetwynd again visited Kiel accompanied by representatives of the Superintending Electrical Engineer and of the firm of Elliott Bros, who held the agency for Anschütz in England.[38] Two more gyro-compasses, each with three repeaters, were purchased for trial and fitted in the battleship *Prince of Wales*, flagship of Vice-Admiral Sir John Jellicoe, commanding the Atlantic Fleet, and in the *Neptune*. Although these early compasses suffered severely from what became known as 'inter-cardinal rolling error', their performance appears to have been very successful and encouraged the Admiralty to order four more.

In 1906 Anschütz-Kaempfe had been joined in the firm by his cousin, Max Schuler, and it was he who five years later discovered that the period of the controlled precessional oscillation about the meridian was a significant factor in the directing property of a gyro-compass. If the precessional period of oscillation is made 84 minutes the acceleration errors largely vanish and a compass with this period will, on alteration of course, precess from the old settling point to the new during the period of the alteration. This became known as 'Schuler tuning'. When, in the following year Anschütz-Kaempfe redesigned his compass to incorporate three gyroscopes[39] it was given this period. The new compass also incorporated a much improved method of damping which greatly reduced the intercardinal rolling error and was able to drive repeaters. Subsequent Admiralty orders were for this type of compass, which became known as the 'Anschütz 1912 model'.

Meanwhile, in February 1911, as a result of experience in the *Prince of Wales* and *Neptune*, the Superintendent of Compasses prepared a set of guidelines for the future fitting of gyro-compasses in the Fleet (the first *Installation Specification*). He recommended that when possible the master compass should be placed in the lower conning position so that it could be used as a steering compass 'without the intervention of a receiver'; he covered such aspects as communications for 'lining-up' and the siting of ancillary equipment (motor generator and switchboard), and he recommended the positions for the three receivers, which included the 'Fore-bridge Steering position' and the 'Plotting Station or other position to meet *gunnery* requirements'.[40] It was not long before the number of repeaters had to be greatly increased to meet the needs of weapon systems. By 1914 the battlecruiser *Tiger* had eight, including the gunnery transmitting station, (TS) the Dreyer table, the range-finder and the torpedo control tower.[41]

The next three compasses were fitted in the battleships *King Edward VII* and *Hercules* and in the battle-cruiser *Indomitable*, while the 1911 – 12 naval estimates included eight more at a cost of £1,975 each[42] for the 'We want eight' programme. When received, one of the first of these compasses was diverted for trials in the submarine *E1*,[43] the first of a class of larger submarine (660 tons surfaced) some of which carried a 4 inch gun.

Despite the improvements introduced by Anschütz there was still a tendency for the compass to wander ($5°$ to $10°$) in anything except smooth water and it could not yet be fully relied upon. However, the wander was slow and, provided frequent comparison was made with the Standard Compass, the advantages of being able to steer an accurate course and to determine precise changes of bearing for plotting purposes were worth having.[44]

It was in June 1911 that Elmer Sperry from the United States entered the European arena. Although he had patented a gyroscopic ships's stabilizer in 1908 and had filed a US patent for a gyro-compass in September 1909, he had not proceeded far with its development when, in June of the following year, he learnt that the US Navy were about to place a substantial order with the firm of

Anschütz. Successful trials with the German compass had been completed early in 1910 and the firm of E. S. Ritchie, (which had designed the improved liquid magnetic compass adopted by the US Navy in 1863 (see p. 74), held the agency and was pressing for a contract. Elmer Sperry immediately stepped up his development and wrote to the US naval authorities that he had 'one of these compasses nearly completed'. He hoped that his compass would make it unnecessary for the US Navy 'to go to Germany'.[45] The contract with Anschütz was evidently held up and in January 1911 Sperry was able to inform the Bureau of Navigation that his compass was ready for factory inspection. Sea trials followed almost at once and during the early summer a compass was fitted in USS *Delaware*, the first American dreadnought and the ship chosen to attend the Naval Review to honour the coronation of King George V.

Elmer Sperry himself came to England in June 1911 and, having met Mr S. G. Brown (who was later to become one of his major rivals), asked him to arrange an interview with the Hydrographer. It is unlikely that the Superintendent was aware of the Sperry gyro-compass at the time and this interview was at first rather curtly refused, the Hydrographer having been given no details of the Sperry invention.[46] It seems likely, however, that it took place later, as by the summer of 1913 the Sperry Company had opened an office in London to handle their European marketing. It is also probable that liaison with the Compass Department became close, as the address of the Sperry Company was 57 Victoria Street, only five doors away from the building to which the Compass Department had moved early in 1912, when they ceased to belong to the Hydrographic Office. The Sperry Gyroscope Company was formed in 1914 and in due course moved to larger premises at 15 Victoria Street. Towards the end of the war a factory was opened at Shepherd's Bush.

The first demonstration Sperry compass to be brought to England was assembled and adjusted at the works of Messrs. S. G. Brown at Acton, who had not at that time entered the compass field themselves. Comprehensive comparative trials between this compass and the Anschütz were conducted at the Royal Naval College at Greenwich during the autumn of 1913, under the superintendance of Professor James Henderson,[47] using a rolling table loaned by the Sperry Company, and these were followed by sea trials of the Sperry compass in the battleship *St Vincent* and in an E-class submarine.

As a result four more Sperry gyro-compasses were ordered at once and five more early in the following year. Meanwhile it was decided to mark time with the Anschütz until further trials had been made under operational conditions.

Captain Creagh-Osborne reports in his history: 'As a result of these trials it was proved that although the Sperry undoubtedly had 'Intercardinal Rolling Error', the errors observed were no greater than in the Anschütz, the design was superior from an engineering point of view and practically a complete set of spares was provided at a lower cost than the Anschütz'.[48] The fact that the heavy rotor of the Sperry compasses enabled it to maintain its heading for up to one and a half hours in the event of loss of electical power, was an added advantage. The Sperry Company at once set to work to overcome the rolling error and shortly afterwards, following advice and suggestions received from Professor Henderson, it introduced the 'floating ballistic', a kind of gyro-pendulum attached to the casing of the main gyro-wheel, which considerably improved matters.[49]

By the beginning of 1914 Anschütz compasses had been ordered for a total of 21 battleships and 2 submarines, 8 of the former having a duplex equipment.[50] Thereafter no further orders were placed, although Elliott's continued to install these compasses well into the war. The Admiralty policy was now to fit Sperry gyro-compasses as fast as possible in all battleships, battle cruisers and submarines, with the exception of a handful of older vessels, priority being given to ships in which the bridge had had to be altered following the hot-funnel problem, leaving the compass in the lower steering position as the only one available for steering. The programme had not progressed far by the time hostilities commenced and the Compass Department thus entered the war with a large new commitment on its hands.

Aircraft

Another problem which pressed for the attention of the Compass Department in the years immediately preceding World War I was the provision of an adequate compass for aircraft. Early aeroplanes, if they carried a compass at all, tended to use any small instrument which might be available. These had, of course, been designed for other purposes, they probably had no antivibration arrangements and they were generally mounted in gimbals. They were thus quite unsuitable for use in the air.

In August 1909, on hearing of these problems, Commander Creagh-Osborne wrote to Colonel Cody, one of the country's leading aviators, as follows:

> I was much interested to see that you were finding the necessity of using a compass for aeroplane work and as Comte de Lambert had also found that necessity and asked if we could assist him, I thought that if you think it worth while I could easily run over from my house at Woking on a Saturday afternoon or Sunday and I might possibly be able to help you to steer a straight course and also at the same time get some experience of the conditions, which would be of use in the future aerial Navy.
>
> We have lately introduced into the Navy a new type of liquid compass as a change became absolutely necessary on account of the excessive vibration of some modern ships. The War Office are also experimenting with liquid compasses of this type and these latter I should say would be the most suitable for your work being much smaller. For long 'flys' probably you would find it an advantage to have the compass adjusted as closely as possible and I have no doubt this could be managed as probably the magnetic conditions are no worse than one finds in a Submarine Boat for example.
>
> Please excuse me for troubling you, but if my experience in ship work will be of any assistance please let me know.[51]

From this helpful but apparently informal approach a whole new field of activity was to open up for the Compass Department.

Colonel Cody evidently responded favourably for it was in his plane, on 27 September 1909, just two months after Louis Blériot's historic 37 minute hop across the Channel, that Commander Creagh-Osborne became the first naval officer ever to fly. Finding that the compass simply spun round the moment the engine was started he rightly deduced that the trouble was vibration and initially effected a cure by simply packing a small liquid compass in a box filled with cotton waste. It is reported that before trying the compass in an aircraft he had first tested it out on the floorboard of a one-cylinder car. In the air it was very successful.

From then on Creagh-Osborne devoted much of his time to the problems of aircraft compasses and air navigation. In May 1910 he was invited by the secretary of the Royal Aero Club to visit Brooklands aerodrome, not far from his home at Woking, to study matters at first hand. In a letter to Mr F. W. Clarke, the managing director of Messrs Kelvin & White, he described this visit as follows:

> I had a most interesting afternoon and as there are already 20 machines there and more due, I had a very good opportunity of inspecting the various types. There seemed to be a general consensus of opinion among those who had got beyond the 'hopping' stage that they wanted a compass but they seemed to look on it as pretty hopeless on account of vibration and the vicinity of the magneto.[52]

Creagh-Osborne clearly thought otherwise. His letter went on to talk about the compasses themselves, the method of mounting them in different types of aircraft (tri-planes, bi-planes, etc.) and of lighting and correcting them. He encouraged Messrs Kelvin & White to be first in the field and offered to try out different fitting arrangements for them. Already he was considering his 'Rules for placing a compass in an aeroplane' (reproduced as appendix 8),[53] and before long he also sent the Royal Aero Club his proposals for laying out the first aircraft swinging base at Brooklands.

Meanwhile, in 1911 Kelvin & White began marketing an aircraft compass designed along the lines suggested by Creagh-Osborne, with the bowl held in a container lined with horsehair and four trunnions fitting into rubber-lined sockets to prevent rotation. This compass had a Chetwynd-type reduced-diameter card with a band running across the float from north to south, painted red and blue, a method of defining north and south which found favour with pilots for some years. Later the markings of the northern half of the card were coloured red and the southern half blue. Compasses by other manufacturers soon followed, including one by Mr E. H. Clift which had a transparent bottom to enable the pilot to look through the compass to the ground below and so estimate drift. Creagh-Osborne was able to make a number of further flights to try out these designs and to study the vibration problem, but for some time there were no regulations governing what instruments should be fitted or for checking their suitability.

In November 1912 the Superintendent of Compasses wrote to the Admiralty as follows:

> At present there is no Standard Pattern of Compass for use in Aeroplanes, various types being in use in the machines of the Naval and Military Flying Wings. They are obtained in a rather haphazard way and in some cases not even subjected to the most elementary tests of efficiency.
>
> In view of the large increase in the number of aircraft requiring these instruments, it is considered advisable to introduce some method into their purchase and testing.[54]

As a result of this submission a conference was held on 5 December 1912, attended by representatives of the leading naval and military aviation interests, at which it was agreed that the purchase, supply and testing of instruments for the Naval Wing should be placed on the same footing as that of compasses for the Fleet. At the same time the aim was to arrive at a standard pattern compass for all service aircraft and a specification was prepared which covered the essential features required – size, weight, presentation, mounting, lighting, and so on. Manufacturers on the Admiralty list were invited to submit samples,[55] and from these evolved the first standardized aircraft compass, the Pattern 200, based largely on the latest Kelvin model. It was a simple, robust instrument with a large steering prism and a cross-wire, capable of being turned in azimuth, for taking rough bearings. A small carrier could be attached for the corrector magnets. This compass proved very successful and was quite adequate for the majority of the early, comparatively slow types of aircraft. The story of subsequent developments to meet the needs of more powerful machines and wartime flying operations will be told in the chapter which follows.

Meanwhile, as early as 1910 the specific needs of airships and balloons had also been studied by the Compass Department and in particular their requirement to be able to fix accurately from terrestrial objects. The compasses provided tended to follow the pattern of marine instruments, even retaining their gimbals, but without their large binnacles. Airships were provided with separate standard and steering compasses and there is also evidence of an ingenious combined bearing-plate and range-finder which incorporated an arrangement for measuring the angle of depression of an object.[56]

Creagh-Osborne was soon established as the leading authority on aircraft-compass design in the country and his opinion was widely sought. During 1910 and 1911 he contributed a number of articles to the two leading aviation journals of the day, *Aero* and *Flight*, in which he dealt at length with many aspects of air navigation, always stressing the need for selecting a suitable position for the compass, following his rules. He also covered the problems of course and drift determination which, he maintained, came naturally to a sailor.[57] In April 1911 he was elected to the Technical Committee of the Royal Aero Club and later that year drafted the navigation requirements for the award of the Club's certificates for 'Pilot' and 'Master Aviator'.

One further incident which occurred during the pre-War phase of aircraft development deserves special mention. Early in 1914 plans were afoot for the first trans-Atlantic flight using a large, twin-engined flying-boat named *America*, especially designed for the project by Glenn Curtiss at Hammondsport, New York. The pilot was to be Lieutenant J. C. Porte,[58] who had earlier been invalided from the Royal Navy, and the attempt excited considerable interest on both sides of the Atlantic.

Porte discussed the matter of a suitable compass with Creagh-Osborne and seems also to have consulted him on all aspects of the navigation, route-planning, meteorology and safety arrangements, receiving a wealth of help and advice. A special compass was designed, based on Pattern 200, but with a 6 inch card and a very large magnifying mirror to simplify steering. It was later fitted with small spheres from a range-finder compass. Creagh-Osborne went to America in June 1914 to fit and adjust it and actually flew on the maiden flight from Lake Keuka. In the event, owing to the outbreak of war, the attempted crossing never took place and in the autumn of 1914 the same aircraft made its first flight from the Royal Naval Air Service base at Felixtowe in Suffolk, having been brought over in the hold of a liner.[59] Creagh-Osborne was again on board. Later, improved versions of the compass were used extensively in flying-boats and airships throughout the war.

Although the Admiralty had made it clear that Creagh-Osborne's trip to America was entirely private and that they were not involved in the attempt, he was nevertheless able to provide them on return with a full report on his visits to the Curtiss aircraft works, the Washington and Brooklyn navy yards and the Sperry Gyro Company's factory.[60] He was very impressed with the gyro test facilities at Brooklyn and determined that the Royal Navy should do its own testing, pointing out that 'At present accuracy tests of the gyro-compass are carried out at the makers and cannot be properly supervised.' Although duplex Sperry gyro-compass systems were then being fitted in all battleships, the Americans still considered the Standard Magnetic Compass essential despite the serious difficulties in providing it with a satisfactory position. On the compasses themselves he reported, 'The efficiency, design and general finish of the Magnetic Compass . . . was very poor . . . and they bear no comparison with the instruments furnished to HM Ships.' In this field it appeared that the Royal Navy had at last regained the lead it had surrendered in 1863.

Compass adjustment

Shortly after taking up his duties in 1904, Chetwynd had suggested to the Admiralty that as navigation officers were all now instructed in compass adjustment there was no longer a need for special swinging officers to be appointed to the home ports. Ships without qualified Navigating Officers could apply to the Commander-in-Chief for assistance.[61] Although this plan was approved, some organization for swinging ships seems to have been maintained in all ports as in 1908 local swinging officers were instructed to forward annual returns of ships swung to the Compass Department.

It seems, however, that different arrangements existed at each port. At Devonport, where responsibility rested with the Captain of the Dockyard, swinging was undertaken by the King's Harbour Master at Plymouth, and there were few problems. At Portsmouth and Sheerness, where the officers in charge of the chart depot were frequently employed for swinging, to the serious detriment of their proper function, things were much less satisfactory. The load was greatest at Portsmouth, where two magnetic huts were available, and the Captain of the Dockyard protested bitterly when the Commander-in-Chief suggested he should take the job over. He did, however, eventually agree to provide experienced staff to man the huts when required. At Sheerness the Commander of the Dockyard agreed in 1911 to undertake the task as an experiment provided he could borrow the senior assistant from the chart depot when necessary. To the Hydrographer's dismay this appeared to happen all too frequently, at the very time that he was giving up his responsibility for the Compass Department. The assistant in question, who appeared to enjoy these duties better than chart-correcting, was eventually transferred to the Commander of the Dockyard's staff as a compass assistant.[62]

At all ports, the task of keeping the Reserve Fleet (later renamed the Third Fleet) ready for immediate commissioning required constant attention. Compasses were earmarked and kept available in the dockyards and ships were periodically swung. Nevertheless, it was considered essential that their deviation tables should be checked before going to sea and this presented a particular problem at Sheerness where, because of strong tidal streams, conditions for swinging were always difficult. With the agreement of Trinity House the Superintendent arranged that a well-adjusted compass should be maintained on the Nore Light Vessel so that ships could swing by 'reciprocal bearings' at any time and would not be restricted to the limited periods of slack water in the River Medway. The facility would be available for individual ships whenever required and would be particularly useful when a large number of vessels needed to prepare for sea at the same time, as on mobilization. Their Lordships approved the idea some nine months before the outbreak of war and a retired officer was given an emergency appointment to the Nore Light Vessel for the purpose.[63] The scheme remained in use until two magnetic huts were established, one on either shore of the Thames estuary, early in 1915.

Transfer to the Controller's Department

In 1910 the Compass Department again found itself under severe pressure with 44 new vessels to be inspected and swung besides a further 19 which were completing major refits. In addition, the *Deviation Manual* and the variation charts were due for revision. Lieutenant Maxwell Anderson from the staff of the Navigation School was seconded to the department for six months, but the pressure remained and when a further addition was requested, the Civil Establishment Committee decided to look at the whole question of staff for the Hydrographic Department. Their report, dated 22 March 1911, had far-reaching consequences.

On the question of terrestrial magnetism, which had been the stumbling block in 1905, they concluded that the Astronomer Royal, Sir Frank Dyson, was in a better position than anyone in the Admiralty to co-ordinate this work. Because of his other magnetic responsibilities, he was prepared to accept the task without increase in staff. Observations from HM ships would, however, still need to be checked by the Compass Department, which would know the magnetic peculiarities of individual ships. The report recalled that but for the work on terrestrial magnetism the Adair committee would have reported in favour of the transfer of 'Compasses' to the Controller's Department in 1905, and it recommended that, provided the new proposals were acceptable, this transfer should now take place. Further, having looked at the load on the compass branch they were satisfied that so long as the present rate of shipbuilding continued, there was sufficient work to occupy three officers for the next three years.

The Admiralty approved these proposals on 1 June 1911. As, however, there was likely to be some delay in obtaining Treasury agreement, they arranged for the temporary appointment of Lieutenant M. C. Allenby, the officer who had relieved Creagh-Osborne as nagivating officer of the battleship *Mars* in May 1904. In the event he remained with the department until the outbreak of war.

To support the negotiations with the Treasury, Chetwynd provided information to show that the number of new ships visited had more than doubled since 1906, when Commander Betty had been withdrawn, and was expected to increase by a further 50 per cent in the coming year. In addition the trial and introduction of new-pattern magnetic compasses, gyro-compasses, range-finder compasses, and so on, had involved considerable extra work while the number of electrical instruments to be tested for their safe distance was growing all the time. Their Lordships concluded their submission to the Treasury by saying, 'My Lords are convinced that, not withstanding the relief afforded by the transfer of the magnetic work to the Royal Observatory, the extra assistance asked for will undoubtedly be required for a period of at least three years.'[64]

News of the Treasury's agreement was received on 6 October 1911 and three weeks later the Admiralty announced their approval for the transfer of terrestrial magnetism to the Astronomer Royal.[65] By the middle of November the Hydrographer was able to report that this was complete,[66] except for the 1912 variation chart, which was already well advanced, and on 23 November Board approval was given to the transfer of the compass branch to the Controller.[67] It was a very logical arrangement which had been a long time a-coming.

The association with the Hydrographic Office, which had lasted since Captain Johnson was appointed as the first Superintendent of the Compass Department on 14 March 1842, had been long, friendly and mutually beneficial, and the Hydrographer seemed reluctant that it should end. He was still responsible to the Board for all navigational matters (the appointment of a separate Director of Navigation did not occur until 1913), and therefore asked that all papers connected with compasses should continue to be referred to his department. However, as the Superintendent of Compasses pointed out, this would defeat much of the object of the transfer and the Hydrographer had finally to be content with seeing papers only 'after action'.[68] Early in 1912 the Compass Department moved from the Admiralty offices at 31 Abingdon Street to new premises on the second floor of 47 Victoria Street, where it remained until the final move to Ditton Park, Slough, in March 1917.

Promotion and retirement of Captain Chetwynd

We have seen how a change in the regulations in 1900 had denied Commander Chetwynd the chance of further promotion on the active list. He had, however, placed his mark indelibly on the fortunes of the Compass Department, not only with his patent liquid compass which had at last made the magnetic compass a thoroughly reliable instrument, but also by the competent way with which he had dealt with the host of new problems which had arisen as a result of 'the general advance in science and magnetism' and in the construction of modern warships. In November 1910, the Hydrographer wrote to the Board, underlining these outstanding contributions and pointing out that 'From the Service point of view it would be very desirable that the Superintendent of Compasses should hold the rank of Captain.' He submitted that Their Lordships' appreciation of these most valuable services should take the form of promoting him to Captain on the retired list.[69] Under an Order in Council of 1902, a retired officer who was voluntarily re-employed might receive promotion at any time and Chetwynd was accordingly promoted on 7 December 1910.

Two years later he relinquished his post at the early age of 56, to become the managing director of Messrs Dent & Co. and Johnson Ltd, compass-makers of London.[70] He was succeeded as Superintendent by his Assistant, Commander Creagh-Osborne, who was promoted to Captain on the retired list on 15 December 1912, and it was he who was to guide the department through the tumultuous years ahead.

NOTES

CHAPTER 7

[1] Having already served the statutory time at sea, Henderson had been selected for promotion to staff captain in a vacancy, on 6 October 1898, the number of staff captains being limited to fifteen by Treasury order.

[2] Hydrographer's Minute Book, No. 54, p. 97.

[3] Ibid., No. 54, p. 148; No. 63, p. 113.

[4] They were made by Messrs Kelvin & James White, the firm becoming Kelvin Bottomley & Bird in 1913.

[5] A description of the working of the principle projector binnacles is contained in the 'R & D Report of the Compass Department' for 1947.

[6] Hydrographer's Minute Book, No. 61, p. 55.

[7] Admiralty Circular Letter, N17187 (1903).

[8] Hydrographer's Miscellaneous File, No. 52 ('Reports on the Hydrographic Office').

[9] Hydrographer's Minute Book, No. 73, p. 152.

[10] The Thomson compass became the Kelvin in 1892, when Sir William Thomson was raised to the peerage.

[11] Hydrographer's Minute Book, No. 59, p. 89.

[12] Ibid., No. 60, p. 298.

[13] Ibid., No. 65, p. 90.

[14] Ibid., No. 71, p. 128.

[15] Ibid., No. 69, p. 7.

[16] Ibid., No. 72, p. 198.

[17] Ibid., No. 69, pp. 86, 168.

[18] Ibid., No. 70, p. 103; No. 72, p. 198.

[19] Ibid., No. 70, p. 295; No. 73, p. 140.

[20] Ibid., No. 76, p. 11.

[21] Ibid., No. 73, p. 148.

[22] Ibid., No. 76, p. 13.

23 Ibid., No. 91, p. 131; (Admiralty Letter, CP 17231, 3 August 1910).

24 Hydrographer's Minute Book, No. 79, pp. 152, 195.

25 Ibid., No. 81, p. 114.

26 The navigating officer of the battle cruiser *Princess Royal*, in a private letter to Commander Creagh-Osborne, reported: 'the heat of the lamp has literally boiled the compass card to such an extent that the decorations in the centre of the card have all been boiled off . . . the heat on the port sphere is so great . . . that you cannot bear your hand on it' (National Maritime Museum, Magnetic Compass Collection, Envelope N 18.). The matter was much improved when metal-filament lamps replaced carbon filaments).

27 Hydrographer's Minute Book, No. 79, p. 246.

28 Ibid., No. 89, pp. 21, 89, 121, 240.

29 Ibid., No. 70, p. 219.

30 Ibid., No. 61, p. 56.

31 Ibid., No. 90, p. 192.

32 Ibid., No. 76, p. 256.

33 Detailed results of these trials are contained in the National Maritime Museum, Magnetic Compass Collection, Envelope N18.

34 *Admiralty Technical History*, Vol. 3, Part 20 (October 1919), p.3.

35 T. P. Hughes in his biography *Elmer Sperry, Inventor and Engineer*, says on p. 133 that Sir William Thomson's invention had been tested by the Royal Navy. However, Sir William's paper to the British Association does not mention this (see p. 155) and no trial details are known.

36 Hydrographer's Minute Book, No. 68, p. 146.

37 Ibid., No. 83, p. 155.

38 Ibid., No. 86, p. 42.

39 The three gyroscopes (1 meridian and 2 control) were set at an angle of 60° to one another in a frame which was supported by a sphere floating in mercury.

40 Hydrographer's Minute Book, No. 91, p. 9.

41 The gyro fitting cards, completed by the representatives of Elliott Bros, gave details of each Anchütz installation. They are still held at the Admiralty Compass Observatory.

42 Hydrographer's Minute Book, No. 91, p. 2.

43 By a strange quirk of history the first American submarine to be fitted with a Sperry gyro-compass was US submarine E-1.

44 Hydrographer's Minute Book, No. 92, p. 169.

45 Thomas Parke Hughes, *Elmer Sperry, Inventor and Engineer*, John Hopkins Press, London, 1971, p. 136.

46 Hydrographer's Minute Book, No. 92, p. 85.

47 Professor Henderson's report, together with other papers concerning the trials, are held in the National Maritime Museum Compass Collection, Envelope N31.

[48] *Admiralty Technical History*, Vol. 3, Part 20 (October 1919), p.4.

[49] A description of the floating ballistic is contained in A. L. Rawlings, *The Theory of the Gyroscopic Compass*, London, 1929, p.122.

[50] A duplex equipent is one in which two compasses feed a single repeater panel (sometimes described as a spare-wheel system). It differs from a duplicate equipment which was introduced during World War I, in which each compass is self-contained, with its own separate repeater panel. Cables from each repeater panel are run to a changeover switch at each outlying repeater.

[51] Letter in National Maritime Museum, Magnetic Compass Collection, to Colonel Cody, August 1909, Envelope N51.

[52] Letter to Messrs Kelvin & White, 27 May 1910, ibid.

[53] Letter to Mr Perrin, secretary to the Royal Aero Club, 16 November 1911, ibid.

[54] Comment on Admiralty paper S 2922/12 (22 November 1912), National Maritime Museum, Magnetic Compass Collection, Item R9.

[55] Admiralty letter CP NS602/2295, 31 January 1913, National Maritime Museum, Magnetic Compass Collection, Envelope N51.

[56] Letter from Kelvin & White, 30 September 1910, ibid.

[57] In April 1911 he conducted trials with Messrs Brocks of Sutton into ways of determining the speed and direction of the wind. Rockets fired to 3000 feet released strings of flags on a parachute which were tracked by theodolite (ibid., letter to Messrs Kelvin & White, 28 April 1911).

[58] Later Colonel J. C. Porte CMG. See Air Marshall Sir Edwar Chilton, 'John Cyril Porte', *Aerospace*, February 1980, pp. 14–21.

[59] The first successful crossing was eventually made in May 1919 by a later Curtiss flying-boat, piloted by Lieutenant Commander A. C. Read USN, following the route planned by Creagh-Osborne, via the Azores and Vigo, finally landing at Plymouth (commemorated by a tablet on the Barbican, next to the Mayflower Steps). This was less than a month ahead of the first direct flight by Alcock and Whitton-Brown.

[60] Reports by Superintendent of Compasses, July 1914, National Maritime Museum, Magnetic Compass Collection, Envelope N51.

[61] Hydrographer's Minute Book, No. 65, p. 235.

[62] Ibid., Files 191, 620 (1914).

[63] ADM 235 'Correspondence Register, 1912–14' (Letter S 23663/13).

[64] Admiralty letter, CE 11758/1911.

[65] Admiralty acquaint, CE 15190/1911.

[66] The transfer included responsibility for a long list of specialized instruments (dip circles, magnetometers, shore and sledge compasses, and so on) many of which were at that time on loan to various expeditions, including Captain Scott's ill-fated Antarctic expedition of 1910.

[67] Hydrographer's Minute Book, No. 93, p. 199.

68 Ibid., No. 93, p. 284.

69 Ibid., No. 89, p. 144.

70 In 1914 Captain Chetwynd underwent an operation in London, and on 14 April he died.

The war years, expansion and a new home, 1914-18

8

'We should provide in peace what we need in war' (Publius Syrus, c. 42 BC)

'We must not forget at this moment how much we owe to those who have gone before us and have created the Fleet as it now is; those who worked so arduously and so long, to be ready for such a moment as has now been forced upon us' (Vice-Admiral Sir David Beatty's message to the 1st Battlecruiser Squadron, 4 August 1914)

In 1911 worsening relations with Germany and concern for the soundness of Britain's war planning combined to bring a new team to the Admiralty. Winston Churchill succeeded McKenna as First Lord, while the First Sea Lord, Admiral Sir Arthur Wilson VC gave way to Admiral Sir Francis Bridgeman. Waiting in the wings, as Second Sea Lord and heir-apparent, was Prince Louis of Battenburg. One of the first acts of the new administration was to set up a Naval War Staff to review the Admiralty's plans which had suddenly been found to be almost non-existent. It also appeared that the super-dreadnoughts had been overtaken, as both America and Japan now had larger battleships, mounting 14 inch guns.

A number of immediate actions followed. The battle-cruiser *Tiger*, which was about to be laid down under the 1911 programme, was radically redesigned and emerged just in time for the outbreak of hostilities as the largest and fastest warship afloat, while the five ships of the new *Queen Elizabeth* class, due to be started under the 1912 programme, were given 15 inch guns, heavier armour, and a speed of 25 knots, almost rivalling that of the battle-cruisers. To strengthen home defence the main fleets were reorganized and now included the Third Fleet, consisting mainly of older warships which, although in reserve, were kept ready for instant manning on mobilization.

Early in 1914 the political situation which had improved during the previous year, began to deteriorate rapidly. The Admiralty decided to cancel the annual Fleet manoeuvres and instead to exercise a full mobilization of all reservists for a week's training. On 15 July, amid rising tension, the Third Fleet threw off its mothballs and only three days later was assembled at Spithead for a review by the King. The ships were then to sail for a brief exercise before dispersing to their home ports for a demobilization planned for 23 July. On that very day, however, Austria delivered its ultimatum to Serbia and war became almost inevitable. Prince Louis of Battenburg, who had been appointed First Sea Lord in 1913, cancelled the order for demolibization and within a few days all fleets sailed for their war stations. By 3 August the Navy was ready for its first major encounter for ninety-nine years.

Since the end of 1912, Captain Creagh-Osborne and his Assistant Superintendent, Commander S. B. Norfolk, had done much to prepare the department for war. The temporary improvement in relations with Germany during 1912–13 had allowed the supply of Anschütz gyro-compasses to be maintained for as long as it was needed, while the fortunate decision taken in December 1913 in favour of the Sperry compass had ensured that urgently needed supplies for modernizing the fleet would continue unbroken. On the magnetic front, most major problems appeared to have been solved; the Chetwynd liquid compass was well established, the compass outfits of capital ships and cruisers had been greatly streamlined and recent improvements in the method of projecting the image of the lower steering compass up to the conning tower had at last led to a highly satisfactory arrangement.

In 1913 a new set of 'Rules to be attended to in the arrangement of structure and fittings in the vicinity of compasses'[1] was issued which for the first time stated clearly that the Standard Compass should be at the position from which the vessel is usually navigated; also that it should be at least 20 feet from large masses of iron (conning towers or turrets) and 32 feet from the nearest 'great funnel', with no iron or steel of any kind within 10 feet, the figure still in use today. The need to determine the safe distance of the many electrical instruments coming into service had led to the establishment of a special test facility in Portsmouth Dockyard where compass staff could conduct the necessary trials, and the 1914 edition of the 'Rules' for the first time included a list of the instruments tested, with their minimum permitted distance from the standard and lower conning tower compasses.[2]

Three hundred gyro-compasses

At the outbreak of hostilities Messrs Elliott Bros had already installed or were in the process of fitting some thirty Anschütz compasses, a proportion of which had had to be converted from the original design to the 1912 model. The Sperry score at the time was roughly a dozen, all of which had been fitted by representatives of the firm. However, although the declared Admiralty policy was to install Sperry gyro-compasses as rapidly as possible in all modern capital ships and large submarines, orders for the new compasses appear to have taken several months to get through the system and it was not until 11 December that Reginald Gillmor,[3] who was in charge of the Sperry London Office, was able to wire Elmer Sperry personally saying, 'I wish I could be in New York for just one day to shake you by the hand and celebrate the finest little victory known to the history of the Sperry Gyroscope Company.'[4] The Admiralty had just placed an order for 55 submarine and 10 battleship compasses. It was to be the first of many substantial orders as the war in Europe created an ever widening demand. In parallel with the British order had gone one for 10 battleship and 1 submarine compass for Russia and before long they were being fitted by virtually every maritime nation except Germany.

The outbreak of war presented the Compass Department with one particularly serious problem. On mobilization the support for magnetic compasses in the Navy was well catered for by the numerous retired navigating officers who were available to take up posts as swinging officers at the different ports around the country. Although they worked under local senior naval officers, these men were regarded as representatives of the Compass Department, and the Superintendent had a say in both their appointments and their employment. Many of these posts were later taken over by RNR and RNVR officers. There was, however, no equivalent organization to support the gyro-compasses of the fleet. Whilst it was possible, in the case of the Anschütz, to call on Messrs Elliott to provide after-sales service, the case was entirely different with the Sperry. At the beginning of the war most of Sperry's civilian employees in the country were American citizens, and the United States was neutral. While it might be in order for them to install equipment in shipyards they could hardly be used in support of an active fleet. The Compass Department had therefore to take urgent steps to recruit and train its own specialists. Men with electrical experience were rapidly signed on as RNVR officers and were soon travelling all over the country from the now very elastic office in Victoria Street. Later in the war Compass Department offices, dealing with both magnetic and gyro activities, were established in Glasgow and Liverpool and it was not long before the new recruits were handling the installation and maintenance problems of Anschütz as well as Sperry compasses. Several of them remained with the department as civilians after the war – two of them, J. C. Hereford and J. H. Cruickshank, until after World War II.

Early in 1915 the Admiralty decided to extend the fitting of gyro-compasses to the larger cruisers and later to the *Glorious*, *Courageous* and *Furious* which were converted to aircraft-carriers. Monitors, of which some twenty were built, were also fitted. However, with the exception of submarines, small ships were not considered as suitable platforms for these instruments and it was not until several years after the war that the first destroyers were able to enjoy the advantages of such a compass.[5] Nevertheless, by the end of 1918 the total number of gyro-compasses that had been fitted exceeded three hundred.[6]

Although the floating ballistic introduced by Sperry at the end of 1913 had done much to cure the intercardinal rolling error, it soon became evident that it was only satisfactory in moderate weather. In heavy seas it was readily upset and could sometimes cause very large errors. In 1916 the battleships *Queen Elizabeth* and *Barham* both reported errors of up to 40° and the Admiralty again wrote to Professor Henderson at Greenwich, seeking advice.[7] In his reply the professor stated that he believed the floating ballistic was insufficiently stabilized and that forced oscillation due to the lateral translation of the ship by the waves could account for the errors. He suggested that the effect could be demonstrated on 'the Admiralty test-bed at Deptford' which had apparently just been completed close to the original observatory, and he went on to propose two possible methods by which the period of the pendulum of the floating ballistic could be increased to make it long in comparison with the period of the waves.[8]

However, in January 1917, before any solution could be tried out, the Commander-in-Chief, Grand Fleet, appointed a committee at Scapa Flow to investigate the whole problem of 'wandering' compasses. The design of the floating ballistic was quickly confirmed as being the root cause of the trouble and many of the detailed criticisms were concerned with its construction and operation. The committee was, however, also severely critical of the procedures for balancing the compass during installation, almost all the compasses examined being found to be seriously at fault in this respect. A much more comprehensive series of balancing tests was eventually introduced as a result of their report.[9] Other possible contributory causes which were identified were the position of the compass with respect to the centre of roll and the stability of the power supplies, on both of which the committee sought advice.

Urgent consultations between the Compass Department and the Sperry Company quickly led to a simple and cheap method of effecting the Henderson solution by the addition of a small weight to the upper end of the floating ballistic to increase its natural period. Four modified equipments were sent for trial in the Grand Fleet, but it was several months before the winter of 1917–18 produced weather that was sufficiently rough to cause the normal, unmodified compasses to wander. Once, however, it had been demonstrated that the modified ballistic could effect a worthwhile improvement, it was widely introduced and, while it did not completely cure the problem, the compass now held the meridian in weather which it would not previously have withstood. It was not until a year after the war that a complete solution became generally available.

As a final recommendation the committee proposed that the navigating officer should assume responsibility for the operation and general efficiency of the whole gyro-compass equipment in HM ships, the torpedo officer remaining responsible for the purely electrical aspects. Also that an electrician should be detailed to carry out the actual work of care and maintenance under the supervision of the navigating officer. This was the beginning of the Gyro EA (Electrical Artificer) scheme which was a boon to navigating officers for the next fifty years. These men were trained by the Compass

Department and on retirement from the Navy many of them returned as civilians to serve at the Observatory for considerable periods.

Before leaving the story of the gyro-compass during World War I, brief mention must be made of two highly significant events which were to have important repercussions on the Compass Department in the years immediately following. The first occurred on 3 August 1916, when Mr S. G. Brown, working with Professor John Perry FRS,[10] patented a gyro-compass with an entirely new method of control known as a liquid ballistic. Although the details need not concern us at this stage, this invention was to open up a whole new chapter in the history of the gyro-compass. It was also to form the subject of litigation and anguish over the next thirteen years as, for reasons which have never been disclosed, the progress of this patent (No. 124529 of 1916) was held up 'at the instance of an Admiralty official' until after the war.[11] In October of that year Captain Creagh-Osborne was invited by Mr Brown to inspect his new compass and Lieutenant Commander G. B. Harrison, who had taken the place of Allenby in 1914, was sent. It is probable that at this stage the significance of the invention was not appreciated by the Compass Department, where effort was mainly concentrated on attempts to cure the troubles of the Sperry. However, in May 1917 Mr Brown showed the department a later development of his compass which he said had been 'greatly improved' since 1916 and now had no quadrantal error (i.e. no intercardinal rolling error). This instrument was also seen by officials of the Compass Department and was later loaned to the Admiralty. After tests at the Compass Observatory it was given an extensive sea trial in the cruiser *Chatham*, where it apparently performed extremely well. Despite this, however, nothing further appears to have been done about it until after the war.[12]

The second event of significance concerned Professor James Henderson, at the Royal Naval College at Greenwich, who had conducted the mechanical tests on the Sperry gyro-compass in 1913 and had been responsible for the suggestions which led to the design of the floating ballistic. He was primarily concerned with the problems of accurate gunfire (and was, at the time, working on the gyro-controlled gunnery firing-gear which bears his name, using an Anschütz gyro). He was thus greatly interested in any method of controlling a gyro-compass which would make it hold the meridian more closely. In June 1917 Professor Henderson evidently heard of Mr Brown's ideas and, although there is no conclusive evidence that he had ever seen the compass itself, nevertheless in that same month he suddenly decided to lodge a provisional specification for his own method of applying a 'liquid control' to a gyro-compass (Patent No. 166570 of 1917). This was followed by a greatly revised complete specification in January 1918.

These events took place during the very period when the modified ballistic was being widely fitted in the Fleet as a palliative, although by no means the final answer, to the problem of intercardinal rolling error, and both ideas contained the essentials of a cure for the troubles which had beset the Sperry gyro-compass for so long. Indeed Professor Henderson apparently considered that his patent could be applied as a modification to this compass. He seems, however, to have mistrusted the Compass Department and did not at first communicate his ideas to them. For their part the department, despite the very successful trial of the Brown compass in HMS *Chatham*, took no steps to discuss with Mr Brown the possible application of his principle of liquid control to the Sperry compasses fitted in the Fleet. With hindsight these failures must be deeply regretted, coming at a time when the fullest co-operation between all concerned could have been of immense benefit in helping to solve the acute compass problems of the Navy at a critical stage in the war. The reasons for this reticence and its subsequent impact on the fortunes of the department will be fully discussed in the next chapter.

Compasses in submarines

We have seen that submarines were given priority for the fitting of gyro-compasses and by the end of hostilities approximately 120 equipments had been installed. With the exception of the first two boats of the E-class which had Anschütz compasses, all were Sperrys. The installations were generally similar to those supplied for surface ships but because of space restrictions duplex or duplicate systems were not possible. An automatic voltage regulator was an essential addition in order to smooth out the huge variations of voltage from the submarine's battery, depending on whether it was on charge or discharge. Two repeaters were provided for use on the bridge (one for the helmsman) and these had to be carried up and down the conning-tower hatch along with 'Faithful Freddie', when diving and surfacing. Pressure tight repeaters, which could remain *in situ* when the submarine dived were not introduced until some years after the war.

Although a submarine can be very lively on the surface, once submerged at a reasonable depth there is little movement and conditions for the gyro-compass are ideal. Navigation in a submerged submarine obviously presents unique and difficult problems and although, by 1914, the projector compasses of the early days had been much improved, it is doubtful whether some of the amazing feats of skill and daring accomplished during the war years, particularly in the Dardanelles, would have been possible without the gyro.

As discussed in chapter 7, the early projector binnacle had the great disadvantage that if the light failed it could not be replaced when submerged. In 1915 the H-type projector was introduced for the H-class submarines building in Canada, with two projector lamps which could be interchanged by a lever from inside the submarine. However, the first fifteen boats of this class did not have a gyro-compass and it is clear that they were not always satisfied with their service magnetic compasses. The Submarine Museum at HMS *Dolphin* at Gosport contains an interesting compass whose inscription tells its own story: 'Compass taken from a Turkish dhow by Midshipman Bettell in HM Submarine H1 in the vain hope that it might serve to check the submarine's own compass, which was highly erratic. 1916'!

The raising-and-lowering (RL) type of binnacle, introduced in 1918, overcame the lighting problem and provided a compass which was further from the steel hull and from the influence of the elctromagnetic fields of the main cables. Although an attempt was made to compensate for this effect by providing corrector coils, fitted to the outside of the binnacle abreast the compass, they were never a success and were not widely adopted.[13]

Aircraft compasses and wartime flying

In chapter 7 an account was given of the early development of compasses for aircraft and of the way the Compass Department had tackled the new problems. The first standardized aircraft compass, the Pattern 200 introduced in 1913, had adequately met the initial needs of both the naval and military flying wings, whilst suitable regulations now governed the problem of supply, fitting and adjustment. However, although in 1912 several successful flights were made from wooden platforms fitted over the foredeck of a number of HM ships,[14] generally speaking the early growth of naval flying was less spectacular. It was only when the naval wing broke away from the Royal Flying Corps in July 1914 to become an independent Royal Naval Air Service[15] that naval aviation began to develop an identity and spirit of its own. Thereafter its activities grew rapidly particularly when, during the second month of the war, the Admiralty was given responsibility for the air defence of Great Britain. With the Royal Flying Corps mainly concerned with operations in direct support of the Army in the field, the RNAS virtually became an equal partner. Its duties were many and varied, starting with responsibility for preventing zeppelins and aircraft from raiding England. They also included attacking German submarine and airship bases in Belgium, maintaining the Dover patrol to protect cross-Channel traffic, bombing coastal targets, searching for enemy shipping and harrying German aircraft, balloons and zeppelins. A wide variety of types of land-based aircraft operated from airfields on both sides of the Channel and these were later supported by sea planes and flying-boats, the latter mainly employed on anti-submarine patrols over the North Sea. Here the problems of navigation for long periods over a feature-less sea demanded great accuracy of the compass, and some remarkable successes were recorded.[16]

The Compass Department was, of course, responsible for all service aircraft compasses and, as the war progressed, many different operational requirements arose. In particular, as aircraft speeds increased, the Pattern 200 compass was frequently found to be unreliable, with a serious tendency for the card to revolve. Experiments by Dr Keith Lucas at Farnborough and by Captain Creagh-Osborne at Chingford soon showed that the engines tended to set up rotary vibrations which caused the card to spin, and a cure was quite simply effected by introducing an inverted pivot, attached to the card instead of the bowl (so that the card would no longer behave like a plate spinning on a billard cue!). The pivot engaged in a jewel cup on a stem rising from the bottom of the bowl and this remained the standard method of mounting the magnet system for aircraft compasses for many years.

The new compass, which was first introduced in 1915, was still basically the Pattern 200, based on Chetwynd's patent, but with an inverted pivot and with the compass points and lubber's line painted with radium compound, another innovation introduced by Creagh-Osborne. The design was very successful and although further modifications which included eliminating the float, were introduced from time to time, the basic compass remained one of the standard types in service until 1928. A larger edition, the Pattern 253, was also introduced in 1915 for use in flying-boats and bombers and it was a compass of this type that was used by Alcock and Brown on their historic trans-Atlantic flight in 1919.

By 1915 it had become difficult in some aircraft to find a suitable position for the 'flat-card' type of compass and at the suggestion of Creagh-Osborne, who was working in co-operation with Henry Hughes, a vertical card compass (i.e. with a compass card shaped like a cylinder) was introduced which could be read in a position either below or above the eye level of the pilot. Again a family of compasses was developed with different sizes for different types of aircraft (patterns 255–259). At about the same time the Royal Aircraft Factory at Farnborough designed a similar compass, known as the RAF Mark II, which had a very slow period designed to counteract the effects of the 'northerly turning error' which had recently been identified by Dr Lucas. This error occurs when an aircraft banks steeply, causing the needles to sense the vertical component of the earth's field. Its effect is that, when turning from a northerly course, the card tends to follow the turn of the machine. However, the Compass Department and the Navy preferred to use a compass with a quick period which although subject to northerly turning error, would more rapidly take up its correct heading after a turn. The two schools of thought persisted until the latter part of 1917, but in time many RAF pilots also came to prefer the shorter-period instruments and eventually the RAF Mark II 'quick period' compass was introduced.

As the war in the air intensified an urgent requirement arose for a simple, cheap aircraft compass that could be easily mass-produced for the rapidly expanding air forces. At Creagh-Osborne's request Messrs Hughes & Son developed a number of experimental designs, all of which had light, floatless cards, strong suspensions and a simple air trap above the bowl instead of an expansion chamber, and it was from these designs that the famous Type 5/17 (signifying design-approved May 1917) was evolved. Although by no means the perfect instrument, it lent itself to very rapid production, and manufacture could be undertaken by firms with no previous experience of magnetic work. Between 50,000 and 60,000 were made before the contracts were cancelled early in 1919.[17]

The compasses described above represent only a small selection of the many different types that were designed to meet the operational needs of the RFC and the RNAS during this period. Others deserving special mention were those based on the *America*'s compass and used mainly by airships and bombers, for which the flat card was still favoured. Some were designed as azimuth compasses to enable the position to be fixed by the land.[18] There was also a special compass (very similar to the hand-bearing compass which appeared some twenty years later) for use in 'kite' balloons, in which an observer was sent aloft to spot the fall of projectiles for the fleet. These and many other examples which illustrate the general evolution of aircraft compasses during this formative period can be seen in the unique collection held by the National Maritime Museum at Greenwich. The technical aspects are fully described in the catalogue written by Lieutenant G. H. Alexander in 1930.[19]

There is little doubt that it was largely due to the great interest in aircraft compass design shown by Captain Creagh-Osborne during the early days of aviation that Britain led the world in this important new field at the outbreak of war. Rumour had it that there was always keen competition amongst German pilots to secure the compass whenever a British plane was shot down behind the lines. It was a fitting tribute to the department when in 1918, after America had entered the war, the superintendent was again invited to visit the United States in order to advise the US Navy and the Air Corps on air-compass matters.

Considerable experience had been gained during the four years of hostilities and about six months before the armistice, Lieutenant Commander G. R. Colin Campbell RN and Dr G. T. Bennett FRS, both of the Compass Department, collaborated to design a compass which would embody the many improvements that had appeared. The result was the first liquid aperiodic compass (in which the card does not oscillate but gradually returns direct to the meridian), the forerunner of many types still in use today, with a magnet system consisting of six very small needles in a light frame which carried a number of radial wires for damping purposes. This compass, which was known as the type 6/18 (June 1918), represented a very considerable advance on all compasses of the period and completely overcame the northerly turning error.[20] It did not, however, come into service until the year after the war.

As a sad postscript, Lieutenant Commander Campbell was killed shortly afterwards when S.S. *Leinster* was torpedoed in the Irish Channel, only one month before the end of hostilities. This is believed to be the only war casualty suffered by the department.

Compasses for military purposes

About 1915 Creagh-Osborne undertook the design of a number of different types of Marching and Bearing (prismatic) compass for military use, to replace a dry-card compass of a type which had probably seen service in the Anglo-Boer War. Some of these had radium-painted cards, much favoured at that time, and some carried a second lubber which could be offset for the variation, so that true courses could be set. A compass of this type was later adapted for use as a wrist compass by observers in the RAF and in a modified form it was also used on a folding tripod when adjusting compasses in aircraft and was then known as the small landing compass. In 1916 the medium landing compass appeared, an excellent instrument which remained in service, as a companion to the old Admiralty Pattern 1 landing compass, until after World War II.[21]

In 1916 the Compass Department was asked to provide compasses for the tanks just entering service on the Western Front, to enable them to reach their objective during the hours of darkness. Initially they were given specially adapted boats' compasses which were corrected as far as practicable but which, because of the amount of moveable iron in the vicinity, often had variable errors in excess of 20°. These compasses were replaced in the following year by aircraft compasses of the vertical-card type (Pattern 259) which could be fitted above the driver's line of sight and appeared to work better. An order for 9550 was placed but by the end of the war only 1800 had been delivered. Most of the remainder were cancelled and for some years after 1918 the problem was shelved. Although interest revived in 1925, when it was learnt that the Americans were doing trials with a gyro-compass in a tank, when these came to nothing the subject remained dormant for many years.[22]

The build-up of staff in the Compass Department

When hostilities commenced in 1914 the staff of the Compass Department consisted simply of the Superintendent, Assistant Superintendent, one naval assistant and a clerk, all housed in the offices at 47 Victoria Street, with the compass-examiner and one labourer at the Compass Observatory at Deptford. Although new tasks and increasing responsibilities were to necessitate a vast expansion before peace returned, at first the growth was very gradual. In 1915 a second testing station for magnetic compasses was established at Glasgow University, run by a scientist lent by the Royal Observatory at Edinburgh, while the appointment of an additional naval assistant relieved Creagh-Osborne of much of his work in the field. Early in 1916 the first three RNVR officers to be recruited as gyro specialists began their duties, and a flight sub-lieutenant of the RNAS became the first air liaison officer. A warrant electrician was appointed to Deptford, where the first gyro-compass test equipment was being installed, so that testing could be done independently of the contractors. At the same time the first woman compass-tester was engaged.

By the beginning of 1917, however, the numbers had begun to rise sharply. Ten gyro-travellers and four naval assistants now operated from the overcrowded offices in Victoria Street, where the Superintendent and his Assistant had already been joined by a second air officer and three more clerks. At Deptford five women compass-testers were now employed on both gyro- and magnetic compasses. It was evident that new premises would soon have to be found.

The move to Slough

New development work on gyro- and aircraft compasses would require laboratories and workshops in addition to test facilities, but there was no more room to be had in the Royal Victualling Yard at Deptford. Meanwhile a new hazard had arisen. The gradual sprawl of London towards the south-east, and particularly the proximity of electric trams, was making accurate magnetic work at the Observatory increasingly difficult. The time had come for the department to look for a new home where its various activities could be concentrated in suitable surroundings and where there would be room for expansion. Fortunately a solution appeared to be readily to hand.

The Manor of Ditton, in Ditton Park near Slough, was the property of Baron Montagu of Beaulieu and had been on the market since 1897. It was only 20 miles from London. The manor house itself, with 14 acres of garden was enclosed by a decorative moat and surrounded by 250 acres of parkland. It had a magnetically 'clean' environment and would make an ideal situation for the Compass Department with plenty of space for development. The Admiralty purchased the house and the 14 acres without delay, paying the very moderate sum of £20,000, and on 17 March 1917, exactly 75 years after its foundation, the department acquired its new premises. The new establishment was named the Admiralty Compass Observatory (ACO). A brief account of the history of the Manor of Ditton is given in appendix 9.

Having been largely unoccupied for some years, the house and grounds of Ditton Park were very run down and there was much to be done to make the place shipshape. The summer of 1917 witnessed many changes as the estate was gradually cleared up and tidied, workshops and a hangar for two small aircraft (with wings folded) sprang up and laboratories, test rooms and offices were established in the ample mansion with its surrounding coach houses, stables and store rooms. Occupation began on 1 June and a considerable work force was quickly built up, largely from local labour, to supplement those who had moved from London and Deptford. Most significantly the first two scientific assistants, Dr R. T. Bennett FRS and Mr A. L. Rawlings joined the staff during the year.

With this move came full departmental status under the Controller, Captain Creagh-Osborne being appointed Director and Commander Norfolk Assistant Director, both with official residences on the site. The establishment was organized into sections under three Superintendents, dealing with magnetic, gyro- and air compasses, a fourth being added the following year to cover instruction and optical instruments. Six-week courses in compass adjustment for bomber pilots of the RFC (at first called compass officers) began late in 1917. The Director also arranged that the establishment should have its own section of the Naval Stores organization on the site, an advantage enjoyed by few service departments but one which has contributed immensely to the efficient support of the Fleet's compasses.

One field in which a considerable improvement could now be expected was that of compass-testing. With the limited facilities at Deptford it had only been possible to test a proportion of the vast number of aircraft compasses being made, but now no compass would escape. Separate test rooms were established in the mansion for marine and aircraft compasses respectively, with a further test facility for gyros in the stables. Here the compasses could be hung in 'swings' which initially had to be swung by hand, hard work for a female tester, but were later modified for electrical operation. Lieutenant Alexander became the Chief Compass Examiner assisted by a second boatswain, a commissioned electrician and a staff of about twenty women compass testers. By the summer of 1918 they were testing as many as 2000 compasses a week.

In order to protect the magnetic integrity of the environment the Admiralty agreed, shortly after the armistice, to purchase the 250 acres of surrounding parkland for a further £24,000,[23] and the sale was concluded in 1919. It was not long afterwards that the Compass Department was attacked in the local press as an 'unnecessary extravagance', the main objection being the presence of cows in the park and the land girls tending them. These were, however, the property of a tenant farmer and a source of revenue to the Crown! Early in the same year arrangements were made to have the moat cleaned out with the assistance of labour loaned from the local prisoner-of-war camp.

Visit of His Majesty King George V

Once everything was in full swing, the Admiralty Compass Observatory was honoured, on 26 August, just ten weeks before the end of hostilities, by a visit from His Majesty King George V, who was accompanied by Prince George. The King took a great interest in the new naval establishment, now settled on his doorstep at Windsor, and planted an oak tree (known as the Verdun oak) in the grounds.

In 1917 Captain Creagh-Osborne had been awarded the Order of St Anne, second class, by the Russian government shortly before it fell, for his contribution to the prosecution of the war. At the end of 1918 he was created a CB,[24] a fitting tribute to the man who had been responsible for guiding the Compass Department through the most intensive period in its history – so far.

NOTES

CHAPTER 8

[1] CN 46448/13 (January 1913), National Maritime Museum, Magnetic Compass Collection, Item T (5) 6.

[2] D 15365/14 (August 1914), National Maritime Museum, Magnetic Compass Collection, Item T (5) 6. The 1914 edition also included the rules for safe distance from chronometers for the first time. The list of instruments tested has been amended and re-issued at frequent intervals ever since and now forms the appendix to CD Pamphlet, No. 11.

[3] Reginald Gillmor, who had run the London office since 1913, was destined to become General Manager and Vice-President of the American company at the age of 31.

[4] T. P. Hughes, *Elmer Sperry, Inventor and Engineer*, Johns Hopkins Press, London, 1971, p. 201.

[5] Five destroyers were fitted with gyro-compasses for trial in 1922. Approval to fit all destroyers followed from 1924 onwards (see p. 229).

[6] Pamphlet entitled *Particulars of Spheres, Flinders Bar, Heeling Error Constants, λ 2 and Values of Constant C for Compasses of HM Ships*, National Maritime Museum, Magnetic Compass Collection, Item P8 (1A).

[7] National Maritime Museum, Compass Collection, Envelope N31. (Admiralty letter, CPNS 28929, 62365, 24 October 1916).

[8] Professor Henderson's letter of 27 October 1916, Archives of the Admiralty Compass Observatory. In 1916 Henderson was already working on his own design for a gyro-compass, which he hoped would be a competitor to the Sperry. He accordingly finished his letter to Their Lordships with the surprising paragraph: 'I hope that My Lords will remember that I have a new gyro-compass now under construction for submission to the Admiralty and that by helping to remove the defects in the present compass I am raising the standard which my own compass has to attain. I am, however, always pleased to be of service to My Lords'.

[9] Confidential Admiralty Interim Order, No. 2746/17, Naval Historical Library.

[10] The uncle of Mrs Alice Brown – see chapter 9.

[11] 'Report of the Admiralty committee on gyro-compass development' under Admiral Philpott, 1927, reproduced in the *S. G. Brown Magazine Gazette*, Vol. 2, No. 1 (January 1930).

[12] Ibid.

[13] 'Notes on the fitting and use of submarine compensating coils', National Maritime Museum, Magnetic Compass Collection, Item R33.

[14] The first flight was in January 1912, from the battleship *Africa*, at anchor.

[15] The Royal Naval Air Service was abolished on 1 April 1918, when it was absorbed into the newly created Royal Air Force. Although it again achieved independence in 1937, RAF personnel continued to operate with the Navy until well into the war.

16 An interesting account of the activities of the Flying Boat Flight based at RNAS Felixstowe is given in Squadron Leader T. D. Hallan, *The Spider Web*, Arms & Armour Press, London, reprinted 1979. In 1915 Commander J. C. Porte took over the experimental wing at this station and made many operational sorties. Captain Creagh-Osborne often flew from Felixstowe.

17 This compass incorporated two of Creagh-Osborne's many aircraft compass patents (Nos 1148 and 17736, both of 1915).

18 A number of qualified navigators from the Fleet were appointed for navigating duties in airships.

19 Catalogue of the Magnetic Compass Collection by Lieutenant G. H. Alexander, 1930.

20 Ibid.

21 Ibid.

22 Admiralty Compass Department, R & D Report, 1946, p. 4.

23 At first this purchase did not include the chapel, built in 1817. However, this was de-consecrated in 1927 and was then made over to the Admiralty by Lord Montagu without further payment. It is sited in what became the naval stores compound, and is now used as a somewhat unusual store for compass equipment. The original altar from the chapel is now in the Church of the Blessed Virgin Mary at Bucklers Hard on the Beaulieu river in Hampshire.

24 Other officers whose services were rewarded were Commander G. B. Harrison OBE and Lieutenant G. H. Alexander MBE.

Ups and downs between the wars, 1919-39

'Pick yourself up,
Dust yourself off,
Start all over again.'

Although on 11 November 1918 the great war machine was suddenly hushed, it could not stop rolling overnight. The change to peacetime working at first happened gradually; contracts were cancelled and plans were made for the disposal or storage of equipment, staffs were replanned and redundancies considered. At the Admiralty Compass Observatory (ACO) the run-down went on steadily through the spring and summer of 1919, dismissals occurring particularly amongst the women testers as the throughput of compasses died down. Before long, however, the Geddes axe began to swing and then it was not individuals but whole establishments that were in danger. It is unlikely, however, that the ACO was seriously threatened at this stage.

For four years after the war not a single new ship was built for the Navy, whilst vast numbers were withdrawn from the fleet to be laid up or sold. Over a hundred ships went to the breaker's yard. If gyro-compasses were fitted these were first removed and sent to Ditton Park for careful storage and preservation. During the next few years the newly established Naval Stores organization took on charge some two hundred equipments, with a total value in excess of £400,000. Soon the workshops developed the skills to strip these compasses down, restore them to 'as new' condition (though it used to be said that a compass reconditioned at ACO was not 'as good as new' but 'better') and modify them as improvements were introduced. However, by 1921 the total workshop staff had fallen to a mere twenty men and as only half of these were skilled operatives, this work was to keep them busy, between the normal day-to-day tasks, for many years.

In January 1919, when Commander Norfolk, the Assistant Director, retired without replacement, an establishment officer was appointed to look after the administration. The three compass sections (magnetic, gyro and air), under their superintendents, continued as before, with two further superintendents covering 'optics' and 'experiments and instruction'. However, as the numbers declined, this rather grandiose arrangement, with five superintendents, quickly contracted and by 1922 was down to two. In 1920 the scientific staff, who had joined the ACO towards the end of the war, were absorbed into the newly formed Scientific Research and Experimental Department and were reappointed elsewhere, Mr A. L. Rawlings joining the gyro group at the Admiralty Research Laboratory (ARL) at Teddington. He was again to figure prominently in the story of the ACO a few years later.

The end of 1920 found the non-industrial strength down to only seventeen, of whom ten were classed as technical assistants. The industrial staff at the time totalled seventy-two, and included such useful craftsmen as a carpenter, a joiner, a bricklayer, a scaffolder and a plumber for the maintenance of the establishment. A naval mess had been formed, largely to cater for the considerable number of serving officers who came for courses of instruction, and there were eight catering staff with, as housekeeper, Mrs Gaskill, who was said to have been a lady's maid in the mansion during more spacious days. Her two daughters were employed as compass-testers but, following the run-down, Madge, the elder, became a mess assistant and later took over from her mother as housekeeper, while Connie Gaskill became a clerk and finished up by running the office and registry (some might have added 'and the rest of the ACO as well') with great efficiency for many years. She was awarded the MBE during the war, and when she retired in August 1967 she had served at the ACO for over fifty years.

In 1922 the establishment officer was withdrawn and the sections reduced to two, with Commander Harrison and Mr Chaffer as the Superintendents, Naval and Civil respectively. Harrison covered compasses and administration while Chaffer, who had served through the war as an Instructor Lieutenant in the Navy, had charge of the workshop and drawing office and of instruction. However, although the non-industrial numbers remained below twenty for the next twelve years, the industrial side of the establishment soon began to build up again. By 1923 it was over 100, with 22 operatives (skilled craftsmen who were later called Compass Mechanics) and by 1930 it was approaching 130 of whom 45 were operatives. The number then remained steady until the mid-1930s when the build-up of both industrials and non-industrials began in earnest as the danger of war was recognized.

Throughout the lean years the ACO remained an extremely happy place in which to work, with a pleasant 'small ship' atmosphere and a family feeling which has always remained with it, surviving the great expansion into World War II and another in the 1960s, when the Ships Inertial Navigation System (SINS) and the Polaris projects led to a doubling of the non-industrial staff in under five years. It was in no way upset by the general strike of 1926, when a detachment of Marines was billeted at the ACO for security purposes, and was greatly enriched in 1929 by the formation of a Sports Club in the grounds. A horse was employed 'on the strength' for pulling a cart round the establishment and it is reported that there was often a gross misuse of official horse power for such essential chores as mowing and rolling the cricket field.

Directors come and go.

Captain Creagh-Osborne retired in December 1926 having been with the Compass Department since 1904. He had led it through the most challenging period in its history, building it up to meet the requirements of the three services throughout a long war, and had then held it together during the testing period of the run-down and doldrums which followed. He died at his home in Lymington on 10 September 1943. Creagh-Osborne was succeeded as Director of the Compass Department (DCD) by his deputy, Commander G. B. Harrison, whose place as Superintendent (Naval) was taken by Lieutenant Commander B. C. Porter from the Navigation School who had recently been the Navigating Officer of the battleship *Malaya*. For reasons which we shall come to shortly, Harrison served less than two years as Director before being relieved in 1928 by Commander (later Captain) H. L. Hitchins and it was he who was shortly to have the task of preparing the establishment for an even greater challenge and then of leading it, with great distinction, through World War II.

Commander Hitchins was a torpedo specialist, the branch responsible for the Navy's electrics, and had been selected for the post by the Controller, who wished to strengthen the technical direction of the establishment's activities. Gradually he put in hand an extensive programme of reorganisation, bringing in scientific and technical staff drawn from the pool recruited by the Director of Scientific Research. Chaffer became the Chief Technical Adviser, having under him five sections which dealt respectively with gyro-compasses and optics; magnetic compasses, including aircraft; the gyro and electrical test rooms; the magnetic test rooms; and the workshop and drawing office. It is interesting to note that at this time the Compass Sections not only handled the Research and Development aspects of new equipment but also acted as Project Managers in the fullest sense, covering financial planning, arranging contracts, writing handbooks and dealing with the problems of manufacture.

Commander Porter became the Superintendent and second in command, responsible for administration and for all naval matters, including instruction which had become an area of increasing importance. Since 1924 the Navigating Officers' qualifying course had included a fortnight at Ditton Park on gyros, whilst a refresher course was later added to the 'First Class Ship' Course. There were comfortable cabins on the top floor of the Mansion and these courses provided a pleasant break from naval routine. Gyro EAs and dockyard fitters came for more extended periods, and ever since 1917 there had been a steady flow of RAF personnel learning how to adjust compasses in aircraft.

When the Chief Compass Examiner, Lieutenant Alexander, retired early in 1929, the job changed in character, and thereafter testing was organized by a member of the technical staff. Since 1844 there had been only three holders of the post, Mr Brunton, Mr Foden and Lieutenant Alexander, a remarkable record of service. Throughout his time Alexander had taken a keen interest in the museum which had grown steadily ever since 1840 and was now admirably displayed in the spacious hall and galleries of the mansion. Before retiring he completed a comprehensive revision of the catalogue which provided the basis for that in use today and the good work was continued by Commander W. E. May, who joined the establishment at this time from the firm of S. G. Brown. He quickly became an expert in both gyro and magnetic compasses and many of the anecdotes in this narrative are from his recollections. Later he was to become an international figure in the field of compass history and in 1951 he left the ACO to become the Deputy Director of the National Maritime Museum.

Compass Representatives and Superintendents of Gyro-Compasses (SGC)

During World War I RNVR officers had been employed as 'gyro-travellers', to fit and test compass equipment in ships and to provide instant support in case of need. This service was maintained after 1918 by civilian technical staff working from the ACO and the organization continued in being until the mid-1960s, providing another fifty-year record of service.

Although the travellers worked closely with the dockyard organizations it was impossible, with their nomadic existence, for them to provide continuity of supervision over work on board ships, nor could they always be available when needed. It was therefore decided, during the mid-1920s, to appoint compass representatives to all the home dockyards, who would work there whenever required. They were essentially an extension of the Director's organization and for many years used to report back to the ACO each Friday. Commander May has given this description of a typical working arrangement:

> When I ran Devonport in 1933–36 I used to visit the yard for a few days when the Fleet came in after a cruise or when a ship came in for refit, calling on each ship and arranging with the electrical department what to do. I then went back to the ACO and returned to Devonport for a week or so before the Fleet sailed to make sure that all was well. I had plenty to do besides this.[1]

In December 1924, a representative was appointed to Malta dockyard, where he was given the title of Superintendent of Gyro-Compasses (SGC)[2] and this name was later adopted by the home yards when the appointment of representatives became full-time on the outbreak of hostilities in 1939. Two years earlier an SGC had also been appointed to Hong Kong to cover the requirements of the Far East Fleet which at that period had no less than 12 submarines, in addition to 4 county-class cruisers. The incumbent, Mr C. W. Somers, was in one of the last ships to escape from Singapore in 1942.

Thus was born a scheme which took care of all local gyro-compass interests and provided a magnificent service to the Fleet for forty years. It was greatly extended during World War II, with SGCs appointed to the many additional naval bases that were established, both around the shores of the United Kingdom and in foreign ports. Whenever a ship came into port, there was the SGC, available to deal with any compass problems there might be. It was not surprising that the scheme was very popular with the officers of the Fleet, providing, as it did, a unique, on-the-spot service by men who had years of experience with gyro-compasses. But it was this very uniqueness that was its undoing. In 1966 the Head of the Civil Establishments Department ruled that the SGCs should be withdrawn and their responsibilities transferred to the local dock-yard officers, thus bringing the compass in line with other weapons systems.[3] The decision was perhaps inevitable, but after the years of personal attention under the direct control of the Compass Department, it was greatly regretted by captains and navigating officers throughout the Fleet.

The Radio Research Station

In 1920 a very happy landlord-tenant relationship was begun in Ditton Park which was to last almost half a century. Admiral of the Fleet Sir Henry Jackson, who was then chairman of the Radio Research Board of the Department of Scientific and Industrial Research (DSIR), suggested that the Admiralty should be asked to provide facilities in Ditton Park for certain experimental work into radio direction finding for which the National Physical Laboratory was unsuitable. A DSIR report later recorded the event as follows: 'A flat and open site of considerable area was here available, on which could be erected wooden huts, so isolated as to enable several experiments to be carried out simultaneously on the propagation of waves and directional wireless.'[4]

Two small groups moved into huts in the north and west park. The only interference that was likely to worry them would be from the cows. In 1924 they were joined by a third group under Robert Watson Watt, whose research into atmospherics, including the location of thunderstorms, had hitherto been conducted at Aldershot. A large hut and a wooden radio mast 210 feet high were erected in the north park. Watson Watt himself takes up the story: 'On the very day in 1927 that I was appointed Superintendent of an officially unified *Radio Research Station* . . . my telephone interrupted my lunch with the news that my main wooden hut . . . built around my 210 foot timber lattice mast was burning fiercely.'[5] Despite the efforts of the Slough and ACO fire brigades, the mast was completely destroyed. A new set of wooden buildings was subsequently erected in the south park and remained in use until 1982.

Relationships between the Radio Research Station and the ACO were always friendly and relaxed. The radio men used the ACO mess facilities until their own were built, they asked permission when they wished to erect new huts or aerials, and the ACO reminded them when they omitted to take them down once the experiment was completed! Social and sporting contacts were frequent. It was from Ditton Park that a van set off for Daventry early one February morning in 1935 for the first ever demonstration of the radar detection of aircraft.[6]

When, in 1950, the DSIR wished to build a new and more spacious headquarters, the open spaces of Ditton Park were a natural venue. It was therefore necessary for the Admiralty to point out that the site had originally been chosen for the ACO because the surrounding parkland ensured freedom from interference with the work of the Observatory.[7] These requirements still prevailed and any encroachment could only be on the Admiralty's terms. After protracted negotiations a modern complex of buildings was eventually built in west park and was opened in 1957 by Sir Edward Appleton, the Admiralty retaining the freehold and the overall control of the environment.

When, in 1965, the newly formed Science Research Council (SRC) replaced the DSIR, the establishment was renamed the Radio and Space Research Station. In 1973 it became the Appleton Laboratory. However, the SRC was not happy about the landlord-tenant relationship and after further negotiations the Ministry of Defence agreed, with suitable environmental safeguards, to a paper transfer of the land. Inevitably the writing was on the wall. Within a few years the

SRC had decided to close down the site in Ditton Park and to amalgamate the establishment with the Rutherford Laboratory at Chilton in Oxfordshire. In 1982 it was sold for commercial purposes – with the magnetic, electromagnetic and seismic requirements of the ACO still suitably safeguarded in the contract.[8]

Introducing the 'mercury control' to the gyro-compass

We must now return to the year 1918, when by far the most pressing problem facing the department as the war drew to a close was to turn the Sperry gyro-compass, already fitted in large numbers in the Fleet, into a reliable instrument of navigation. Although its performance had been much improved by the simple modification to the floating ballistic suggested by Professor Henderson, it was very soon clear that the cure was by no means complete.

The following is an account, in roughly chronological order, of the main events which ultimately led to the introduction of a liquid level control for the Sperry gyro-compass, now known more generally as the mercury control, an improvement which, without doubt, made the Sperry the most reliable compass then available. Unfortunately it also led to a long chain of enquiry and litigation which adversely affected both the fortunes of the Compass Department and the supply of compasses to the Navy for many years.

When judging the actions described in this account it must be borne in mind that the various parties concerned were not necessarily aware at the time of what others were doing or, sometimes, of their motives. As a consequence the various court hearings which took place during the 1920s in an endeavour to establish rights and priorities were necessarily lengthy and involved.

The whole matter was investigated, from different aspects, on three separate occasions: first, in the Chancery Court, when Mr S. G. Brown sued the Sperry Gyroscope Company for infringement of his patent. This case was heard before Mr Justice Tomlin in 1924; second, by a committee of enquiry set up by the Admiralty under Admiral E. M. Philpott CB in 1927; and third, by the Royal Commission on Awards to Inventors, in a hearing before Lord Justice Tomlin in August 1929. The reader will be able to assess the findings of each of these bodies against the background of the following narrative.

In the previous chapter we noted that in 1916 Mr S. G. Brown patented a new gyro-compass with a novel system of blown-liquid control (Patent No. 124519) which was inspected at the firm's works at Acton by Lieutenant Commander G. B. Harrison on behalf of the Compass Department. However, at the direction of 'an Admiralty official' the patent was apparently treated as 'secret' and was withheld from publication. By May 1917 Mr Brown had completed further improvements to his compass which, he claimed, now had 'no quadrantal error' (i.e. no intercardinal rolling error).

During the summer of 1917 two Compass Department officials, Commander Harrison, by then the Superintendent (gyro) and Dr G. T. Bennett FRS, were shown the new compass and shortly afterwards it was made available for tests at the Admiralty Compass Observatory. These were followed by an extended sea trial in the cruiser *Chatham*, where its performance was shown to be greatly superior to the Sperry compass already fitted, particularly during very rough weather. In October 1917 the ACO team was joined by Mr A. L. Rawlings from the Sperry Gyroscope Company, and from then on he too was associated with these trials.

In parallel with these events, on 23 June 1917 Professor J. B. Henderson, working at the Royal Naval College at Greenwich, also lodged a patent for a method of controlling a gyro-compass 'using liquid for gravity control' (Patent No. 166570). He stated that he had long entertained the idea of such an improvement but frankly admitted that he had only filed his patent 'on hearing that Brown was using a liquid level control'.[9] He had not, at the time, made an experimental apparatus to test his theory, neither could he recall exactly where he had obtained the information about Brown, although he believed it to be 'from an official in DNO'.[10] He was, however, adamant that he had not seen the Brown device and had no details of it. Mr Brown, on the other hand, was convinced that Henderson had visited his factory on more than one occasion, in the company of officials from the Compass Department.

It is probable that on first being shown the Brown invention in 1916, Commander Harrison had not fully appreciated its significance as efforts in the Compass Department were wholly directed towards improving the Sperry. There can be little doubt, however, that after the *Chatham* trials all the officials concerned at the ACO would have been aware that the system represented a fundamental change of principle and a clear breakthrough in gyro-compass control. Initially the Sperry compass had been controlled by a pendulous bail weight, which had been supplemented in 1915 by the addition of the floating ballistic and in 1917 by the modified ballistic (see p. 197). These devices had each had the effect of making the compass less pendulous but neither had been able to compete if the motion became too complex or violent. On the other hand, in the Brown system the compass was not pendulous but in neutral equilibrium and the mobile liquid ballistic was able to counter the effects of *all* the complex movements which might result from rolling, pitching and changing course or speed, even on intercardinal courses.

In 1916, in an attempt to save the export of currency to America, the Admiralty had suggested that Messrs Barr & Stroud of Glasgow should undertake the manufacture of gyro-compasses and, as a start, they were invited to build a laboratory model of a twin-gyro system designed by Professor Henderson.[11] When, therefore, in the autumn of 1917, Henderson decided to put his ideas on liquid level control into practice it was to Barr & Stroud that he sent his drawings. A rig was developed and was fitted experimentally to a Sperry-type gyro-compass. Henderson did not at first inform the Compass Department directly about his ideas but the arrangement was undoubtedly seen by Commander Harrison during a visit to the Glasgow works early in the following year.

During the spring of 1918 Henderson prepared a thesis on the application of the gyro-compass to gunnery problems, in which he proposed applying a liquid level control to a compass of the Sperry type and enclosed a blueprint of such an arrangement.[12] The paper was forwarded to the Director of Naval Ordnance and a copy was sent to the ACO where it was seen by Harrison and Rawlings. It was also remarked upon at length by Dr Bennett whose critical commentary opened with the words, 'Professor Henderson proposes to modify the Sperry compass for the purpose of securing a steadier reading than it gives at present. He would replace the bail by the Henderson level control and claims that the compass will then be aperiodic and free from ballistic deflection.' Significantly, when forwarding Dr Bennett's detailed comments to the Admiralty, Harrison omitted these opening words. When questioned later, he was unable to give any explanation for the omission.[13]

Meanwhile during the early summer of 1918, having apparently seen both Brown's and Henderson's methods of control at work,

Harrison and Rawlings began developing their own ideas for applying a form of liquid control to the Sperry gyro-compass, and on 31
July they decided to file a provisional patent (No. 131981). It is
clear, however, that their original concept underwent considerable
modification during the months which followed and, in particular,
as a result of a conference held at the ACO in October, which was
attended by Henderson. Consequently their complete specification,
dated 11 December 1918, differed in many respects from their
provisional patent and neither version agreed very closely with the
copy that had been lodged with the Admiralty in August. Yet a
further major revision took place before the patent was finally sealed
in September 1919. The first three paragraphs from the Harrison-
Rawlings patent, as submitted to the Admiralty, are significant in
view of what was to follow:

> The present application refers more particularly to compasses
> which are not pendulous but in which the effect of pendulousness
> is obtained by causing a flow of liquid between the North and
> South sides of the gyro when the spin axis of the gyro is tilted.
>
> We are aware that compasses on this principle have already
> been constructed in which the flow is caused by an air blast
> controlled by a valve operated by tilting the gyro casing. [This
> was the Brown method.]
>
> In our invention however we rely on gravity to cause the
> liquid to run from the higher to the lower side of the gyro, and
> we employ special means to prevent the level of the liquid in the
> North-South direction from being disturbed by the rolling of the
> ship, while at the same time it is sensitive to acceleration due to
> change of speed in latitude, so as to give a ballistic deflection and
> prevent oscillations resulting from such a change of speed.[14]

The 'special means' mentioned in the last paragraph referred to
constricting the connecting pipe containing the fluid so that the
natural period of oscillation of the flow from one side of the compass
to the other would be long in comparison with the rolling of the
ship. This statement also acknowledged Brown's patent but stressed
the difference between a gravity-controlled ballistic and one controlled by an air blast. In its final form, as sealed in 1919, the
specification also recognized the pre-existance of liquid controls of
the Henderson type and it described for the first time a system of

dividing the mercury boxes into three compartments in order to make appropriate adjustments to suit a wide range of latitudes. However, the Admiralty, which was clearly an interested party, was never informed of these changes or of the considerable reduction in the scope of the final patent from that originally submitted.

The first model of the Harrison-Rawlings mercury control for a Sperry compass was made in the ACO workshops during the summer of 1918 and was given comprehensive laboratory tests on the new gyro testing swings at the ACO. Meanwhile, having lent his latest gyro-compass to the Admiralty late in 1917 for sea trials in the cruiser *Chatham*, Mr Brown apparently heard no more until a few weeks before the armistice. He then received what he described as 'a drawing of an adaption of [my] liquid control system, suitable for use with *other compasses* . . . with a request that [I] should make a model.'[15] This request was followed by a contract for six Brown's compass equipments and, shortly afterwards, by an order for a further twelve liquid controls. Mr Brown stated later that he complied with these requests in the belief that he was co-operating with the Admiralty in introducing his system of control to the Sperry compass, clearly accepting the fact that the Admiralty was committed to Sperry for the bulk of the compasses of the fleet. He was, of course, quite unaware at that time of either the Henderson or the Harrison-Rawlings patents.

Early in 1919 a Sperry gyro-compass, fitted with the latest mercury control, was installed in the destroyer *Rapid*. An Anschütz and a Brown compass were also fitted for comparison in addition to a standard Sperry with a modified ballistic. All were given a very thorough trial in home waters and subsequently in the Mediterranean, where extremely rough weather was experienced, and the new control was shown to operate very satisfactorily. The following is an extract from a letter dated 2 January 1920 from Commander Harrison to Mr Jackson, managing director of the Sperry Gyroscope Company:

> The *Rapid* having now returned, we are in a position to assert definitely that by using the Mercury Control fitted to a standard Sperry Compass, the rolling error has been completely overcome. Exceptionally severe weather was experienced in the Mediterranean, when the Floating Ballistic in the ordinary Sperry broke

clean off and the Anschütz compass, when not using the 4th gyro, was useless.[16]

The letter makes no specific mention of the Brown compass and there is no record of how well its performance compared with that of the Sperry fitted with the Harrison-Rawlings control. Although the trials were continued during 1920, the Compass Department resolutely declined to allow the firm to witness them and interest in the Brown compass appears to have evaporated altogether by the end of the year. The order for six compasses, placed in 1918, was cancelled, although three of these were subsequently accepted.

Following the *Rapid* trials of 1919, events at the ACO moved swiftly. In November Harrison and Rawlings had approached the Sperry Gyroscope Company with a view to exploiting their 'invention' and two months later Sperry acquired an option on their patent rights. A firm agreement to purchase was signed on 7 June 1920, the Admiralty's right of usage being duly safeguarded. Subsequently patents were also filed in America, France and Italy and in due time these too were made over to the Sperry Company. Eventually the two men were paid a total of £4,000 for all their patent rights.

The Harrison-Rawlings mercury control completely revolutionized the Sperry gyro-compass and was greeted with fullsome praise on both sides of the Atlantic, as well as in the many other countries where trouble had been experienced with the floating ballistic. Mr Herbert Thomson, the patent attorney of the Sperry Gyroscope Company, New York, summed up the breakthrough in these words:

> This invention has proved one of the greatest steps forward since the gyroscopic compass was invented, firstly since it eliminates at one stroke the causes of serious deviations due to rolling and pitching of the ship, especially when on an intercardinal course, and secondly since no extraneous damping means need be employed, the very element which imparts meridian seeking properties being employed also to damp the compass.[17]

Meanwhile, what of Mr Brown? Although his curiosity had been aroused by the orders placed with his firm in 1918, it was not until September of the following year, when the Harrison-Rawlings patent was finally sealed, that he learnt that what he considered to be an adaption of his device had been separately patented by the two Admiralty officials over a year earlier and four months before the end of the war. On visiting the Shipping Exhibition in London in 1920 he observed on the Sperry stand a unit described as an Admiralty Pattern compass, to which 'was attached an apparatus so similar to that in use on the Brown gyro-compass as to be indistinguishable from it'.[18] He was not, however, aware even then that the patent rights had been sold to the Sperry Company and assumed that the Admiralty was entitled to use the patent for its own compasses. He did, however, raise the matter of priority with Captain Creagh-Osborne, receiving a somewhat evasive reply which nevertheless contained the apparently reassuring comment: 'I am sorry that any question of priority should have arisen. If there is one thing more than any other upon which I shall always endeavour to insist, it is that inventors can come to this department with absolute confidence of a fair deal.'[19]

But the damage had already been done. When Mr Brown visited the Shipping Exhibition at Olympia in 1923 he saw on the Sperry (America) stand, two American compasses fitted with the Harrison-Rawlings mercury control. He no longer had any doubt that he must sue Sperry for infringement of his patent. Everything would now be brought into the open.

Before looking at the outcome of the three separate investigations which were to assess and pass judgement on this intricate series of events, it would be as well to remind ourselves of the various patents that had been taken out for devices using a liquid for damping purposes in a gyro-compass. These had been filed by:

Anschütz-Kaempfe in 1906 and 1911. These did not effect the present case.

Professor Perry, working on behalf of S. G. Brown, in 1916 (Patent No. 124529). This had been held up at the insistence of an 'Admiralty official' and was not finally sealed until 1922.

Professor James Henderson in 1917 (Patent No. 166570). Although this was Henderson's only patent dealing directly with liquid control, he had filed a total of sixteen patents between 1914 and 1917 on subjects concerned with correcting errors of the gyro-compass.

Commander Harrison and Dr Rawlings in 1918 (Patent No. 131987).

Mr Brown's case against Sperry was heard in the Chancery Division before Mr Justice Tomlin, during the autumn of 1924, and judgement was given for Sperry. The judge ruled that although the Sperry Company had embodied principles of the Brown liquid ballistic in their equipment, the method of application was sufficiently different to allow them to escape the strict reading of the claim. Mr Brown took his case to the Appeal Court but the judgement was upheld, and it is said that this litigation cost him almost £40,000.

Having lost his case in law Mr Brown was free to speak his mind. The *Brown Budget* (the company's house magazine) for March 1926 contained an article by Mrs Alice Brown, also a director of the firm, which included the following passage:

'Unfortunately for Mr Brown these two Admiralty Officials, Harrison and Rawlings, applied his liquid ballistic correction principle, without his knowledge, to the American compasses in the British Navy.'

The company was thus openly accusing the ACO of taking ideas from one firm and selling them to another. Although the lawsuit had gone against Brown, the company resolutely maintained its position, pressing the case for fair treatment for British inventors and pointing out the injustices it considered it had suffered at the hands of Admiralty officials. In April 1927 they made a direct request for the whole matter to be investigated further and in September of that year the Admiralty decided to appoint its own committee of enquiry, under Admiral E. M. Philpott CB, with the following terms of reference;

(a) To investigate the changes made to the Sperry Gyro-compass from the time of its introduction into HM Naval Service to this date, with particular reference to the origin and development of inventions and of modifications in respect of principles of the apparatus commonly known as Level Control, for which Patents have been granted to Mr S G Brown, Sir James Henderson and to Captain [an error: Harrison was never promoted to Captain] Harrison RN and Mr Rawlings.

(b) As a result of this investigation, to report upon the development of the apparatus, stating to whom, in the Committee's opinion, credit is due for the successive steps by which the apparatus now in use has been evolved.[20]

The committee under Admiral Philpott consisted of: Sir Thomas H. Holland FRS, an eminent scientist; Mr Kenneth R. Swan OBE, a barrister; Mr A J Edwards, from the contract and purchase department; and Mr T. J. Gibson (secretary) of the Admiralty.

They met at intervals during October and November 1927 to take evidence, also to visit the ACO and the works of Messrs S. G. Brown. In addition to studying the official Admiralty files they were given a comprehensive set of extracts from the correspondence of the firm of S. G. Brown whose approach to the investigation appeared to be not so much one concerned with patent claims and priorities as with the betrayal of trust by Admiralty officials. On 15 December the committee produced its report, from which the four principal conclusions were as follows:

> 1. After careful consideration . . . we are of the opinion that the idea of applying liquid level control to the Sperry gyro-compass . . . is *not* the original conception of Harrison and Rawlings but is due partly to the invention of Brown and partly to the inventive suggestions of Henderson.

Conclusions 2 and 3 then dealt with the extent to which the committee considered Brown and Henderson had contributed. Finally they gave as their opinion:

> 4. We are satisfied that Harrison and Rawlings were sufficiently acquainted with the ideas of Brown and Henderson in regard to gyro-compass design to disqualify them from making any broad claim to originality in applying liquid level control to the Sperry compass in the manner in which it has been applied.[21]

By the time the Philpott committee was appointed in 1927 Commander Harrison had relieved Captain Creagh-Osborne as Director of the Compass Department and Dr Rawlings had moved to the Admiralty Research Laboratory at Teddington where he was working on the design of the gunnery gyro-compass. Both officers were required to leave the Admiralty's service and Dr Rawlings returned to the firm of Sperry which he had left in 1917. Shortly afterwards he was appointed to their New York office.

Thus ended an unhappy episode in the history of the Compass Department in which human frailty was once more much in evidence. The foregoing account must inevitably be regarded as little more than a summary of the principal events which influenced the outcome. It has been written with the advantage of hindsight and has been presented as factually and impartially as possible, without assigning motives to any party. S. G. Brown's own account is presented in full in the firm's house magazine for 1928. That of Dr Rawlings is given in an appendix to the first edition of his excellent book *The Theory of the Gyroscopic Compass* (1929). However, the following remarks which occur in a letter from Sir Thomas Holland KC to Mr Kenneth Swan, both members of the Philpott committee, during the final phase of their deliberations appear to express succinctly the real heart of the matter:

> The distracting influence of the desire for priority in securing patent rights led to reticence among those who were all seeking, at the instance of the Admiralty, for a solution to the difficulty which had been discovered by the Navy. Instead there ought to have been the freest co-operation, under conditions of war. . . . Henderson was anxious to keep his inventions from the Compass Department, and events justified his suspicions. Brown was frank and helpful in 1916–17; less so afterwards and then wholly secretive, as he still is. Those 'outsiders' who contributed most to the solution of the difficulties of the Navy were 'done' in turn by the men whose one business should have been to serve the public interest first.[22]

To conclude this account of the enquiries connected with the introduction of what was, without doubt, an excellent invention, brief mention must be made of the hearing of the Royal Commission on Awards to Inventors which took place in 1929 before Lord Justice Tomlin. It was a long-drawn-out affair as Tomlin ruled that the report of the Philpott committee was inadmissible as evidence. The whole story had therefore to be heard again. Awards were made as follows: Professor (by then Sir James) Henderson was granted £1,000 in respect of the floating and modified ballistics, for which he had been largely responsible. He and Mr Brown were then each awarded £5,000 in respect of their contribution towards the invention of the liquid ballistic. In view of the fact that Dr Rawlings had already received a grant from the Admiralty, and had been allowed to dispose of his patent rights, no further reward was recommended. Commander Harrison was not represented at the hearing.[23]

Mr Brown was totally dissatisfied with the award made to him, on two counts. He had been treated in exactly the same way as Sir James Henderson over the liquid ballistic yet he was convinced that Sir James, because of his privileged position as a government employee, had knowledge of the Brown patent before filing his own. Further, he contended that he was entitled to compensation for loss of revenue over a number of years as a result of having his patent 'frozen' during the war. He again took up his case with the Admiralty but Their Lordships declined to discuss the matter any further, with the regretable result that relations between the firm of S. G. Brown and the Compass Department were strained for many years, to their mutual embarrassment and disadvantage.

It was a distressing period in the life of the Compass Department but one from which, under the stirring leadership of the next Director, Captain Hitchens, it rapidly recovered.

Developments and improvements in the Admiralty gyro-compass

By the end of 1919 a cure for the wandering Sperry gyro-compass had been perfected and the first fifty of the new mercury controls had been ordered. Harrison and Rawlings had started negotiations with Sperry for the sale of their patent rights and, pending agreement, the workshops at the ACO had begun the task of modifying the Sperry compasses in store. The first *Admiralty Handbook of the Gyroscopic Compass* was written by ACO staff and published in 1925.

Meanwhile, with an eye to the commercial market after the war, the Sperry Company had, in 1918, developed a small twin-gyroscope compass, the Sperry Mark III, which was followed in 1919 by the Mark IV. Both were tested at the ACO but as their performance showed no significant improvement over the Modified Mark II, which was already in service, they were not adopted for the Navy. From that time on, although there was often close co-operation with the ACO, Sperry's commercial interests and Admiralty gyro-compasses developed along separate lines. In 1924 the firm introduced the Sperry Mark V, a development of the Mark II, with a single but improved rotor and more robust bearings. At the time, however, the Admiralty had a large number of gyro-compasses in store, many more than were needed for the postwar fleet and, whilst much of this surplus was later taken up in equipping destroyers, few additional compasses were needed for new construction. Furthermore, master gyro-compasses do not wear out and could be reconditioned to 'as new' condition, and there was much to be said for adhering to a single type of instrument throughout the service. It was not therefore until the mix-1930s that the greatly improved Mark V rotor was adopted by the Admiralty.[24] This basic unit survived, albeit with considerable peripheral variations and additions, for some sixty years.[25]

Naturally it was not long before other small improvements began to appear and, whilst undue attention to technical detail would be out of place in a narrative such as this, there were a number of modifications which may be considered of general interest and worthy of mention. As already stated, gyro-compasses were generally introduced into destroyers from 1924 onwards,[26] and must have been a great boon, particularly in rough weather. However, the well known 'hunt' of the gyro, much liked by early destroyer captains as an indication that 'the thing was working', was a nuisance, particularly for weapon control, and a new design of 'commutator transmitter' (as opposed to the original 'finger' type) was introduced, incorporating a lost-motion device which allowed the master compass to hunt approximately half a degree without moving the repeaters. A highly ingenious instrument known as a balancer was also introduced to deliver smooth transmissions (2 minute and 10 minute) for gunnery and torpedo purposes. It was widely fitted in capital ships and cruisers until the introduction of the Admiralty Gyro Transmission Unit in 1943 (see below) and although never entirely adequate for the more exacting requirements of anti-aircraft gunnery, particularly in indirect (radar-controlled) fire, it remained at sea in older ships until 1949, enjoying a useful life of some twenty-five years.[27]

In 1936 Chaffer introduced a major redesign of the gyro-compass mercury-control arrangements for the first time since Harrison and Rawlings had completed their work in 1919. In place of the single, divided mercury box on each side of the gyro-wheel, four mercury 'pots' were provided, connected in pairs. The volume of mercury in each could be varied by means of bakelite domes which were set against a latitude scale, and this design has been used on all Admiralty gyro-compasses ever since. The 1930s also saw the introduction of the latitute rider and the Admiralty speed-corrector.

Shortly before the war work was begun to improve the transmission arrangements from the gyro-compass in order to compete with the ever growing demand for gyro-compass information. M-type transmission was now gradually replacing the original Sperry type and in order to cater for the increasing number of gyro-repeaters a new multiple repeater motor was introduced, driven by the transmitter on the compass. Early in the war a bottle-transmitter, which could handle Sperry, Anschütz or M-type transmission was designed, and this later proved extremely useful in enabling Admiralty-type equipment to be driven by the many other types of commercial gyro-compass encountered in ships taken up for war service. Work also began on a new version of the Admiralty gyro-compass itself, which was fitted with a novel form of follow-up system (known as the 'valve follow-up') to provide a smooth, deadbeat transmission, and eliminated the 'hunt' altogether. This compass, which later became known as the Type 2005, was not however completed until 1943. It proved very popular but because of postwar developments, it had only a limited operational life.

The design of the Admiralty gyro-compass was gradually drawing away from that of the original Sperry and was now very different from their current commercial range. Although the second edition of the handbook, written by Chaffer in 1931, had been entitled *Admiralty Manual of the Sperry Gyro-Compass*, by the end of the decade it had been decided to refer to the instrument simply as the 'Admiralty gyro-compass (Sperry type)'.

The provision of a gyro-repeater on the bridge of a submarine presented a number of obvious problems, and for many years it was necessary to carry an instrument up from the control room, along with 'Faithful Freddie', when coming to the surface. In 1929 submarines were given a watertight plug on the bridge to obviate the hazard of trailing leads up through the conning-tower hatch, but unplugging it took up valuable seconds when diving. The problem was finally solved in 1937, with the design of a pressure-tight gyro-repeater which could be left *in situ* on the bridge when the submarine dived. Surprisingly it gave remarkably little trouble and was still in service in non-nuclear submarines some fifty years later, despite the greatly increased diving depths.

Finally, in this necessarily brief list of small but often vital improvements, mention must be made of the tape repeater, in which the direction of the ship's head is clearly displayed in an illuminated window from a moving 35 mm tape, printed to show the 360 degrees. As each degree is a quarter of an inch long, small variations in heading are easily seen. This very simple idea, first introduced for trial in 1937, has been a great boon to helmsmen ever since and has greatly increased the accuracy to which a ship can be steered.[28]

One other interesting instrument which appeared in the years between the wars was the Mountbatten station-keeping equipment, invented by Captain Lord Louis Mountbatten and aimed at giving destroyer captains greater flexibility in control of their ships when keeping station in close company.[29] Although this was not designed at the ACO responsibility for introducing it into service was placed with the Compass Department as it required modifications to be made to the bridge pelorus. By the outbreak of hostilities it had been installed in the three latest flotillas to be built, (the *Inglefield*, *Jervis* and *Kelly* classes) after which fitting was stopped. Although it was reintroduced in 1951 in five destroyers of the *Daring* class, it was not perpetuated. An example is, however, held at the National Maritime Museum.

Further trials with the Brown compass

In 1929, following the Philpott enquiry, it was decided to buy four Brown gyro-compass outfits for trial in the Navy. It was agreed that the firm should superintend the installation of the first two and the Compass Department would be responsible for the second pair. Commander May again takes up the story:

> The four compasses were duly fitted in the Mine-laying Cruiser *Adventure*, the *Alresford*, (Navigation School training ship) and in the capital ships *Marlborough* and *Repulse*. At that time I was working for the firm of S. G. Brown as an Installation Engineer, though chiefly employed on experimental work. Thus because of my knowledge of the Royal Navy I was selected to supervise the installations of the first two ships to be ready. At this time Lieutenant Alexander, the Chief Compass Examiner, was about to retire and in the consequent re-organisation of the ACO Staff the Director offered me the vacancy. Mrs Brown, Managing Director of the firm, thought it might well be an advantage if there was someone in Admiralty employ who had an intimate knowledge of the Brown compass, so was only too willing to

agree to the cancellation of my contract. In consequence it came about that I superintended the fitting of the second two compasses as well, this time for ACO. In due course reports on the trials were received. Those from three of the ships were reasonable, their only complaint seems to have been the nuisance of having to allow for the Course and Speed Error in the Brown. The report from the *Marlborough* merely stated that the compass was useless. Asked for the grounds on which this statement was made she replied that the Brown and Sperry compasses frequently differed and as everyone knew that the Sperry was always correct the Brown must be useless.

Commander May concluded his account as follows:

The *Marlborough* was about to make an overnight passage from Chatham to Portsmouth and I embarked in her. At dawn the weather was calm and clear and I got permission to turn the ship through 360°. The officer of the watch called out the ship's head every 15° and the Navigator and I then took bearings of the rising sun, the time being noted. He used the Sperry repeater, while I used the Brown. As the ship's head passed through North the Brown bearing naturally differed as that compass had no course correction, and the Navigator shouted out that I could see that it was useless. I then realised that he had taken so little interest in the trial that he had not appreciated that the Brown had no course correction. We continued to record for a while after steadying again on a westerly course. I subsequently got out the sun's azimuths, corrected the Brown bearings for course error and plotted the bearings from the two compasses. These revealed that the Brown compass had behaved slightly better than the Sperry, and had settled quicker after the ship had steadied. So much for a ship report that the Brown was useless!

After two years of very thorough comparative trials it was apparent that there was very little to choose between the performance of the Brown and the Sperry, Mr Chaffer's conclusion being, 'These records are, on the whole, consistent. Brown . . . appears to be *at least* as good as Sperry.'[30] Although the excellent workmanship of the Brown compass was frequently commented upon, there was still doubt about whether the delicacy of the mechanism would withstand service conditions as well as the more robust Sperry, once the skilled maintenance provided during the trials was no longer available. Naval support and training was, in any case, already completely geared to the Sperry. No further Brown compasses were therefore ordered until the outbreak of war in 1939.

The ARL gunnery gyro-compasses and the Admiralty gyro transmission unit

Attempts to develop a gyro-compass capable of meeting the standards demanded by the Director of Naval Ordnance (DNO) went on for most of the interwar years. Professor Henderson's thesis in May 1918 had stressed the need for a compass with a very slow wander rate, even after rapid manoeuvres, to provide a datum in azimuth and this would best be met by an aperiodic or deadbeat compass. (This implies a compass which, if disturbed, will return gradually to the meridian and will not overshoot.) The current navigational compasses were periodic and, while they might more quickly return to the meridian after a disturbance, they would also oscillate about it before settling. The DNO had stated that he required a compass with an accuracy of $\pm$ 10′ at all times, a very tall order.

Suspicion of the Compass Department following the events of 1917 probably encouraged the DNO to continue the development of an independent gunnery gyro-compass after the war, based on the original proposals of Professor Henderson. At first the work was concentrated at Greenwich, with Henderson continuing to act as consultant after his retirement in 1920, but in 1925 the team moved to the Admiralty Research Laboratory (ARL) at Teddington, where it joined the gyro group under Mr A. L. Rawlings, formerly of the ACO. The ACO kept in close touch with the developments of this compass through a regular exchange of information and ideas and, on occasions, by participating in the sea trials which occurred at intervals throughout the 1920s and early 1930s.[31]

Initial experiments in the *Rapid* in 1925 were followed two years later by more extensive trials in another destroyer, the *Thisbe*, with no less than six different compasses including a gunnery compass developed by S. G. Brown. Mr Brown himself was in attendance.

The principle employed in these gunnery compasses was to use a completely separate gyro whose function was to act as a 'slow wanderer'. It was monitored by the main gyro compass so that the readings of the two instruments agreed fairly closely, but it would not follow any unduly rapid movement of the gyro-compass such as might occur after violent manoeuvres.

The year 1927 also saw the appearance of a new design of Anschütz gyro-compass with two gyroscopes in a floating, sealed sphere. This performed very well in laboratory tests at the ARL but on sea trials in the battleship *Nelson* it was said to be only 'slightly better than Sperry' and was not pursued.[32] Further trials with three ARL gunnery compasses took place in the battleship *Iron Duke* in 1933 and again in 1935, after which they were adjudged to be ready for Fleet trials and fitted in the cruisers *Devonshire*, *Shropshire* and *Sussex* in the Mediterranean.[33] By now the accuracy requirement had been relaxed and only called for a $\pm$ 20′, a more realistic figure.

At this stage the ACO unwittingly became fully involved. The compasses, which had performed well in the laboratory under expert supervision, gave considerable trouble at sea and it was not long before the SGC at Malta (Commander W. E. May) was called in to help. These were not 'his compasses' and were officially only allowed to be touched by 'ARL personnel', who were not always available. If he helped, would any subsequent failure on trial be blamed on his department? Enquiry from the Director of the Compass Department showed that he was also worried lest the compass might be accepted by default, because no one had actually reported against it. The solution was simple. May was permitted to assist and was thus able to render a report on the maintenance aspects of the compasses which rightly showed that although their performance might be adequate they were insufficiently robust for sea service.

By this time the nation and the Navy were preparing for war and the situation was becoming critical. At a meeting called by the Director of Naval Ordnance in 1938 it was decided not to proceed with the ARL compass but to retain the standard Admiralty gyro-compass (Sperry type) and to provide it with a slow wanderer, as described above. The new instrument would be called the Admiralty Gyro Transmission Unit (AGTU) and its design would be undertaken by the Director of the Compass Department. It must have been a disappointing end to twenty years of endeavour at the ARL.

Design of the AGTU was carried out at the ACO and a prototype assembled in the workshops. Laboratory trials on a rolling platform at the ARL were followed by successful sea trials in the battleship

Royal Sovereign, and later in conjunction with the master stabilizer unit (MSU) in the cruiser *Charybdis*. Production was then undertaken by Sperry whose new factory at Brentwood had been opened in 1931, the instrument being called the AGTU Mark I. It was fitted in all modern battleships, aircraft-carriers and cruisers from 1943 onwards and remained in service until more modern gyro-compasses were introduced in the mid-1960s. An AGTU Mark II was also developed at the ACO during the early 1940s for use in certain Fleet destroyers fitted with an American fire-control system (the Mark XXXVII director).

Magnetic compass development for ships and aircraft

In the field of magnetic compasses the period between the wars appears to have been mainly one of consolidation and tidying up, with few major advances. At the ACO the technical staff had been reduced to the bare minimum required for the routine tasks of procuring, testing, fitting and supporting the gyro- and magnetic compasses of the fleet. Research and development remained at a comparatively low level until stimulated in the late 1930s by the likelihood of war. Nevertheless a number of significant developments had been made of which a selection deserve to be briefly mentioned.

In 1919 it was pointed out that if the outer gimbal of a compass is supported in an athwartship direction, as was the case with most service compasses at the time, a heading error can be introduced when the ship is both rolling *and* pitching.[34] This does not, however, arise if the outer gimbal is supported fore and aft. Although the resultant error was not serious, the Director decided that a new range of compasses, gimballed fore and aft, should be introduced in parallel with those already in service, the latter being gradually phased out. One of the compasses introduced under this scheme was the Pattern 195, the 'flotilla-type' Standard Compass for destroyers, which first appeared in 1922 and, with minor modifications, remained the standard Admiralty magnetic compass more than sixty years later. At the same time it was decided that compass-makers should no longer be allowed to advertise by putting their own name on compass cards made for the Admiralty. A standard design of card was introduced which incorporated the fleur-de-lys used on the original Pattern 1 compass of 1840 and cards were to be labelled with the pattern number of the compass for which they were intended. This practice does not, however, appear to have lasted long.

The wider introduction of aircraft carriers in the early 1920s with their bridge to one side, gave real emphasis to the problems of slewing the spheres and Flinders bar when adjusting compasses. Whilst the theory of this problem had, of course, been well covered in the *Admiralty Manual of the Deviations of the Compass* since the days of Archibald Smith it was not a matter which normally arose at a well-placed compass. Now it had to be taken seriously and special binnacles were introduced to facilitate 'slewing'. Calculating the amount to slew became a favourite examination question for officers qualifying in navigation.

In trawlers, drifters and similar minor war vessels, lack of space for a good steering compass in the wheelhouse led, in 1935, to the development of an excellent overhead trawler binnacle, designed by Commander May, which was to prove of immense value a few years later when hundreds of these craft were taken up for Admiralty service during the war, in many cases with compass equipment that was quite inadequate. This binnacle (Pattern 922) also proved ideal for motor minesweepers, corvettes, landing craft and numerous other small vessels and was still in regular use in the 1980s.

In 1936, at the suggestion of the Director of Naval Equipment, the Compass Department took over responsibility for the design of submarine projector binnacles from the Director of Naval Construction and in the following year there appeared the first of a series of ACO projector binnacles (see p. 163) which, as already discussed, offered many advantages over the RL types.[35] Considerable assistance was given by the Admiralty Research Laboratory at Teddington with the design and specification of the optical glassware.

The concept of a transmitting magnetic compass for ships was still attractive, although little progress had been made since the pre-war Siemens-Halske compass. However, in 1929 Mr E. L. Holmes, working with Messrs Henry Hughes & Son, obtained a patent for a new system using a Wheatstone's bridge principle in which the compass fluid was electrically conductive and electrodes were fitted to the card and bowl. An alteration of course would unbalance the bridge and the resulting error signal was used to cause the bowl to be rotated so as to realign it with the magnet system and restore the balance. The bowl was thus made north-seeking and the same drive would operate the repeaters. Variations of this type of compass were tested at the ACO between 1931 and 1933 but although the idea was sound it had not yet been adequately developed.[36] Ten years later a considerably improved instrument, the Holmes telecompass, was to form the basis of the first of the successful family of transmitting magnetic compasses that were developed at the ACO during and after the war (see p. 295).

In the air, the first major innovation to appear during the 1920s was the development of separate compasses for pilots, who simply required to steer a course, and observers, who needed to take bearings. These compasses, referred to as P1, P2 (etc.) and O1, O2 (etc.) respectively began at the ACO in 1924 with the P1, which was an attempt to make use of a large stock of obsolete RAF Mark II compasses by giving them light cards similar to the Type 5/17. It was not a success and was followed quickly by the P2, a grid compass based on a greatly improved Type 6/18, and by the P3, with a vertical card for dashboard mounting. A number of developments of these two types followed, culminating in 1943 in the P12 which had the latest form of T-grid steering and a course-setting ring. It also had a reflecting mirror below it which enabled the compass to be mounted high up, clear of other instruments, yet to be viewed in an approximately horizontal plane. The P12 is still being made (1984) and although little used in service aircraft it is popular in light civil aircraft and has sometimes been fitted in marine applications where space is limited.

The 'O' series of compasses were mainly of the azimuth type for observing bearings of landmarks, although they were also provided as telltale compasses for bomber navigators. The most notable survivor of this series is the O.6, the hand-bearing compass, designed at the ACO in 1935. It was developed from the 'Kite' balloon compass used during the war (see p. 203) and is still much in demand for many applications half a century later.

Corrector boxes, using scissor magnets, were available for the majority of these compasses. Whilst at first these only catered for coefficients B and C it was later found necessary to introduce heeling-error magnets because of the difference in the attitude of the aircraft in level flight and when 'tail down', on the ground, while being swung. When armour plate was introduced into aircraft, early in World War II, the ACO carried out experiments using spheres to counteract coefficient D, but these were never adopted.

The RAF Distant Reading gyro-magnetic compass (DR compass)

The advent of all-metal aircraft, together with the wide introduction of electrical equipment, required the magnetic element of the compass to be removed from the cockpit and sited in a part of the aircraft where there was a more stable magnetic field. This implied having a compass with a repeater system. Gyro-stabilization was a logical development, greatly reducing temporary misalignments due to acceleration or turning error and thus combining the stability of the gyroscope with the heading provided by the magnetic compass.

It is probable that early experiments with gyro-stabilisation were started at the ACO in 1919[37] but that they were shelved through lack of staff. Work began in earnest at the Royal Aircraft Establishment at Farnborough in 1925 but it was 1937 before the first compass proved satisfactory on trials. Even then many difficulties remained and it was the spring of 1941 before the DR compass was first used operationally, in Stirling bombers of No. 7 squadron.

The master unit contained a double-pivoted magnetic compass needle and a small gyroscope with a horizontal spin axis, which rotated at about 12,000 rpm and provided a very stable datum in space. The direction of the gyroscope axis was controlled by the *mean* position of the magnetic needle so that whilst it indicated the correct course of the aircraft, it would not react to short term fluctuations. The complete master unit was normally placed in the tail of the aircraft, well away from sources of local magnetic interference, and the aircraft's heading was transmitted to repeaters which could be sited wherever required in the aircraft. Variation and deviation could also be fed in so that the repeaters would indicate the true course.[38]

During the war this excellent compass played a vital role in furthering the effectiveness of the bombing offensive. Unfortunately it proved too large to be fitted in single-seater fighters. Its upkeep and repair were destined to feature largely in the workload on the ACO workshops during the years ahead.

Staff changes

Before closing this chapter on the interwar years, mention must be made of certain important staff changes that occurred below the level of Director and Superintendent. Although basic research and development work was necessarily limited during this period, Mr Chaffer had nevertheless been able to achieve many worthwhile advances. In 1921, on the departure of Mr Rawlings, he had succeeded to the post of Superintendent (Civil), in charge of experimental work, and with the arrival of Captain Hitchins had been appointed Chief Technical Assistant to the Director, serving in this capacity until he left the ACO in 1936. After a brief spell at the Admiralty, where he was responsible for assessing inventions, he was appointed to the important post of Superintendent of the Admiralty Reseach Laboratory at Teddington.[39]

Chaffer's place as Senior Technical Officer at the ACO was taken by Mr J. E. Wright, one of the original group of gyro-travellers who had joined as lieutenants RNVR in 1915. At the same time the department was joined by Mr W. G. Heatley, a scientific officer from ARL who had started his career as scientific assistant to Professor Sir James Henderson at Greenwich and had worked on many of his inventions. In 1925 he had transferred to Teddington, where he initially worked in the gyro group under Mr Rawlings, and he was thus ideally qualified for the ACO. It was not long before he was actively involved in the development of the type 2005 gyro-compass, the bottle transmitter, the tape repeater and the AGTU Marks I and II, as well as many items of associated equipment. By the end of World War II he had become the Chief Scientist at the ACO, with the rank of Principal Scientific Officer.

Another officer to join the ACO at about this time was Lieutenant Commander A. V. Thomas, who became a Naval Assistant in 1938. Having been invalided from the submarine service in 1929 he had then qualified in navigation, but ill health had continued to dog him and he had to give up all hope of an active service career. On 1 June 1939 he was sent to swing the submarine *Thetis* off Liverpool on the first day of her sea trials and, as an ex-submariner, it was his normal practice on such occasions to remain on board for the passage to the Clyde. On this occasion, however, as he was needed for another compass adjustment at Newcastle early the following morning, he disembarked immediately after the swing. Later that day the *Thetis* made her first and fatal dive, from which she was unable to surface. There were only four survivors.[40] Such is the hinge of fate. Commander Thomas went on to serve at the ACO for twenty-four years, becoming the Deputy Director in 1954, the post in which the author relieved him eight years later.

Rearmament and preparations for war

Throughout the 1920s and early 1930s the world had discussed disarmament. The Washington treaty of 1922 had come and gone, leaving Britain with two of the strangest-looking battleships of the century.[41] The several London and Geneva conferences between 1927 and 1936 had failed to produce any sort of agreement on naval ship-building and had finally been flouted by Germany in 1935 and Japan the following year. Britain found her forces once again woefully unprepared for a future that was filled with foreboding and the country had now to undertake the production of warships and aircraft on a scale unparallelled in history. The ship-building programmes approved for the three financial years up to the beginning of 1939 included 5 new battleships, 5 aircraft-carriers, 16 cruisers, 24 destroyers and 22 submarines, with many other supporting vessels.

At the ACO the build-up of industrial strength, particularly of skilled craftsmen, had begun in the late 1920s, when gyro repair work and the manufacture of magnetic compasses as an in-house activity had been stepped up. By 1934 the one workshop that had been hurriedly put up in 1917 was proving inadequate for a workforce of fifty operatives, nor could it provide the clean conditions necessary for modern assembly work. A large new workshop (No. 2) was built in 1935 and from then on the number of industrial staff increased rapidly. There was still much unemployment in the country and there was no shortage of volunteers for the interesting and skilled jobs available. By the summer of 1939 the total stood at 327, which included 162 skilled craftsmen as well as a large number of women workers for such tasks as luminizing compass cards and grid rings. All aircraft work was now concentrated in the new workshop.

By the summer of 1938, the urgent need for all types of compass, particularly those for aircraft, required regular overtime not only in the workshops but in the test rooms as well. Described as 'the ACO's Munich celebration', this continued until August 1939 when, about a week before war was declared, the factory, for that is what the workshops had become, went over completely to shift working. This was to continue without a break until the war was over.

Meanwhile the build-up of non-industrial technical staff had been more restrained, the number of technical officers having only risen from ten in 1930 to seventeen in 1939. This was understandable. The demand before a 'conventional' war is inevitably for proven, conventional equipment. Only as the war proceeds does the requirement for new devices, to meet new and unforeseen eventualities, arise in earnest. It is then that the designer and innovator are needed as never before. And so it was to prove.

NOTES

CHAPTER 9

[1] Private letter to the author.

[2] ACO Archives. Admiralty office memorandum No. C 12172/24.

[3] Defence Council Instruction, No. 1013/66.

[4] Department of Scientific and Industrial Research, 'Annual Report 1928/29'.

[5] Robert Watson Watt, *Three Steps to Victory*, Odhams, 1957.

[6] Ibid. p. 110.

[7] ACO archives. Admiralty Letter, C. E-in-C 52023/50.

[8] ACO Archives. Ministry of Defence, Minute No. 6LA/SLO(72)/210/DLW/ JWH (20 October 1981).

[9] 'Report of the Admiralty Committee on gyro-compass development', 1927.

[10] The Director of Naval Ordnance was the Admiralty department responsible for gunnery-control matters, on which Henderson was working at Greenwich.

[11] This compass did not get beyond the laboratory stage but the idea formed the basis for the design of the ARL gunnery compass after the war (see p. 220). It is surprising, however, that this invitation was not put to S. G. Brown, whose patent for a gyro-compass had been 'frozen' during the same year.

[12] Document G02682/18 (29 May 1918), in DNO, Vol. G 0388/19.

[13] Records of evidence given to Admiral Philpott's committee. National Maritime Museum Compass Collection, Envelope N32.

[14] Compass Department, paper CD 452/18 in CP Patents 453/21.

[15] These words were taken from the *Brown Marine Gazette* for July 1927.

16 The fourth gyro was an additional 'stabilizing' gyro introduced by Anschütz during the war. Harrison's letter is held in the National Maritime Museum Compass Collection, Envelope N32.

17 Ibid.

18 Ibid. Mr Brown's own words in a memorandum to the Admiralty in 1941 (paragraph 13).

19 Ibid.

20 Ibid. (Admiralty letter, 23 September 1927).

21 Ibid.

22 Ibid. (Letter, 30 November 1927).

23 National Maritime Museum Compass Collection. Envelope N33. (Report on the hearing of the Royal Commission on Awards to Inventors in the *Brown Marine Gazette*, Vol. 2, No. 1 (January 1930).

24 Admiralty Fleet Order, 1437/36.

25 The author suspects that, despite modern developments (see chapter 12), the Admiralty gyro-compass will still be found at sea in the year 2000!

26 Admiralty Fleet Order, 1906/23.

27 Admiralty Fleet Order, 3050/49.

28 Admiralty Fleet Order, 1249/39.

29 Admiralty Fleet Order, 1273/37 and BR132.

30 National Maritime Museum Compass Collection, Envelope N34. (Report on the trials in *Adventure* and *Alresford*).

31 ACO Historical Section, Part 5 Reports of trials of the *ARL* gunnery compass are contained in Item R37 (series).

32 ACO Historical Section, Part 5. (Item R37/(22)).

33 A copy of the draft handbook of the ARL gunnery gyro-compass (1936). by Mr W. G. Heatley, is held in the ACO Historical Section, Part 5. (Item R31).

34 Theory of the deviations of the magnetic compass (1948), Part 9 (BR101/48).

35 R & D Report of the Compass Department, 1947.

36 ACO Historical Section, Part 5. (Item R11).

37 Admiralty Technical History, Vol. 3, Part 20. (October 1919), p. 8.

38 A description of the DR Compass is contained in Air Ministry Publication A.P. 3456D.

39 Clifford Chaffer died of a heart attack in July 1939. A new laboratory block for gyro work, built at the ACO early in the war, was named the Chaffer block in his memory. This building was demolished in 1980.

40 The *Thetis* was subsequently raised. She was later renamed the *Thunderbolt* and saw service during World War II.

41 The *Nelson* and *Rodney* had all their main armament (nine 16 inch guns) forward of the bridge and appeared to be 'all forecastle'. This unusual arrangement had been introduced to meet the severe tonnage restrictions imposed by the Washington treaty, but they were nevertheless a very successful design.

World War II, 1939-45

'When I looked upon that densely packed congregation of fighting men of the same faith, of the same fundamental laws and same ideals, and now to a large extent of the same interests, and certainly in different degrees facing the same dangers, it swept across me that here was the only hope, but also the sure hope, of saving the world from measureless degradation. And so we came back across the ocean waves, uplifted in spirit, fortified in resolve.' (Winston Churchill, in a broadcast to a nation after returning in the battleship *Prince of Wales* from signing the Atlantic Charter, 24 August 1941[1])

On 3 September 1939 the Special Telegram 'Total-Germany' went out to the Fleet. The war was on and no one was surprised. The breathing-space since Munich and 'Peace in our time' had been devoted wholly to preparing for war – a desperate attempt to make up for those lost years when many politicians had found it easier to accept Hitler's reassuring words than to take note of what he was doing. Within days came the further signal to announce 'Winston's back', as Churchill again took up the reins at the Admiralty that he had last held in 1914. This time, however, the Navy was far less prepared numerically than it had been then.

At the ACO work was already organized on a war footing, with much of the labour force working in shifts around the clock. An air-raid shelter had been dug in the director's garden to the side of the mansion[2] and more were later prepared under the hallowed turf of the green oval by the front doors. During the hours of darkness fire-watchers took turns in a look-out post on the roof, while an officer was on duty each night to deal with emergencies or urgent calls for compass equipment. The valuable museum collection was stowed away for safety in the cellars. The air-raid siren for the eastern half of Slough was established on top of the de Molyens tower and operated by the ACO telephonists. Everyone wondered how soon the first air raid would come.

Compasses for ships and aircraft were now needed as never before and the number of ships requiring attention rose very rapidly. Each day brought its new crop of problems and challenges. So much occurred at the ACO during those six hectic years that it would be impossible to present a clear account in strictly chronological order. Instead it has seemed best to treat each main subject briefly on its own and to leave the reader to form his or her own picture of the hive of activity that went with it.

Responsibilities of the Compass Department

To set the scene it might be helpful to summarize briefly the responsibilities of the Director of the Compass Department in 1939. These had grown considerably during the interwar years and were now as follows[3]:

1. To undertake all the responsibilities of an Admiralty department under the Controller. This included, in particular, designating the compass equipment for each type of ship and checking the appropriate plans showing its installation.

2. As a design and experimental establishment, to undertake the development of all magnetic and gyro-compasses for the Navy, the Army and the Royal Air Force. To produce handbooks, as necessary, for naval compass equipment.

3. To inspect the magnetic compass positions of all new ships during building and to carry out the initial compass adjustment.

4. To maintain a travelling staff to attend on board any HM ship experiencing difficulties with its gyro-compasses and to supervise the testing and adjusting of these instruments after they have been installed. To provide the resident staff (SGCs) in certain dockyards.

5. To act as production officer for all gyro- and magnetic compasses, producing the necessary manufacturing drawings and specifications for the compasses and associated equipment, and the plans for their installation.[4] To arrange manufacturing contracts and to monitor their progress.

6. To provide an inspection and testing organization for all gyro- and magnetic compasses. Inspection covered all parts of the compass and might be done either at the ACO or at the manufacturer's works. Testing of each gyro-compass occupied 10–14 days.

7. To provide instruction on gyro-compass matters and in magnetic compass adjustment to officers and certain specialist ratings; also to dockyard officers and fitters, as appropriate.[5]

8. In the workshops, to build prototypes of new equipment and to undertake production to prove the drawings. Further production, repair and reconditioning of equipment to be undertaken as required.

9. In addition, the Director of Stores maintained a naval stores depot at the ACO which by 1945 had a staff, including labourers, of 145.

Workshops and test rooms

Early in 1939 it was apparent that more workshop space would be needed and a large extension was quickly built onto the north-east corner of the mansion. It was constructed on two floors to accommodate machines (lathes, grinders, etc.) below and gyro-compass refurbishing above and was known as No. 3 workshop. A service lift ran between the floors, and it was not long before the lift shaft was requisitioned for mounting the long submarine projector binnacles for test. Later in the war it was also used for X-craft periscopes. With an eye to the future, a large drawing office was added on top of the north wing of the mansion, and by the end of the war the original five draughtsmen had increased to twenty. At this period the duplication of drawings was still being done by Sun-printing, a slow and tedious process.

In 1941, at the request of the Ministry of Aircraft Production a further large workshop (No. 4) was built in the north park and for the first two years handled nothing but the RAF's DR Compasses, which were needed for the bomber offensive. Special test rooms were provided on the spot and by 1943 No. 4 workshop alone was employing some 400 men, in two shifts. As it was a quarter of a mile from the rest of the establishment it provided useful factory dispersion against the risk of air-raid damage. In 1942 a further workshop (No. 5) was built to handle the large amount of painting and 'stoving'.

The throughput of compasses coming in for repair, both for the Navy and for the Ministry of Aircraft Production, continued to grow throughout the war and, by 1945, amounted to almost 3000 a month of which some 250 were the delicate and complicated DR compasses. Recruiting skilled men to handle all this work was difficult and they had to be accepted from many trades including jewellers, silversmiths and watchmakers, even musicians and meter-readers. Those who were not indentured craftsmen were entered as 'dilutees' and employed on the more routine tasks. Later they were supplemented by women. It was popular employment and qualified as a reserved occupation, not liable to call-up. At the same time some of the skilled young men already at the ACO volunteered to join the forces and were away for much of the war. There was thus a continual turnover of industrial staff. As women were less liable to be called up, the test rooms and inspection did not suffer as severely as the workshops. Two large houses, Langley House and Kenwood, were requisitioned locally for overflow work and were mainly used for the inspection and assembly of components for aircraft compasses and bomb sights. They were reported to have been bitterly cold in winter, with large rooms, ancient grates and practically no coal! Nevertheless the fifty or so women employed there wrapped up well and did first-class work.

By 1945 the number on the industrial payroll had risen to 850, of whom almost half were women, and compasses were being tested and certificated at the enormous rate of 20,000 a month. Almost all distribution was made direct from the ACO, through the Naval Stores organization which, at the height of the war, was despatching as many as 750 packing-cases or crates of compass equipment each week.

Compass positions and compass adjustment

The complementary tasks of siting compasses and swinging ships, which had been the traditional role of the department since 1842, now proved to be among its most difficult. From the start there was a tendancy on the part of constructors and others responsible for fitting guns, armour and other equipment to think that in war the 'Rules' could be forgotten. The situation became so bad that on one occasion the Director reported that five members of his staff were away simultaneously, curing unnecessary compass problems, and it required a top-level showdown with the Director of Naval Construction before order was restored. Even then mysterious craft would sometimes appear, designed by other authorities, who had generally omitted to think about the compass until the last minute.

No sooner had the Admiralty issued a memorandum[6] reminding all authorities that the Compass Department must be consulted at an early stage, than craft began arriving from Canada and the United States where, it appeared, safe distances had not been heard of. In many of these ships the bridges had to be considerably altered to make the magnetic compass of any use whatsoever. In the Merchant Navy the position as every bit as bad, and here the commercial compass-adjusters were unable to exercise the same authority. The case of the *Empire Knoll* is worth quoting as just one example of the iniquitous practice of placing a compass in a position where it could not be corrected. Owing to the inefficiency of her compasses the *Empire Knoll* was unable to lay a course to join her convoy on her maiden voyage. She tried to return to Newcastle but the port had been mined and she was forced to remain at sea all night with her compasses 'swinging wildly'. At 4.0 o'clock in the morning she ended up on the breakwater, where she finished her brief career.

Swinging ship for the adjustment of compasses was another requirement which naval operators ashore tried all too frequently to ignore in the belief that they were 'getting on with the war'. Although the Compass Department's responsibility officially ended after the first swing of a new ship, it was soon apparent to the director that he would have to exercise far wider control over this activity. As the following narrative shows, it was an uphill struggle.

On the outbreak of war four retired Commanders (N) were called up for swinging duties with the Compass Department and each was given responsibility for the new ships round a certain section of the coast. These men were 'rusty' and must at first have had a difficult time dealing with ship-builders intent on cutting corners to get ships to sea. After the first adjustment, responsibility for swinging rested with the senior naval officers of the ports, many of whom did not have swinging officers on their staffs. If they were lucky they might recruit the local commercial adjuster to assist; otherwise they tended to detail any officer for swinging duties. The ACO had therefore quickly to organize ad hoc swinging courses on top of an already full programme. Matters were brought to a head in 1940 by the introduction of degaussing (see p. 252), followed soon afterwards by the fitting of compass-corrector coils, which had to be adjusted, and this proved too much for many of the commercial adjusters, let alone the new recruits. The director therefore urged on the Board the necessity of appointing Admiralty swinging officers at all the major ports and, as a start, in 1941 arranged for three officers to be sent to these ports to train the local 'swingers' in the new techniques. They were not always made welcome.

At last, in March 1942, approval was given for the Compass Department to take over the training and appointment of all swinging officers, and thereafter regular four-week courses were held at the ACO, followed by four weeks practical work with an experienced swinging officer, generally in a naval dockyard.[7]

The establishment of the Combined Operations organization in 1942 soon brought further problems. Not only did 'combined ops' develop a whole new language of its own but its members had a tendency to divorce themselves completely from the rest of the Navy. They had a job to do and time was short. Officers-in-charge of landing-craft bases were often reluctant to accept the need for compass adjustment or to allow time for it to be carried out. After one senior officer had claimed that the compasses in his craft were perfectly satisfactory, a member of Compass Department staff was allowed to take passage from Northney, round Hayling Island to Portsmouth. He noted that the north point of the compass was locked to an adjacent bulkhead and that the compass did not alter its reading for the entire trip. Even when the need was demonstrated, landing-craft bases were often reluctant to make their craft available to be swung, possibly due to a failure to understand the problem. Commander May recalls visiting a base to adjust the compasses in a flotilla of landing craft. He was given a dozen compasses and one LCA and asked if he would mind adjusting them all in the same craft!

Another incident was far more serious. In the summer of 1942 an officer from the ACO was asked casually, while in Greenock, whether assistance could be given to swing a number of craft from the local base 'for an exercise', and the director agreed to lend an officer for the purpose. After the North African landings, complaints were made that the ACO had given insufficient assistance during the build-up, as less than half the craft which took part had been swung. Because of the secrecy surrounding the operation, the Compass Department had been told nothing about the impending landing, and the assistance of one officer was all that had been sought.

The report on the North African landings at last brought home to Combined Operations Headquarters the importance of compass adjustment, and the department was asked to train the necessary swinging officers to deal with the many hundreds of landing craft then being built. Only sub-lieutenants RNVR were available and as these officers generally had no experience of handling craft, let alone of compasses, it was arranged that they should do a fortnight's theory at the ACO followed by a further intensive fortnight of swinging at a landing-craft base under an instructor from Slough. Not surprisingly the most difficult part was still to persuade the base to make craft available for this training.

Unlike other 'swingers' the appointment of these officers to bases was handled by the Chief of Combined Operations. Late in 1943, when preparations for the Normandy landings were well advanced, the ACO was asked, at very short notice, to provide still more swinging officers for the individual Assault groups. Once again ad hoc arrangements had to be made but this time the lesson was evidently learnt as, after the invasion, the Director was asked by the Chief of Combined Operations to take over full responsibility for landing-craft swinging officers. These men were then gradually withdrawn for a thorough training so that they would be ready to be sent out East for the impending Japanese landings.

The maximum number of trained swinging officers in the field at any one time during the war was 110. They embraced officers of the RN, RNR, and RNVR, both active and retired, ranging in rank from commander to midshipman and in age from 19 to 60. They covered a total of 60 different ports, at home and abroad, 12 of which were entirely used as combined operations bases. Throughout they did a magnificent job. At the height of the war the complex pattern of their appointments and movements was being organized entirely from the ACO by Commander W. E. May, one of the naval assistants, who had himself been carrying out compass adjustments on behalf of the department since 1929.

Compass joiners

An interesting carry-over from compass adjustment in the nineteenth century was the employment of compass joiners in dockyards, the natural successors to the men responsible for embedding the corrector magnets into the wooden deck or redrilling the pillar (see p. 93). In later years these men not only carried out any necessary repairs to the binnacles but often gave invaluable assistance to the adjuster, particularly when a number of compasses had to be corrected simultaneously. During the war approval was given for swinging officers at other ports to employ a skilled labourer for this duty but when the manpower situation made this impossible, several swinging officers obtained the assistance of a Wren. These young women took the greatest interest in their work and were even known to take away motor boats out of working hours to practice adjusting compasses for themselves.

The magnetic mine and Degaussing

The story goes that on the morning of 22 November 1939 Captain Hitchens was summoned from his bed at an early hour as the Prime Minister wished to see him. The first German magnetic mine had been discovered and rendered safe and the Prime Minister now wished to know what the 'magnetic department' was going to do about the safety of our shipping around the coast. It was no doubt with some relief that Captain Hitchins explained that his 'magnetics' were compasses, whereas *mines* belonged to the Director of Torpedoes and Mining.

The harrowing problems that beset the operating authorities who had, at the time, no method of sweeping the new menace, did not immediately concern the ACO. However, it was essential that an antidote to the magnetic mine should be found with all speed, in order that ships could again move freely and safely around the coast, and as experts in magnetics the ACO was very much involved in the early discussions. Before long, however, a new department of degaussing (DG) was established to co-ordinate this work and thereafter the ACO's interest lay principally in overcoming the serious disturbing effect which any degaussing system must inevitably have upon the magnetic compass.

Degaussing was the collective name given to the various methods and techniques employed to reduce or nullify a ship's magnetic field. This could be achieved either by fitting permanent electric coils round the ship or by applying various magnetic treatments to the hull, such as wiping or flashing. The most effective and widely used method was, however, to wrap the ship with one or more electrical degaussing coils in which the current could be varied to neutralize, as far as possible, the various parts of the ship's magnetic field.

Degaussing-coil systems can vary in complexity from one simple coil round the whole ship, as was used in most merchant ships, to a comprehensive set of coils, wrapped round different parts of the ship, as is used in warships, important merchantmen, minesweepers and other vessels needing special protection. The current in the appropriate coils can be varied to match the changes which occur in the ship's magnetism as a result of change of latitude or alteration of course.

Naturally these coils produced a considerable disturbing effect on the compass, the size of which varied according to the current used. The ACO had therefore to find a means of nullifying this effect so that once a compass had been adjusted in the normal way, with magnets and soft-iron correctors, it would remain reasonably correct whether the degaussing coils were in operation or not. This was achieved by fitting small corrector coils to the binnacle, close to the compass, which would produce an equal and opposite effect at the compass from that produced by the main DG coils. By connecting these corrector coils in parallel with the main DG coils, any change in the current in the main coils would result in a proportional change in the current in the appropriate compass corrector coil.

In an earlier chapter it was noted that when correcting a compass for the effects of the ship's magnetism, separate magnets are used to reduce coefficients B, C and heeling error. Separate B, C and HE corrector coils were therefore provided to cancel each component of the error produced in the compass by the main DG coils. Once these corrector coils had been balanced against the main DG coils, the compass should be largely unaffected by the use of degaussing. The ACO had therefore to organize provision of the necessary corrector coils and resistance boxes to enable this to be done, to work out simple techniques for their adjustment and to arrange the necessary training. As the Admiralty also had responsibility for the safety of merchant ships in wartime, this task extended to them as well. With the numbers of ships involved it was an enormous task.

At first DG-travellers worked from the ACO, inspecting the installation of the compass corrector coils and making the initial adjustments necessary to balance them against the main DG coils. This had, of course, to be done before the ship sailed for her swing as it was normally unsafe to switch off her DG coils on the swinging ground. In due course this adjustment became a normal part of the swinging officer's duties, as it is today. However, it is seldom easy to teach an old dog new tricks and some of the senior commercial compass-adjusters clearly did not take kindly to these new practices. They had always corrected compasses with magnets and they had no wish to start doing so with electrical coils, which they did not understand. There were several instances where the more rebellious were deliberately obstructive, losing no opportunity of interfering with the coils, of which they heartily disapproved, and dangerously misleading merchantship captains as to their value. Later, however, wiser counsels prevailed and the more enlightened adjusters, encouraged by the British Nautical Instrument Trade Association and the Board of Trade, agreed to attend courses in degaussing at the ACO. These eventually became very popular and were continued into the mid-1960s.

In ships which were not degaussed by coils, a treatment known as wiping or flashing could be used to neutralize much of the permanent magnetism of the hull and provide a measure of immunity against magnetic mines, although the effect of this treatment would wear off in time. Submarines and trawlers generally came into this category. The ship had to be swung in the normal way after each treatment, and a careful watch then kept on the deviation of the compass, which would gradually change as the effect of the treatment wore off.

The whole degaussing operation took up a considerable amount of ACO effort, but it was a real success story. DG compass corrector coils were provided for the binnacles of ships whenever degaussing coils were fitted. They were also incorporated as an integral part of the design of new binnacles and this practice was extended retrospectively to the older types, as appropriate. The majority of HM ships are still (1984) fitted with degaussing but since 1975 it has been the policy only to equip certain selected important merchantmen.

Magnetic-compass development

Not surprisingly the development of special craft to meet specific wartime tasks led to demands for new designs of compasses. The operational requirements of coastal forces, submarines, chariots, canoes, yachts and many other vessels, to say nothing of the wide variety of new assault landing craft, all brought their own challenges. The requirements of aircraft and of the host of tanks and armoured fighting vehicles, particularly those required for the invasion forces, all added to the problems to be solved. In all, thirty-six new patterns of magnetic compass were designed and introduced during the war in addition to a number of transmitting compasses and many modifications to existing equipment.[8]

In submarines competition for space on the bridge, particularly for radar, soon led to a reduction in the size and weight of the ACO projector binnacles. The bridge steering position was removed and a number of slimmed-down versions of the projector were introduced to meet the needs of different classes. A very small projector binnacle with a 2 inch card (the Mark XXI) was designed for use in X-craft (midget submarines) and constructed so as to be completely retractable inside the hull. As these boats also carried a small Brown gyro-compass, specially adapted to follow their very rapid alterations of course, and an emergency directional gyro indicator, fitting all the equipment into the very limited space available presented special problems. An X-craft was therefore transported by road from Gosport to Ditton Park, where it remained camouflaged among the trees for several weeks whilst ACO staff carried out tests and juggled with the task of fitting everything in.[9]

Compass adjustment in X-craft required special care as the degaussing system consisted of electro magnets fitted along the keel. Their side cargoes (limpet mines or 2 tons of high explosive) also had a considerable effect on the compass. As no corrector coils were fitted,[10] these craft had to be provided with separate deviation tables for a variety of conditions, and the boat had to be re-swung whenever the side cargo was changed.

The pressing need for convoy escorts during 1940 led to the rapid construction of a very large number of Flower-class corvettes, for which at first no gyro-compasses were available. These ships were therefore given an interesting magnetic compass and binnacle which had been developed shortly before the war for antisubmarine trawlers, in which the bearing of the asdic oscillator was projected from below the compass as a line of light onto the compass card and the oscillator itself was trained manually by a small wheel mounted on the binnacle.[11] It was a primitive but effective arrangement which served them well until gyro-compasses and more modern asdic equipment became available in 1942.

In battleships, cruisers and aircraft carriers, the introduction of new equipment onto the bridge for fighter direction or target indication made it increasingly difficult to maintain a good magnetic position, while the space taken up by the standard compass, which was seldom used, could be ill-afforded. Some ships took the law into their own hands and removed the Standard altogether. Although the more prudent navigators maintained the integrity of the compass position so that it could be replaced in the event of gyro-compass failure, others planned to rely simply on an uncorrected boats compass. Not surprisingly the Compass Department was disturbed at this flouting of authority and alarmed at the suggested use of an uncompensated compass which would be both useless and dangerous.

A Fleet order was issued,[12] pointing out the large errors which might be expected from such a compass (amounting, in a battleship, to as much as 180°). Eventually towards the end of the war approval was given for battleships and aircraft carriers to be given a third gyro-compass, a Brown, Type B (without transmission), mounted in the primary steering position, and for the Standard Compass to be removed.[13] Cruisers were provided with a 'Faithful Freddie' on a portable stand for shipping when required. This compass, which was especially fitted with DG corrector coils, was also used as the Standard Compass in certain landing craft.

Admiralty transmitting magnetic compasses

The need for an efficient transmitting magnetic compass had still not been met when in 1942 Mr E. L. Holmes sent his improved telecompass to the ACO for examination. This compass, which was designed primarily for aircraft, represented a considerable advance over the instrument that had been tested during the 1930s (see p. 236), and although still not entirely satisfactory as an operational compass, it convinced the ACO that the principle of the electrolytic pick-up was sound. Development work was therefore put in hand in 1943, using a valve amplifier in place of the relay system provided, and by this one step most of the defects in the original compass were eliminated.

Extensive laboratory tests were followed in the summer of 1943 by trials at sea in a motor torpedo boat (MTB) where an urgent requirement had arisen for a repeating-compass to provide heading information to positions below decks (e.g. to the plot and the radar). An Air Ministry DR compass had already been fitted in a number of motor launches (MLs) and MTBs for this purpose but it was not proving satisfactory in a seagoing environment.

The Admiralty transmitting magnetic compass, Type 1 (ATMC1), which was designed for shelf-mounting in small craft, was an immediate success and, on completion of the official trial, the prototype was left on board the MTB where it gave very little trouble for the next fifteen months. It was quickly put into production for both MTBs and MLs and proved very popular.

The success of the ATMC1 suggested the possibility of a similar equipment for larger ships and for other vessels not fitted with a gyro-compass. A new instrument, the ATMC2, was therefore designed, based on the standard Admiralty compass (the Pattern 0195A) and incorporating many of the lessons learnt during the trial. It had a full-sized binnacle, with built-in DG corrector coils, and was quickly shown to have a superior performance. Experimental models were fitted in the wheelhouse of the destroyer *Wizard* and in the battleship *Duke of York*, where it was sited on a sponson on the fore side of the after funnel. This was an early attempt to solve the problem of banishing the Standard Compass from the bridge but, although the position was magnetically satisfactory, the idea did not meet with favour and was not pursued. In the *Wizard*, however, the compass proved entirely successful and a changeover switch was provided to enable the ATMC to drive all the gyro-repeaters on board, including those concerned with fire control, an arrangement which later became standard in all destroyers and frigates. Finally a total error corrector, fed manually with variation and deviation, was incorporated so that repeaters would show true rather than magnetic heading.

Neither the ATMC1 nor the ATMC2 was extensively fitted until after the war, but both equipments played an important part in the early development of the family of transmitting magnetic compasses which were to come into service over the next fifteen years.

Transmitting compasses for aircraft

The aircraft DR compass introduced in 1941 continued to be widely fitted throughout the war but, because of its size, could only be carried in multi-engined aircraft. It was much favoured in the Mosquito aircraft of the Pathfinder force. In an attempt to cater for lighter aircraft, the principles of the ATMC1 and 2 were applied to a small P8 deadbeat aircraft compass, and a prototype equipment known as the ATMC3 was developed. Although this compass was not gyro-stabilized and was therefore subject to the usual acceleration errors in aircraft, it had a good performance and could provide a self-synchronous transmission to repeaters. It was adopted by the Ministry of Aircraft Production in September 1944 for use with a new, small air-position indicator but was never put into wide production.[14] After the war it did, however, lead to the development of the ATMC4 for use in tanks, and eventually to the ATMC4G for coastal forces. These and the further development of the gyro-magnetic compass Mark 4B will be covered in the next chapter.

Meanwhile, in 1942 two American remote indicating aircraft compasses arrived in the United Kingdom, both of which were designed to have their sensitive elements fitted in a stable magnetic position in the wing. These were the Magnesyn compass, in which a static transmitter coil sensed the movement of a compass needle fitted in a float, and the Pioneer gyro-fluxgate compass, in which the sensing element was an earth-inductor coil system, stabilized in the horizontal by a gyroscope. Both compasses were sent to the ACO for evaluation before being subjected to operational trials by the Royal Air Force. The pioneer compass became the standard system in all American heavy aircraft while the magnesyn was widely fitted in the Hornets, Meteors and Vampires of the RAF.[15] Before long the ACO workshops were actively involved in repairing both these compasses.

Compass-installation problems in aircraft

It was inevitable that the rapid progress in aircraft development during the war should threaten compass performance. Mild steel airframes, armour plating, heavier armament, increased electrics, radio, radar and much ancilliary equipment all played their part. Occasionally difficulties could be overcome by demagnetization, as in the case of nose-wheels and certain airframe components; sometimes a change of material could help, as with the armour plate. Unexplained changes in the magnetic state of the airframe often occurred after gunfire and could sometimes be shown to be dependant on the aircraft's heading during firing. For this reason 'Beaufighters' always fired a final prolonged burst on a northerly heading to remove earlier changes in magnetism. Occasionally there were unexplained polarity changes in the guns themselves, while bombs, mines and torpedoes all had their separate effects. Mine-laying aircraft, for which accurate navigation was essential, always had a check swing before each sortie, the pilot being given a separate deviation card which he was to destroy as soon as the mine had been laid.

Before the United States entered the war its aircraft manufacturers had tended to pay less attention to safe distances than those in Britain, and in aircraft bought from American sources considerable compass interference was often experienced. Their habit of using single-wire electrical systems with an earth return could cause errors of between 5° and 50° and necessitated many modifications.

The introduction of radar and more powerful radio naturally received the highest priority but its installation was often done with little regard for the existing compass positions. On one occasion the navigating officer of a coastal command base complained to the Compass Department about the large and frequent changes of deviation taking place in his Wellington bombers. Over a period of three weeks one aircraft had been swung five times, showing a change of coefficient B of 6–9 degrees on each occasion. Contact with the radio section revealed that the radio transmitter had been changed five times during that period, quite unknown to the aircrew or the navigation section. At first, radar sets fitted with powerful electromagnets produced the most bizarre effects until a special soft-iron screen was developed by the Royal Aircraft Establishment (RAE) at Farnborough.

These and many similar problems kept the air department of the ACO at full stretch throughout the war. They also highlighted two vital areas requiring urgent action. The first was the need for a remote indicating compass suitable for light aircraft which could not carry the heavy DR compass; the second, for an organization responsible for examining the plans of all new types of aircraft at the design stage, to ensure the integrity of the compass position. As discussed elsewhere, the first requirement was being gradually met, from both American and British sources. These 'compasses', however, were departing radically from the normal pivoted type, whose research and development had traditionally formed part of the Compass Department's responsibilities. Further, R & D on aircraft equipment as a whole belonged to the RAE at Farnborough and there was a growing tendency in the Ministry of Aircraft

Production to regard the compass as just another item of aircraft equipment.

Arranging for a good compass position in RAF aircraft was particularly difficult as many authorities were involved, each of which exercised considerable autonomy in its own field. Under the Ministry of Aircraft Production the Director of Technical Development (DTD) was responsible for providing a reliable compass but normally delegated this duty to two other authorities, the RAE at Farnborough and the ACO, both of which had responsibilities for advising on magnetic integrity. As RAE also looked after the arrangement of electrical cables and the safe distance testing of aircraft equipment, the whole organization was very complex.

In November 1945 Captain Hitchins put forward a 'Memorandum on aircraft compass installation' in which he proposed to rationalize these responsibilities, as far as they affected the compass position, making the ACO responsible for co-ordinating the final report to the DTD and the Ministry.[16] It was a simple, straightforward statement – after all, the Compass Department had performed the same task in ships for over a hundred years – but it as not accepted and in 1947 an Air Ministry memorandum[17] gave the RAE this overall responsibility. The memorandum did, however, safeguard the ACO's position as design authority for pivoted compasses and restated their responsibilities for compass inspection, test and repair.

There the matter rested until 1958, when the Ministry of Supply decided to close down the section at RAE which dealt with magnetic compasses. Over the next few years a new working agreement was negotiated between the Admiralty and the Ministry of Aviation under which the ACO was given new responsibilities including many of those originally suggested by Captain Hitchins in 1945. This whole subject, which took several years to tidy up, will be further discussed in Chapter 11. In the meanwhile the Admiralty still retained responsibility for *Naval Aircraft* and the Compass Department continued to advise on the acceptability of their compass equipment, as it had done since 1913.[18]

Gyro-compasses

At the beginning of the war the supply of gyro-compasses to meet the needs of a rapidly expanding ship-building programme was woefully inadequate and the shortfall was further aggravated by the large number of merchant vessels requisitioned for war service. There was a limit to how quickly the output of the Sperry factory at Brentford could be increased and, because of the large stock of Admiralty compasses held between the wars, the firm had had little experience in manufacturing this equipment. The principal Sperry compass on the market was the Mark XIV, introduced in 1938 and known in the navy as the Sperry Commercial. It was a large, robust instrument with little to go wrong and the firm was immediately asked to produce it as rapidly as possible. Later this compass and the Admiralty gyro-compass were also purchased in large numbers from the Sperry Company of Brooklyn, New York, under the lend-lease agreement.

Captain Hitchins, as Director of the Compass Department (DCD), was now responsible, through the Controller, for the supply of gyro-compasses required by the Royal Navy and the Merchant Navy. Under the Emergency Powers (Defence) Act (1939), both the Sperry and S. G. Brown factories were scheduled as controlled undertakings, and this required DCD to direct their production, to appoint supervisors and inspectors, and to monitor their standards. At Sperry's this arrangement seems to have caused no particular difficulty.

However, relationships between the Compass Department and the firm of S. G. Brown had, for many years, been somewhat cool. No Brown compasses had been purchased by the Admiralty since the early 1930s and a suggestion by Mr Brown in 1938 that they should try out his newly designed gunnery compass had been politely declined, the ACO having recently taken over responsibility for developing the AGTU from the Admiralty Research Laboratory. Nevertheless, on the outbreak of war the factory had immediately started to step up its production which, up to that point, had been running at no more than thirty compasses a year, and their small stock of available compasses was offered to the Admiralty. In January 1940 a contract for 100 compasses was placed with the firm, followed four months later by a second.

From the start, however, the arrangements proposed for the control of the factory under the emergency regulations were clearly disliked by the directors, Mr S. G. Brown and his wife, Mrs Alice Brown. The business had been their personal concern for more than twenty-five years and they resented Admiralty inspection or the presence of an Admiralty representative (whom Mrs Brown described as 'an intruder') at their works. They therefore consistently declined to sign the agreement with the Admiralty which would legalize the position.

During lengthy negotiations there were undoubtedly faults on both sides. The Browns had had sufficient cause in the past to be suspicious of Admiralty officials when dealing with the firm's 'secrets' and it would therefore have been tactful if, when Mr Heatley the Chief Scientist from ACO, was being shown details of the Brown gunnery compass, the firm had been told that he had worked on the Admiralty's equivalent project at the ARL for some twelve years. Far worse, however, was their discovery that Dr Rawlings, who had been dismissed from the Admiralty service in 1929 for his part in the mercury-control controversy, was once more employed at the ACO.[19] For this they blamed Captain Hitchins. In an effort to resolve the impasse the Vice-Controller, Rear Admiral F. T. B. Tower CBE, held a meeting of all parties on 15 January 1941, but the firm declared that 'they refused to co-operate in any way with the Director of the Compass Department or to submit their compasses to him for inspection'.

Surprisingly, through the patient negotiation of the Director of Contracts, the dialogue was maintained, and by March 1941 the directors of the firm expressed their willingness to enter into a slightly modified agreement. Meanwhile the Admiralty had put a lot of money into the factory, which had suffered considerable air-raid damage in 1940, and had purchased the adjacent premises (belonging to Philips Rubber Soles) as an extension in order to increase production still further. By April 1941 matters had improved considerably. A Compass Department representative, Mr Hesketh, was installed at the firm's works and a third contract for 100 compasses had been placed. Compasses were now being delivered at the rate of 4–5 a week and discussion over the disputed clauses of the agreement was apparently proceeding amicably. On 21 August Mrs Brown acknowledged receipt of a draft from the Secretary to the Admiralty which she hoped 'in the course of a few days to be able to return . . . duly signed'.

Unfortunately at this very moment two letters from the Compass Department reached the firm and once more muddied the waters. The first was a copy of a letter from Captain Hitchins to the Anglo-Saxon Petroleum Company, who had ordered a number of Brown compasses for their Fleet, enquiring whether they 'particularly require a Brown as opposed to a Sperry gyro-compass'. It may well have been an innocent enquiry, but to Mrs Brown its implication was obvious. The second letter was more serious for it contained an outspoken attack on the workmanship of the firm based on 'the numerous reports of bad performance of Brown compasses at sea'. Both letters were no doubt justified but their timing was most unfortunate and their arrival undoubtedly contributed to the undoing of six months patient negotiation.

Whether or not Mr and Mrs Brown would ever have signed an agreement acceptable to the Admiralty will never be known but their attitude now visibly hardened. On 21 October the Vice-Controller made one further effort to resolve the situation by visiting the factory in person, but it was of no avail. The directors pointedly refused to associate with Captain Hitchins or his technical advisors although they declared their willingness to work with his deputy, Commander Porter. On 3 November 1941 the Admiralty, acting under regulation 55 of the 'Defence (General) Regulations, 1939', decided to take over the factory and to put in their own controller. Mr and Mrs Brown then left the scene.

This had been a further regrettable and unhappy phase in the relationships between the Admiralty and S. G. Brown during which there were undoubtedly mistakes on both sides. Friction, resentment and mistrust clearly had an adverse effect on many of the actions taken and throughout 1940–41 personalities figures more and more in contacts between the firm and the Compass Department. Whilst it is difficult not to have sympathy with Mr Brown at the end of a long and distinguished career (he had filed the first of his many patents in 1899 and was a Fellow of the Royal Society before World War I), Captain Hitchins had a clear directive to follow and his task had been made unnecessarily difficult by the attitude of the firm's directors. Although the Browns went so far as to petition the Prime Minister and considered taking legal action against the Admiralty this was, in fact, the end of the matter.[20]

Once the firm had settled down as an Admiralty factory, production was maintained at a high level throughout the war. S. G. Brown remained under Admiralty control until 1959 when it was returned to private ownership and became a member of the Hawker-Siddley Dynamics group (see p. 348).

Gyro-compasses were fitted in ships as fast as they could be made available but for the first years of the war the demand considerably exceeded the supply and many (e.g. the Flower-class corvettes) had to make do with magnetic compasses alone. As the war proceeded the need for gyro-compasses or for additional repeaters was further increased by the introduction of new equipments, particularly radar, modern asdic sets and anti-submarine weapons, H/F D/F and fighter direction. Although the requirements of the huge number of landing craft could be largely met by magnetics alone, gyros were essential in the larger vessels (e.g. LST) and in some of the strange assault craft such as the LCT(R),[21] in which the magnetic state of the hull as so altered by the firing of their rockets that a magnetic compass would have been virtually useless.

The number of gyro experts required in the field was considerable. In addition to the Superintendents of Gyro-compasses (SGCs), appointed to the main naval bases at home and abroad, Compass Department representatives were also stationed at the twelve most important commercial seaports in the United Kingdom. These men, with the gyro-travellers from the ACO whose numbers were gradually built up to a force some thirty strong, were responsible for supervising the installation of almost 1500 new gyro-compasses during the years 1939-45. Added to this were the calls arising from action damage, for trouble-shooting or simply due to the introduction of other new equipment which required gyro-compass information. The movements of all these men needed careful planning and dovetailing and this was undertaken personally by the Superintendent, Commander Porter. During their rare spells at the ACO between jobs the gyro-travellers worked under the head of the gyro test room but there were many occasions when they hardly had time to report their return from one job before they were off on the next.

Stories of the achievements of the SGCs and gyro-travellers during the war are legion. The author himself, when navigating a hunt-class destroyer in 1943 off the beachhead at Salerno, had the suspension of his gyro-compass broken as a result of a near miss. After remaining on antisubmarine patrol for a week, using the magnetic compass, the ship was detached to Malta for twenty-four hours for fuel and repairs. Although the gyro compartment was only 40 inches square, the compass was stripped down, rebuilt, balanced and tested, and the ship sailed on time. On another occasion in 1940 the battleship *Barham* signalled for assistance at Liverpool because of a 'gyro-compass which is damaged by sea-water'. The request went on: 'This gyro is in a compartment which was flooded due to an explosion and was totally immersed for 8 days'. A gyro-traveller was despatched with a new compass and it was changed in forty-eight hours.

The majority of the 1500 new gyro-compasses to be installed were either Sperry commercials or Browns,[22] with a leavening of Admiralty gyro-compasses for the major Fleet units. However, compass problems had, of course, also to be dealt with in the ships of our allies, the French, Dutch, Belgians, Poles, Greeks, Norwegians and Russians, in addition to ships from America and the Empire. Altogether during the war Compass Department representatives were called upon to handle twenty-six different types of gyro-compass from five different manufacturers around the world. It seems likely that the compasses fitted in the fifty lend-lease destroyers from America (the '4-stackers') were amongst the most unsuccessful ever designed, as every one had to be changed on their arrival in England. The line of discarded compasses outside the workshops at the ACO became known as 'Arma Avenue'. However, the greatest single challenge to face one man probably occurred when a group of eight Free French ships arrived in Portsmouth early in 1940 and the SGC discovered that they had no less than six different types of compass between them.

Compasses in armoured fighting vehicles[23]

The problem of providing compasses for armoured fighting vehicles (AFVs) received very little attention during the interwar years although officers of the Royal Tank Corps stationed in Egypt are reported to have considered the use of sun compasses[24] as an aid to navigation. During the Middle East campaign a variety of sun compasses were successfully used on desert operations but they had no official status and no attempt appears to have been made to standardize either the instruments or their methods of use. Later it was found possible, by adding a second gnomon, to operate at night, keeping the two gnomons in line with the North Star. The Compass Department does not appear to have been involved with these instruments until after the war, when it undertook to modify an astro-compass by the provision of an automatic drive.[25]

It was early in 1939 when the war office accepted an offer from the Compass Department to fit and correct a compass in a tank. This was regarded mainly as a safety precaution to prevent tanks turning inadvertently in smoke and attacking their own side, and it was agreed that a stability of ± 40° would be acceptable. Preliminary trials showed that an aircraft P8 compass, with suitable correctors, was satisfactory, but that it was most important also to correct heeling error. Whilst on trials tanks had been required to move across a valley to a point on the other side and as soon as they dipped, going down the slope, the heeling error caused their compasses to deviate considerably. When climbing the hill on the far side the heeling error operated the other way, with the result that they moved round the arc of a circle.

After this nothing more was done until April 1940, when the War Office suddenly asked the ACO to provide compasses for all AFVs and to assume responsibility for their design and installation – a very tall order. Only a month later came Dunkirk, when the bulk of the Army's vehicles were left behind in France. Nevertheless, military liaison officers, representing the Ministry of Supply, were appointed to DCD's staff and a start was made on the tanks as they became available, one of each type being sent to Ditton Park so that installation arrangements could be worked out. As they were in very short supply each tank could only be spared for one week, during which a position had to be agreed upon and the compass installed, corrected and tested. Compass positions were inevitably unstable but it was found that the P8 compass, mounted in an anti vibrational suspension and fitted in a dwarf binnacle to house the correctors, including spheres, could be kept accurate to within 5° in light tanks and 10° in medium tanks, provided it was adjusted at frequent intervals.

It was not long before desert operations showed up the need for a compass in *all* AFVs and the original instruction to the department was extended to include armoured cars and scout cars, in which conditions were even more cramped than in a tank. The situation was improved by the design of a completely new compass, designated the WD2, which had a vertical card and could be mounted above the driver's line of sight. Nevertheless some thirty different installation arrangements had to be worked out at the ACO to meet the many different vehicle requirements.

PROJECTOR BINNACLES

When, in 1942, heavy tanks and self-propelled (SP) artillery appeared, with much thicker armour,[26] it was quickly apparent that the magnetic conditions at the driver's position would be quite unsuitable for a compass. Moreover the army had by now decided that they really needed an accurate, as opposed to an approximate, heading. The problem was analogous to that in submarines and the solution was to provide a projector binnacle, based on that designed for the X-craft, which could be raised and lowered through a hole in the roof of the turret. Early in 1943, in anticipation of the North African landings, twenty-four projector binnacles were hurriedly made in the ACO workshops and fitted in the 25 pdr Valentine SPs. This was the PA binnacle which was later modified to become the PB for use in the Sexton SP, where it was extremely successful. The Royal Artillery became expert at using a deviation table, so making it possible for their first round to be directed onto the target by compass bearing and obviating the former hazardous method of laying out aiming posts, which had hitherto frequently to be done under fire.

Many of the special vehicles designed for the Normandy invasion produced their own special problems. Crab tanks (with flails) which were effectively land-mine sweepers, were required to keep in accurate formation while clearing a path up to the beach. They were therefore given RAF directional gyros to steer by, in addition to their projector binnacles. Sherman DD tanks which were designed to wade ashore through quite deep water, were also given a directional gyro for the driver but in addition, had a PB compass mounted on a stalk on top of the turret for the 'helmsman' who did the initial guiding ashore.

CROSSING THE RHINE

In February 1945, during General Montgomery's preparations for the assault across the lower Rhine, the Compass Department was urgently requested to send a military officer to 21st Army Group Headquarters to advise on the navigation of amphibious vehicles. The river was five hundred yards wide and its crossing was expected to require, as Eisenhower had put it, 'the largest and most difficult amphibious operation undertaken since the landings on the coast of Normandy.'[27] The problem was to ensure that the vehicles would be able to navigate the river and touch down at preselected points under cover of darkness and smoke. The Sherman DD Tanks had, of course, already been well equipped navigationally for their landing in Normandy, but it was necessary also to fly out a large number of directional gyros for fitting in the other vehicles taking part. The crossing took place in the early hours of 24 March and by dawn the infantry was moving inland, supported by the DD tanks which had swum the river.

THE FUTURE OF COMPASSES IN AFVS

By the beginning of 1944 the decision by the Royal Armoured Corps to provide thicker armour for their vehicles and light tanks made the provision of reliable internal compasses impracticable and led to a review of the policy regarding directional equipment. On the recommendation of the director, the fitting of these compasses was therefore discontinued. Although experiments were made, with the help of the Superintendent of Degaussing, to demagnetize a number of Sherman, Cromwell and Centaur tanks, the results were not satisfactory and tended to make them magnetically unstable. The idea was therefore abandoned. Clearly the solution lay in the provision of a transmitting compass, either magnetic or gyro, but this had to await the end of hostilities and will be discussed in the next chapter.

British Admiralty Trade Missions

Early in the war a British Admiralty Trade Mission was established in Ottawa[28]. Mr J. E. Wright of the ACO being appointed as the Director's representative in July 1940. His instructions were 'to arrange the manufacture of magnetic compasses, binnacles and accessories in Canada as a reserve and addition to compasses manufactured in the UK' but it was soon apparent that his activities were to extend far beyond this brief. In addition to the equipment purchased and shipped to England, all of which had first to be inspected and tested, compasses were also ordered, installed and adjusted in all vessels built for the United Kingdom in Canada, and this included responsibility for their DG ranging. Organizations for DG ranging and compass adjustment were therefore established on both coasts, also at Quebec although there the range was destroyed by ice during the winter of 1943 and was not replaced. Commander F. G. S. Peile was sent out to relieve Mr Wright later that year and, in 1944, he was joined by Mr J. L. Howard who was destined, some twenty-five years later, to become head of the magnetic section at the ACO.

Over 6000 marine magnetic compasses and binnacles were manufactured in Canada during the war in addition to many thousands of accessories and the Mission worked closely and cordially with the Royal Canadian Navy. Once a satisfactory compass testing organization had been established it was also used by the RCN for their own compasses whilst, as a quid pro quo, the RCN Electrical department provided considerable assistance in dealing with degaussing and gyro-compass defects.

Until the middle of 1942 arrangements for the purchase of gyro-compasses from Sperry, New York, under the lend-lease agreement, were also handled from Ottawa but in that year Commander F. H. Bishop was appointed to a similar mission in Washington where he was joined the following year by Dr A. L. Rawlings. When the United States entered the war this mission was able to give American firms considerable assistance with the preparation of compass positions and the adjustment of compasses in aircraft,[29] very much as Captain Creagh-Osborne had done when they entered World War 1.

Compass Department pamphlets

As the war developed the Compass Department found itself with representatives in many parts of the country and indeed of the world. Offices had been established in Manchester, Glasgow and Newcastle; gyro-compass representatives and swinging officers were stationed at all the main ports in the United Kingdom, with many more abroad; missions had been set up in the USA and in Canada; inspectors were appointed to the works of all the main contractors. In addition representatives were constantly on the move from the ACO itself, covering gyro- and magnetic compasses and degaussing, and dealing with many strange craft.

All these people needed up-to-date information concerning the latest equipments and techniques in order to keep pace with an ever changing situation. A series of departmental pamphlets (CD pamphlets) was therefore started early in 1940 to keep all ACO representatives acquainted with new developments and to issue new instructions or procedures. This series later became a valuable source of historical data and although it was discontinued in 1971, when the establishment was taken over by the Admiralty Surface Weapons Establishment, a number of the original pamphlets still (1984) remain in force.

Staff and facilities

To compete with the increasing workload and widening responsibilities, the staff of the ACO continued to grow throughout the war and by 1945 numbered 1068,[30] made up as follows:

        2 Captains
        7 Commanders (Naval Staff)
        6 Army and RAF Officers (Military and Air Assistants)
       40 Scientific and Technical Staff (R & D Staff)
       21 Naval Officers
        6 Technical Staff   Magnetic compass duties in ships
        4 Naval Officers
       36 Technical Staff   Gyro compass duties in ships
       10 Instructional Staff
        2 Naval Officers
       14 Technical Staff   Compass testing and inspection
       37 Compass Examiners
       17 Clerical, typing and telephone staff
       16 Foremen and chargemen
      850 Mechanics and labourers

This total included a number of staff who were appointed to out stations or to missions abroad and, of course, the department's gyro-compass representatives in dockyards and naval bases. In 1944 the post of Superintendent of the Compass Department was elevated to that of Deputy Director and Commander Porter was promoted to Captain on the retired list.

Probably the most significant expansion had come in the research and development section, of which W. G. Heatley had become the Chief Scientist on Mr Wright's departure for Canada. Here the numbers had increased from a mere handful in 1939 to a total of forty full-time scientists, supported by many other naval and technical officers attached to other sections. In May 1941 Captain

Hitchins was appointed as one of the two naval members of the august Admiralty advisory panel on scientific research, on which the two scientific members were Professor R. H. Fowler and Sir Edward Appleton, both Fellows of the Royal Society.[31]

As has already been discussed, among those recruited early in the war to strengthen the scientific team at the ACO was Dr A. L. Rawlings who, since the S. G. Brown enquiry in 1927, had been with the Sperry Company in New York. On the outbreak of hostilities he had immediately offered his services to Captain Hitchins and been accepted, but this was not a wise move. Although he was mainly employed on degaussing work and was only indirectly concerned with gyro-compasses, his very presence was sufficient to give the directors of S. G. Brown grounds for suspicion. In 1942 he returned to America to join the British Admiralty Trade Mission.

Call up to the forces naturally continued throughout the war although many posts were classified as reserved occupations. The first man to be taken for an operational appointment on the outbreak of hostilities was the RAF liaison officer, Squadron Leader Booth, who was recalled on 3 September 1939 to take charge of the balloon barrage defence of Great Britain. He had once been navigator of the airship R101. A notable volunteer for the forces at this time was a temporary experimental assistant, Class III, P. A. Watson who, on informing the director of his wish to sign on was given a short lecture about the requirements of a 'scientific war' and 'sticking to one's post'. As he walked away, somewhat crestfallen, the director's door was heard to open again and the same voice called out 'The recruiting office is in Reading'. The young man went on to become Vice-Admiral Sir Philip Watson, KBE, MVO, FIEE, FIERE, the Director General (Weapons).

The increase in scientific and technical staff and the explosion in new R & D work had raised an urgent requirement for additional laboratory space. A prefabricated concrete building, put up in 1940 for gyro-compass work, was named the Chaffer laboratory in memory of the late chief scientist who, having left in 1936 to become head of the Admiralty Research Laboratory, died of a heart attack only two months before the outbreak of war. This building, expected to last a maximum of ten years, was only finally demolished in 1980. Next came a long hutted structure, erected behind the mansion in 1942, just after the victory at El Alamein, and named the Montgomery block. Although intended to last for the duration of the war it continued to give useful service until 1965, when it finally gave way to a new purpose-built laboratory block. An all-wooden laboratory was also erected amongst the trees of the boschetto behind the mansion, for accurate magnetic work, and in 1946 was named the Turner laboratory,[32] in memory of Mr D. A. Turner, the head of the magnetic compass section who tragically died of a heart attack at the early age of 37. Forty years later this building is still used for all work requiring the highest grade of magnetically clean environment.

Meanwhile, following Dunkirk, the ACO contingent of the Local Defence Volunteers (later the Home Guard) had been formed under its commander, 'Major' Joys.[33] It comprised three companies and formed the 10th Buckinghamshire Battalion. The unit paraded at 8.00 a.m. on three days a week, and its members were kept on their toes by frequent night exercises against other units, or the local Windsor Military Contingent, who were generally not at all amused. However, the only live round fired throughout the war is reported to have gone through the ceiling and scored a bulls-eye on the director's bed (the director fortunately being absent) while 'opening bolts to clear rifles'. The establishment was fortunate in suffering no enemy damage during the war, although an incendiary bomb was found caught by its parachute in a tree close to the gyro test room. (The silk parachute is reported to have been made into underwear by the Deputy Director's wife and daughter.) On another occasion flack from a local anti-aircraft battery landed on the oval.

On 14 March 1942 the centenary of the foundation of the Compass Department passed quietly by as the establishment got on with the war, but the event was suitably marked by an article in the *Naval Review* by Commander W. E. May.[34]

Finally a word must be said about the director who had shouldered the burden of command throughout the greatest war in history. Captain Hitchins had been appointed Director of the Compass Department in 1928 and, having taken over the ACO at its nadir, had built it up to be in every way prepared for war when it came. He had his sixtieth birthday six months before VE day. In 1982 there were still men serving in the establishment who remembered him in those early days. To them he was 'The director' who seemed to know everything that was going on, to give his personal attention to every detail and to be everywhere at once. The establishment was working round the clock yet he always appeared to be available and approachable, always having the tact to send his dog into a workshop ahead of him. He was strict but fair. He knew his employees and formed the habit of sharing the long night vigils with them, often reading aloud in the canteen during the break periods (normally naval stories, but also the classics, particularly *Pickwick Papers*[35]). This was the man who before the war used, with his superintendent, Bertie Porter, to put on an annual garden party for all employees and their families. It was small wonder that the ACO once again emerged at the end of the war as a 'happy ship' with a job well done.

NOTES

CHAPTER 10

[1] W. S. Churchill, *The Unrelenting Struggle*, 1942, p. 236.

[2] Two human skeletons were unearthed while this shelter was being dug. They were 'very old' but had no distinguishable clothing.

[3] Compass Department, 'R & D Report', 1946, Also ACO archives (CE219/5, July 1935).

[4] Where gyro-repeaters were embodied in instruments belonging to other authorities, the Compass Department's responsibility was confined to the supply of data from the gyrocompass.

[5] During 1945 some 650 officers attended at the ACO for courses of all sorts, varying in length from a few days to several months.

[6] ACO archives, DNE 253/40, 4 April 1940.

[7] Admiralty Fleet Order, 4015/42.

[8] 'Records of Admiralty Wartime Research and Development, 1939–45,' Part N (Navigation).

[9] Shortly afterwards, on 21 September 1943, three of these craft made a daring attack on the German battleship *Tirpitz* in Altenfjord, for which Lieutenants Place and Cameron were each awarded the Victoria Cross.

[10] The compasses of the later, improved XE-craft were fitted with degaussing corrector coils and were the only submarine compasses to be so fitted until the ATMC11 in the 1960s (see p. 297).

[11] A/S outfit 123, Compass Pattern 0195TA in Binnacle Pattern 196T.

[12] Admiralty Fleet Order, 1685/44.

[13] Admiralty Fleet Order, 7383/45.

[14] This air-position indicator was fitted in the Fairey Spearfish Mark I, a strike

and anti-submarine aircraft which, in 1946, was the most powerful carrier-borne aircraft in existence.

[15] Compass Department, 'R & D Report', 1948.

[16] ACO archives, (File 2/3, No. 25).

[17] Ibid., (AD/3/0134, 11 November 1947).

[18] Admiralty Fleet Order, 1676/46.

[19] Dr Rawlings was not in fact employed on gyro-compass work, but on solving the problems raised by degaussing. Nevertheless his very presence at the ACO was sufficient to give rise to grave suspicions in the minds of the Browns.

[20] The correspondence between the Admiralty and Messrs S. G. Brown was collected as a submission to the prime minister: National Maritime Museum, Compass Collection, Envelope N32.

[21] Landing ships (tanks) were vessels of 3000 tons and upwards. LCT(R)s were rocket-firing landing craft used to saturate a section of the beach with rocket fire before an assault.

[22] Commander May contributed another anecdote which could well have been true: 'Owing to a shortage of compasses a flotilla of minesweepers was fitted, one division with Brown and the other with the commercial Sperry. After being in service for a while the senior officer of one division asked for the replacement of their Sperrys by Browns while his opposite number asked for the replacement of their Browns by Sperrys'.

[23] A comprehensive account of this subject is contained in Compass Department, 'R & D Report' 1946.

[24] The sun compass is a simple instrument in which the direction of the shadow of a gnomon or stile pin is read against a scale on a flat plate which is set and orientated according to the values of solar time, declination and latitude. An improvement on this instrument is the astro-compass, which can also be used with the stars and was widely employed by the RAF during the war.

[25] National Maritime Museum, Magnetic Compass Collection, Item R18.

[26] Churchill tanks had front armour 90 mm (3 1/2 inches) thick.

[27] Chester Wilmot, *The Struggle for Europe*, the Reprint Society, 1954, p. 759.

[28] ACO Historical Section, Item R21.

[29] Ibid., Item R32 (4).

[30] Compass Department, 'R & D Report', 1946.

[31] ACO Archives, (Admiralty Office acquaint, CE/SRE, 602/41, 20 May 1941).

[32] For convenience, the safe-distance testing laboratory, which is sited near the new Turner laboratory, was named Turner II. This building was the original aircraft hangar of 1917 and is still in use (1985).

[33] This excellent man had been a stoker petty officer at the battle of Coronel in 1915. He was employed at the ACO as head porter.

[34] *Naval Review*, Vol. 30 (February 1942).

[35] Captain Hitchins's own publications included four editions of *Canterbury*

Tales: Chaucer for Present Day Readers, John Murray, 1946–56, and, in conjunction with Commander W. E. May, *From Lodestone to Gyro-compass* Hutchinson's Scientific and Technical Publications, 1952. He was a Fellow of the Royal Astronomical Society and a member of the Royal Institution, to whom in 1946 he delivered an address on 'Compasses past, present, and future;' National Maritime Museum, Magnetic Compass Collection, Item P11 (15). He died in 1961 at the age of 76.

A struggle for survival and a new dawn, 1946-61

'The Tumult and the Shouting dies,
The Captains and the King's depart'. (From 'Recessional' by
Rudyard Kipling)
'the stone which the builders set at
nought, the same is become the head of the corner'. (1 Peter, 2:7)

VE day on 9 May 1945 was soon followed by VJ day, and the war
was suddenly over. This time the run-down happened quickly. After
six years of war the jewellers and watchmakers, the lecturers,
musicians and housewives, were keen to hurry back to their peacetime occupations. By the late summer of 1946 the total workforce
at the ACO had shrunk to less than half its wartime strength, with
the scientific staff down to a 'holding-force' of about a dozen.

Meanwhile, as soon as the war in Europe was over, technical
teams from all branches had been despatched to Germany to learn
what they could of the enemy's progress. They returned with a
vast array of scientific reports (The Director of Naval Intelligence
amassed a library of over 30,000 German documents) and, in the
case of the compass team, with a fair amount of equipment for
examination.[1] In addition, a number of German scientists were
'invited' back to the United Kingdom in order that our own
specialists could talk to them and no doubt also to ensure that they
did not find themselves working behind the iron curtain which was
shortly to descend across Europe. Such a man was Dr J. Gievers,[2]
a leading scientist in the fields of inertial navigation, advanced gyro-
compasses and stabilizer techniques. He was interviewed at the ACO
in 1946 and eventually worked at the Admiralty Research Laboratory
for four years before emigrating to the United States.[3]

Under the supervision of Commander May, opportunity was taken to update and extend the museum collection. In the introduction to a revised edition of the catalogue he comments on the wartime and immediately postwar periods as follows:

> As time passed the compasses in the ships of our Allies became defective and had to be replaced by British types. With the co-operation of the Naval Stores Department, their old compasses were added to the Museum. In this way examples of the compasses of America, France and Holland were acquired, besides some German ones from Polish vessels. At the end of the war a very large selection of German material fell into our hands. Japanese compasses were obtained through the keen assistance of a navigating officer who reached Singapore in the early days of the Japanese collapse. The magnificent Kaiser binnacle[4] with quadrantal correction by auxiliary compasses, was presented by the Instrument Department of the Dutch Navy in recognition of the assistance given to them. With the return of peace it became possible to lay out the Museum once more.

Changes in senior staff

In 1946, Dr W. F. Rawlinson was appointed as Chief Scientist in place of Mr Heatley, who moved back to Teddington, a great disappointment to him. His ten years at the ACO had been extremely fruitful, covering the development of the Admiralty Gyro Transmission Units, the ACO projector binnacles, the valve follow-up compass, the bottle-transmitter as well as many new compasses and ancilliary equipments, only a selection of which it has been possible to cover in this narrative. After the rush of meeting wartime requirements he had hoped to concentrate quietly on the development of the new types of gyro-compass he believed would be wanted to meet the needs of the future, both ashore and afloat. But the gods had other plans. His successor, Dr Rawlinson, had spent much of his career at HM Signal School at Portsmouth,[5] a misleading name for an establishment which not only dealt with communication systems but which in the early 1920s housed the asdic research section which he headed. Before his retirement in 1959 he was to see the ACO started on its most important project yet, the development of the Ship's Inertial Navigation System (SINS).

Further changes followed quickly. In 1948 Captain Hitchins retired after twenty very successful years as Director and was replaced by his deputy, Captain B. C. (Bertie) Porter who had been second in command since 1926. He was a genial, popular figure, whose never-failing good humour and understanding of human relationships had done much to maintain the spirit and morale of the establishment, particularly during the difficult period of rapid expansion at the beginning of the war and then during its sudden post-war contraction. He had been disappointed not to have succeeded Harrison when, in 1928, the latter had been relieved of his post prematurely following the findings of the Philpotts committee (see page 226). However he had loyally served his new director and his tact and charm often did much to smooth ruffled feathers. Indeed in 1941 Mr and Mrs S. G. Brown had expressed their willingness to co-operate with him rather than Captain Hitchins.

Porter was, however, allowed only three years as director, largely during a period of economic crisis when money was tight, the way ahead for the Navy was still far from clear and research and development were, of necessity, in a low key. He retired in 1951, after 25 years loyal service to the ACO, having earned the affection and respect of all who served under him, and he died at his home in Poole on 3 November 1959.

The Admiralty had appointed Commander C. J. Wynne-Edwards, DSC and bar, as Deputy Director in 1948 and it was he who succeeded Porter as Director, being promoted to Captain on the retired list. Amongst many accomplishments in an outstanding career he had been responsible for the navigational aspects of the brilliant evacuation from Dunkirk and for the laying of the northern mine barrage. After the war he had commanded HMS *Boxer*, the first R. N. Aircraft Direction and Radar training ship. His time in the Navigation Division had given him an intimate knowledge of the often curious workings of the Admiralty which was later to stand him in good stead. After a period of relative calm his appointment was to mark the beginning of another momentous phase in the Compass Department's history.

Hitherto, naval officers serving permanently on the staff at the ACO had been taken from the retired list, giving them the great advantage of continuity, but it was inevitable that, with a rapidly changing navy, their experience of modern conditions at sea would become outdated. Believing that a periodic injection of recent sea experience would be beneficial, Wynne-Edwards arranged that his deputy should be an active service commander, but the officer concerned took a long time to settle into what had become a somewhat tradition-bound environment and in 1954 he was relieved by Commander A. V. Thomas, the senior Naval Assistant, who had been on the staff since before the war. At the same time an active-service Electrical Officer was appointed to the staff, to serve in the vital role of Technical Application Officer, and the Electrical Officers' qualifying course began to come to the ACO for a fortnight's instruction, in the same way as the long navigation course.

Two other changes in the senior staff deserve special mention. In 1948 Mr J. C. Hereford, who had joined the department as a Lieutenant RNVR in 1917 and had run the gyro test room for many years, left to take over the 'school' at the Sperry factory at Brentford. Three years later Commander May left to become the Deputy Director of the National Maritime Museum, a post he held for the next seventeen years.

May's contributions to the ACO, spanning a quarter of a century, had been considerable. He was equally expert in gyro- and magnetic compasses, having served both as swinging officer and superintendent of gyro-compasses. He took immense pains to attend to the compass needs of the fleet and, to many young navigating officers during World War II, his name was almost synonymous with the ACO. His work in arranging and documenting the museum collection, particularly after the war, was invaluable, and his knowledge of the historical aspects of compasses was probably unsurpassed.

The postwar research and development programme

With the small scientific staff remaining, the requirement in 1946 was for a programme of consolidation to be followed by forward planning once the direction could be ascertained. This was a period of uncertainty, when the pattern of the future navy could not yet be clearly seen. However, the war had shown up many desirable avenues for research and development which it had not at the time been possible to pursue. Smaller and more accurate gyro-compasses were needed and there was likely to be an increasing requirement to define the vertical for weapon control; better transmitting magnetic

compasses were essential for both ships and aircraft; more convenient compasses were required for armoured fighting vehicles. Each
of these subjects covered a broad spectrum of activities. Considering
the rate at which staff were leaving, it was remarkable how much
was achieved in those early years.

Three new types of gyro-compass were envisaged to meet particular needs. The first was a small compass for use in armoured fighting
vehicles and the second a lightweight compass for Coastal Forces.
It was hoped that these two requirements could be largely combined
in one instrument and it was obvious that such a compass would
also have wider uses. Third, an accurate compass was needed for
fire-control purposes, particularly in capital ships and cruisers, to
replace the Admiralty gyro and AGTU. The Staff Target specified
a true accuracy of 10 minutes at all times, with a wander rate which
would at no time exceed 2 minutes of arc per minute – almost
precisely the requirement laid down nearly 30 years before, but
never achieved (see p. 233). In addition, in 1948 the Ministry of
Supply asked for a fourth type of gyro-compass which could be
used for rapid and accurate artillery survey purposes.

The Naval Staff decided that efforts should be concentrated on
the first two requirements. By 1949 an experimental master compass
had been built and was undergoing preliminary laboratory trials. It
employed two 4 inch gyros, a north-seeker and a vertical stabilizer,
linked in a double gimbal-ring assembly similar to that used in the
AGTU Mark II, and mounted in a frame some 20 inches high.
To achieve the desired performance certain electrical components,
motors and amplifiers had to be designed from scratch. However,
although promising results were achieved, there was still much
doubt about the direction which future naval requirements would
take and, for reasons which will become apparent, in 1952 the
project was dropped.

This was the only gyro-compass ever to be designed exclusively
at the ACO,[6] and it seems that the establishment was ahead of its
time. The requirements of both Coastal Forces and the Army were
eventually satisfied when variants of the miniature Arma-Brown
gyro-compass became available early in the 1960s. By this time too,
an accurate compass from the Sperry Company, New York (the
Mark 19), had become available, and it was this instrument which
was eventually widely introduced as a compass-stabilizer. Finally
the artillery's requirement was satisfied in 1963 by an ingenious

instrument known as a PIM (precision indicator of the meridian), designed by the British Aircraft Corporation, the acceptance trials of which were conducted at the ACO on the lawns of Ditton Park.

Another avenue of development during this early postwar period concerned compass transmissions. Big ships carried a very large number of gyro-repeaters (the battleship *Vanguard* had over 200) and it was clear that a self-synchronous transmission system was needed to obviate the labour of lining them all up by hand. Plans were also made for a bulkhead-mounted retransmission unit which would contain suitable banks of transmitters to meet the needs of all users. This would incorporate the necessary corrector for speed error, so simplifying the gyro-compass itself.[7] But scientific effort was scarce and many Admiralty departments whose equipment would need gyro-compass information were not yet able to define their requirements for the future, and so work proceeded slowly. Further, doubts still existed about the integrity of synchronous transmission, and for navigation repeaters, on which the safety of the ship depended, it was decided to retain the well-proven M-type and with certain exceptions this policy was maintained for the next two decades. Nevertheless a useful start was made on the development of this equipment and the lessons learnt were later incorporated into the next generation of Admiralty gyro-compasses, the 5005 series (see p. 295).

Yet another problem which had caused great concern during the war was the large number of broken gyro-suspensions which had resulted from explosions or near misses, despite the introduction of the improved *Escapade* mounting in 1940. A new type of mounting was designed which would allow the ship to move as much as ± 12 inches in the vertical direction relative to the compass. This was named the *Proteus* anti-shock mounting (it was first tried out in the submarine *Proteus*) and it proved so successful that during later trials in the destroyer *Ambuscade*, the compass remained undamaged although the shock of the explosion broke the ship's back within 2 feet of the compass position.[8]

Admiralty Transmitting Magnetic Compasses

During the years immediately after the war, work on transmitting magnetic compasses in surface ships consisted mainly of consolidation. Coastal Forces were at first reasonably happy with the ATMC1 while, following the trials of the ATMC2 in the destroyer *Wizard*, which had completed a cruise of some 45,000 miles without serious problems, plans were made to fit it as the Standard Compass on the bridges of all destroyers and frigates. Bridges were, however, becoming very crowded and when, in 1948, it was decided to fit centre-line torpedo sights in the *Battle-* and *Weapon*-class destroyers, the Standard Compass was moved to the wheelhouse where, with repeaters on the bridge, it still gave adequate results.[9] This was the first significant step towards the eventual removal of magnetic compasses from the bridges of all major war vessels.

Meanwhile all Coastal Force activities had been concentrated at HMS *Hornet* at Gosport, where an experimental flotilla was formed with which the ACO worked closely over the next ten years. The simple MGBs and MTBs, which had won the battles of 'E-boat Alley' in the North Sea and English Channel, were giving way to larger craft with sophisticated equipment and there was soon a requirement for no fewer than thirteen repeaters. The compasses in these boats were, of course, required to withstand considerable buffeting and the ACO arranged a series of rough-weather trials which eventually showed their latest transmitting compass, the lightweight ATMC4 designed for the Army (see below), to be the most adaptable.[10] A watertight, shockmounted version was designed and this was later fitted with a gyro-stabilized control, making it the ATMC4G. It was installed in the *Gay* and *Bold* classes of fast patrol boats (FPBs),[11] both of which could achieve 40 knots, and gave good service under extremely severe conditions of acceleration, shock and roll. A very light azimuth repeater was also designed for use in these craft and this was later extensively fitted in the coastal and inshore minesweepers built during the 1950s.

Armoured fighting vehicles

After the war the Army still had many compass problems unresolved and for several years Ditton Park continued to resound to the roar of tanks and self-propelled artillery. Following the severe winter of 1947, during which many tanks sank axle-deep in the mud, a reinforced concrete tank track was laid out in the south park for compass adjustment, with its arms lying along the cardinal and half-cardinal compass points. There was even a ramp at one end on which tanks could be tilted to an angle of 30° to adjust their heeling error.

By 1945 the requirements of tanks and self-propelled (SP) artillery had diverged. The Royal Tank Corps now simply needed a compass for the driver to steer by and this was best provided by a telescopic projector binnacle which, in view of the very limited space in the driver's compartment, was made portable for ease of stowage. The Royal Armoured Corps, on the other hand, required the commander, gunlayer and driver each to have a compass-repeater. A Sexton SP mounting was therefore fitted with a modified aircraft compass, the ATMC3 which became known as the ATMC (WD) and proved very steady when placed 6 feet above the hull. During trials on Salisbury plain in 1947 the average accuracy of the opening round, fired on a compass bearing at targets up to 13,400 yards away, was within one degree.[12] It was a remarkable result which, however fortuitous, did much for interservice relations. Meanwhile the ACO had been developing the ATMC4 especially to meet this requirement.[13] This was a considerable advance on the Type 3 and, after further proving trials, gave very good service for many years. Various retractable binnacles were also tried out,[14] the most notable being the Giraffe (a telescopic binnacle, which was finally adopted) and the Jack-in-the-box, the action of which was self-evident and tended to be lethal both to the compass and the operator, so that it was finally dropped.

After the formation of the Fighting Vehicle Research and Development Establishment (FVRDE) at Chobham in Surrey in 1952, work on navigation systems for AFVs was undertaken there by Dr G. H. Harvey, who had served at the ACO through most of the war and this led to the development of the Chobham navigator, which took its direction from a pair of inductor compasses. What was really wanted, of course, was a very small gyro-compass and this at last became available in 1961, when the firm of S. G. Brown placed on the market their Arma-Brown compass Mark V, especially designed for land vehicles.

Although tanks and self-propelled artillery no longer visit Ditton Park and, since 1965, the site of the tank track has been occupied by a magnetic measuring range used to test equipment for magnetic mine-sweepers, the ACO still maintains its links with the Army, acting as the design authority for any new military compass equipment required.

It is interesting to note that when in 1959 Sir Vivian Fuchs made his historic crossing of the Antarctic Continent in his Sno-cat 'Rock'n Roll', it was the ACO which lent him a modified tank projector compass for the trip. This is now displayed in the main hall of the mansion.

Aircraft compasses

In June 1944 the Air Staff had stated a requirement for a distant-reading compass having an accuracy of $\pm$ 1°, to supersede the heavy and already dated DR compass which had given such excellent service. The detector or magnetic sensor was to be light enough to be placed in the wing. Design work was started at the ACO and at the Royal Aircraft Establishment at Farnborough, both using a type of saturable inductor[15] with gyro stabilization. A third attack on the problem came from the Sperry Gyroscope Company, with a development of their gyrosyn compass, which worked on the same principle but employed a different form of inductor which they called a 'flux valve'.[16]

By 1949 the ACO compass, known as the Admiralty Gyro-Inductor Compass[17] had been successfully developed to the proto-type stage by Alfred Hine, the head of the magnetic section, but by that time it was apparent that the Sperry development, which became the famous GM4B (the fighter aircraft version was the GM4FA) was the preferred solution. Nevertheless the basic design work carried out at the ACO on this project, which necessitated much fundamental research into the magnetic behaviour of various alloys under differing heat treatments,[18] was to stand the department in good stead during later developments in the 1950s.

Meanwhile the ATMC3, which was a transmitting modification of the original aircraft P8 compass, had been further developed by the addition of a gyro unit, to make it the ATMC3G. A prototype model of this compass was subjected to the full acceptance procedure in a York aircraft at the RAF's Aeroplane and Armament Experimental Establishment at Boscombe Down during the summer of 1949, with a view to its possible fitting in certain naval aircraft for which the GM4 was not immediately available. The results, although satisfactory, were unfortunately limited by the indifferent performance of the gyro.[19] Further trials were carried out later that year in a Firefly Mark V of the Naval Air/Sea Warfare Development

Unit at Lee-on-Solent but it was finally decided to wait for the GM4.[20] To the ACO this must have been a grave disappointment as this was the last substantial in-house aircraft-compass design project to be undertaken. Since 1950 all major aircraft compass design has been done by industry under contract from the Admiralty or Air Ministry, with the ACO providing technical oversight.

A very simple compass designed at the ACO in 1946 was the E2, a neat spherical compass, with correctors, which can fit comfortably into a 2 inch cube. Versions of this compass are still in regular use in the 1980s as the emergency compass in the majority of British aircraft, including Concorde.[21] It has also proved extremely popular as a car compass.

During 1945–47 the ACO was closely associated with many of the long-distance flights carried out by the Empire Air Navigation School at Shawbury in their Lancaster bomber, *Aries*, to investigate navigational problems in anticipation of establishing the Empire air routes. The 1945 flights over the Arctic regions were particularly concerned with compass performance in high latitudes, and *Aries* carried a number of instruments supplied by the ACO which, in addition to aircraft compasses, included a liquid boats compass and an Admiralty gyro direction indicator, both of which performed well.[22] Much use was also made of a specially adapted astro-compass (see p. 264) to provide a datum. This first magnetic survey of the Arctic regions from the air showed the north magnetic pole to be considerably further north than hitherto believed[23] and the variation shown on some charts to be greatly in error. Because of the large number of compasses carried, maintaining the magnetic integrity of the compass positions presented many difficulties, and the ACO was later called upon to investigate this matter further when a trip to South Africa by the Lincoln bomber *Aries II* in 1949 showed that the magnetic conditions of the aircraft could change considerably during a long flight.[24]

In 1949 at the request of the Ministry of Supply, the ACO undertook the design of a datum compass to replace the medium landing compass which had been in use for the calibration of aircraft compasses since 1916. Although development was completed and the compass met the design specification, comparative trials at Boscombe Down in 1952–53[25] showed that an instrument developed by Messrs Hilger & Watts from their standard optical mining dial was more accurate and offered greater facilities. This was later named the Watts datum compass and was adopted as the standard instrument for adjusting aircraft compasses and for the magnetic survey of swinging bases on airfields.

In 1958 a new landing compass (the Pattern 2), designed at the ACO, was introduced to enable more accurate observations of variation to be made by HM ships abroad.[26] It was a small, neat and very accurate compass, mounted on a tripod, and was soon widely adopted for the less important calibrations of aircraft compasses, being simpler to use than the Watts datum compass. Because of the extreme accuracy of both these compasses, they are always transported by hand.

The working agreement between the Admiralty and the Ministry of Aviation

It will be recalled that under an agreement reached between the Admiralty and the Ministry of Supply in 1947, the Compass Department would be responsible for research and development on aircraft compasses of the pivotted type while the Royal Aircraft Establishment (RAE) at Farnborough handled all other varieties. The RAE was, to be the final arbiter on questions of the magnetic integrity of compass installations, except in naval aircraft, and also undertook the surveying of compass bases on airfields. Under this agreement, which was reviewed and reissued in June 1955,[27] the Ministry of Supply undertook to nominate one or more officers to the staff of the Compass Department for liaison duties.

In June 1958, in order to release effort for work on inertial navigation, the Ministry of Supply decided to close down the section at the RAE which dealt with magnetic compass matters. No alternative provision was made for its outside responsibilities and by October Wynne-Edwards was forced to draw the Ministry's attention to the large number of requests being directed to the ACO, asking for help in clearing aircraft designs or surveying compass bases.[28] He suggested that the agreement needed revision. Meanwhile the ACO air liaison staff, a Wing Commander and a Lieutenant Commander (Observer), did what they could to handle the more urgent demands. As they had no official authority for this work (which belonged by right to the RAE) their advice was often ignored by both contractors and Ministry officials.

On 7 October 1960, after two years of negotiations (during which both parties changed their titles) the Ministry of Aviation called a meeting between their Director of Air Navigation (DA Nav) and the Director General, Weapons (Compass Division) (DWC), at which a new working agreement was discussed. Although DA Nav would still retain overall responsibility, the ACO, which was recognized as the centre of technical knowledge on all magnetic compasses for the three services, would undertake the following tasks on behalf of the Ministry whenever requested:

1. To act as design or R & D authority for all aircraft magnetic compasses. This might include the need to organize fundamental research.

2. To advise on the suitability of the compass arrangements for all new types of service or civilian aircraft, at the design stage, and to conduct trials with the first prototype in order to prove the acceptability of the compass installation provided.

3. To carry out periodic surveys of the compass bases at airfields belonging to the Navy, the RAF, the USAF in the UK, the Ministry of Aviation, civil airlines and aircraft contractors. Initially this covered a total of ninety-seven bases.

4. To determine the safe distances of all new items of aircraft equipment.

It was further agreed that the Wing Commander should organize this work from headquarters at the Ministry of Aviation, informing DWC of the tasks required. The second liaison officer would be integrated with the magnetic section at the ACO, on whom he would rely for his technical support. In addition the normal routine testing of aircraft compasses would be continued. The ACO was thus once again to provide full support in all magnetic compass matters for all branches of the flying services, as it had done for most of the past fifty years.

To clear the backlog of surveys a Flight Lieutenant and a Flight Sergeant were loaned to the ACO and, during 1961–62, dealt with a total of fifty swinging bases at home and abroad. When the time came for the Lieutenant Commander (Observer) to be relieved, he was followed by a Flight Lieutenant (Spec. N), and this remained the pattern thereafter.

The terms of the working agreement were implemented at 'desk level' without delay and were shown to be entirely satisfactory. However, in the regrettable manner of these things, it was not until

January 1963, more than a year after Wynne-Edwards had retired, that it was ratified by the Admiralty and the Ministry of Aviation.[29] As the new Director, Captain Ross, reported to his Director-General, 'This agreement has taken nearly two years to prod through the machine!' but, after sixteen years, things were pretty well back to where they had been before 1947.

Other magnetic compass work

In addition to the work on transmitting compasses for ships and aircraft already discussed, several minor items deserve to be mentioned. A successful small luminized compass with a grid steering ring was introduced for canoes and similar craft; also a compass which would withstand dropping by parachute was designed for the inflatable dinghys used by the Royal Marine Commandoes. The canoe compass was tried out by the British Olympic sailing team in 1948 and one was loaned to Captain John Ridgeway and Sergeant Chay Bligh for their successful row across the Atlantic in 1967. In addition many weaknesses that had shown up as a result of wartime experience were rectified and, where appropriate, degaussing corrector coils were incorporated within binnacles.

GRADUATION OF MAGNETIC COMPASS CARDS

We have noted that from earliest times, whenever degrees were printed on magnetic compass cards in addition to points, they were shown in the quadrantal system (e.g. S60°E rather than 120°). The Americans had changed to the 0°–360° notation in 1895 but the Royal Navy had declined to follow and when the matter was reviewed in 1913, in connection with the introduction of gyrocompasses, it was decided to retain the quadrantal notation for magnetic courses and bearings to emphasize the difference. In 1943 the Royal Canadian Navy pointed out to the Admiralty that the Royal and Commonwealth Navies were now the only ones 'out of step'[30] and a change to 0°–360° was accordingly agreed in principle. However, in view of the enormous number of vessels in service and the thousands of 'hostilities only' ratings who had been trained in the quadrantal system, it was decided to take no action until after the war.

The changeover officially took place on 1 January 1948,[31] and the Director of Stores was allowed £1,000 to alter all compass cards.

No change was made to the pattern numbers of the compasses but the work involved placed a heavy load on the ACO workshops.

TESTING COMMERCIAL COMPASSES FOR THE BOARD OF TRADE

Ever since the early days at Charlton the Compass Observatory had undertaken to test batches of commercial compasses for the Board of Trade whenever requested to do so. It was not until the 1920s, however, that testing for the Merchant Navy was established on a regular basis, ship-owners then being required to obtain a certificate for their Standard Compasses from the National Physical Laboratory's testing station at Kew Observatory. In 1952, when the National Physical Laboratory gave up work on compasses, the ACO agreed to take over the task and this very satisfactory arrangement has continued ever since, bringing in a modest but steady revenue to the Crown. The ACO thus became the standard national authority for testing magnetic compasses, analogous to the Greenwich Observatory for chromometers and the National Physical Laboratory for sextants, and the 'ACO certificate' was soon recognized and accepted by the principal maritime nations of the world. Some thirty years later, again at the request of the Department of Trade, the establishment was to assume the same role for gyro-compasses (see p. 376).

This association between the ACO and the Board of Trade flourished and led eventually to the setting-up of a working group under the authority of the International Standards Organization (ISO) to establish agreed standards for commercial marine compasses and binnacles of all types. For many years the British delegation to this group was led by Commander A. V. Thomas of the ACO, and later by the author. The establishment became recognized as one of the internationally accepted testing stations for ISO certificates and its new magnetic test room, built in 1968 in the gardens of the mansion, is amongst the best equipped in the world.[32]

SONOBUOY COMPASSES

In 1947 an urgent requirement arose for a compass to be fitted in a new type of radio directional sonobuoy. The object of a sonobuoy is to pick up the underwater noise of a submarine by means of a hydrophone and to transmit the information by radio to a ship or aircraft. A compass was therefore needed to indicate the orientation of the hydrophone. It was required to operate at a depth of 40 feet and to withstand dropping, with a parachute, from heights up to 5000 feet, a very severe test.

Design was undertaken by the ACO, whilst responsibility for development and production was placed with S. G. Brown, which was still an Admiralty factory. Because of the urgency, a conventional pivoted compass system was used, but this resulted in many broken pivots before a satisfactory shock-absorber could be devised. However, once successful dropping trials had been achieved, tens of thousands of these compasses were made and, with certain modifications, the design was still in production some thirty years later.[33] A more modern version, using a compass on the 'fluxgate' principle, with no moving parts, was designed during the late 1960s by Ultra Electronics, the ACO both monitoring and participating in the development.

THEORECTICAL WORK

During the late 1940s a considerable amount of theoretical work was undertaken by Commander G. N. Harvey and Mr T. H. O'Bierne, both of whom had joined the technical staff during the war, into possible ways of using the transmission arrangements of a marine compass to correct residual deviation and into the possible use of electromagnetic correction for compass adjustment.[34] Whilst this method is standard in remote-reading aircraft-compass systems it is, of course, contrary to the seaman's accepted practice of 'correcting like with like', and although it was successfully demonstrated at sea, it was not generally adopted. In 1947 Commander Harvey was awarded the degree of Ph.D. by the University of London for his thesis on 'The correction of transmitting magnetic compasses, using devices driven from the transmission of the compass'.[35] Work was also carried out into the problem of producing a truly vertical correcting field at the compass needles from heeling error magnets that inevitably have an unwanted inductive effect on the Flinders bar. This led to the development of the Harvey-Raynes sloping-magnet corrector[36] which, although theoretically sound, was unnecessarily complex for handling the now simple problem of correcting heeling error and was not introduced (it was aptly described by Commander May as 'that quaint conceit'!).

Before leaving the ACO to become chief scientist at the Fighting Vehicles Research and Development Establishment at Chobham, Commander Harvey completed a new edition of the *Admiralty*

Manual of the Deviations of the Magnetic Compass, which was published in 1948.[37]

Inevitably requests for odd jobs continued to arrive in the department to add variety to the everyday problems. Such tasks as fitting compasses to the land-rovers of the International Red Locust Control Service to enable parallel lines of insecticide to be laid in the African bush; or to the Weasels used by the British North Greenland Expedition to aid navigation on the icecap. The department was also called upon to assist in surveying the undulating 'horizontal' bore holes drilled during experimental work on underground gasification of coal seams, to enable them to be picked up by vertical holes drilled from the surface. This was accomplished by 'rodding' a saturable inductor along the narrow holes for distances up to 450 feet.[38] In 1947 two reproductions of Gowan Knight's famous compass of 1851 (see p. xxi) were made for the binnacle of HMS *Victory*, at Portsmouth, which had stood empty for many years.

Reorganization and policy changes

In 1948 the technical staff belonging to the Department of Scientific Research were reorganized and were allocated either to the Scientific Service or to the Production Pool. Mr A. G. Akehurst was appointed to ACO as Head of Production, with a staff of production pool officers, and assumed responsibility for the procurement of compass equipment, including its factory inspection and performance testing. At first this did not include the production contracts for gyro-compasses and their transmission units which, in common with much other electrical equipment, traditionally came under the Director of Electrical Engineering (DEE), but in 1952 after a considerable tussle, this anomaly was rectified and DCD became responsible for *all* compass equipment 'from the cradle to the grave'.[39]

The management of the ACO was reorganized into three departments under the Deputy Director and two Assistant Directors, who covered research and development and production respectively, the latter also embracing the workshops and inspection arrangements. A more detailed breakdown of the organization as it stood in the mid-1950s is given in appendix 10.

When peace returned the extensive production facilities built up during the war were no longer needed and for several years, despite the considerable run-down of personnel, it was difficult to keep the workshops adequately loaded. All Admiralty gyro-compass work and a considerable amount of magnetic-compass repair which would normally have gone to industry was kept at Slough. In 1947 it was arranged that the workshops should also undertake the repair of marine sextants which had hitherto been done entirely by the manufacturers. A sextant test bench, which had been taken out of service at Kew in 1913 when the optics staff moved to Teddington, (but brought back into use during both world wars) was now acquired and set up at the ACO.[40] The Compass Department had taken over responsibility for the procurement of sextants and star globes from the Hydrographer in 1942 and, with this new test facility, it was now authorized to issue its own certificates[41] (hitherto the sole prerogative of the National Physical Laboratory). When, in 1967 the National Physical Laboratory wished to give up its traditional role, the ACO agreed to test commercial sextants as well, and so became the only official sextant certification authority in the country.

Domestic and operational clocks and watches (but not chronometers) were also accepted for repair and before long the Compass Department became the procurement authority for these items too, a task which remained with it until 1968, when it was handed over to the Hydrographer. In addition the Director of Stores found the ACO useful for repairing small items, such as fans and motors, for which it was not always easy to find a contractor.

Despite these additional tasks, finding suitable high-grade work for a large number of craftsmen remained a struggle for several years but by dint of much lobbying for repair work on equipment other than compasses (e.g. asdic recorders and electric motors) it was possible to justify retaining the main core of excellent craftsmen, many of whom had been at the ACO since before the war. It was an effort that was well justified when, in 1959, the workshops undertook their most ambitious task yet, that of manufacturing the first two models of the British SINS equipment.

Meanwhile changes introduced during the war called for a review of the compass-fitting policy for HM ships, and in September 1946 the Director of the Compass Department restated the position. The following is a brief summary of his paper[42] which, in view of the long tradition of deference to the needs of the magnetic compass, represented a bold change in outlook.

1. *Large ships (battleships, carriers, cruisers and Daring-class destroyers).* These ships will normally have two Admiralty gyro-compasses with a Brown (Type B, without transmission) fitted at the primary steering position. If there is insufficient room at this position, a third Admiralty gyro may be fitted elsewhere. In cruisers, if room cannot be found for a third gyro, a portable magnetic compass is to be carried in lieu of the Standard. Otherwise large ships will not carry magnetic compasses.[43].

2. *Destroyers.* Two Admiralty gyro-compasses plus an ATMC2, fitted in the wheelhouse.

3. *Submarines.* One Admiralty gyro-compass, a magnetic compass in a projector binnacle and a portable compass ('Faithful Freddie').

4. *Smaller ships (sloops, frigates, minesweepers, etc.).* One gyro-compass, plus standard and steering magnetic compasses.

5. *The valve follow-up compass* is to be fitted in all new construction ships, except submarines, and to be introduced into older ships still fitted with balancers, as opportunity offers.

6. *Replacement of compasses.* As a general rule master compasses are to be renewed every five years. Sperry Commercial and Brown compasses, introduced during the war, will be gradually phased out of service and replaced by Admiralty types, except as in (1).

For many years the necessity to fit electrical and other equipment on the bridges of HM ships had made the satisfactory siting of the magnetic compass progressively more difficult, whilst the improved reliability of the gyro-compass had rendered an accurate magnetic compass less essential. In 1947 a system of graded compass positions was introduced[44] in order that, when acceptable, less stringent rules for ferrous structure and safe distances could be applied, so easing the problems of the naval constructors. A Grade I position still corresponded exactly with the traditional Standard Compass requirements, but in ships fitted with a gyro-compass a Grade II position was acceptable for the main magnetic compass as it was only the secondary means of navigating the ship.[45] Grades III and IV referred to positions for the standby and emergency compasses, for which the tolerances and safe distances were considerably relaxed.

The shape of the post-war Navy

When hostilities ended Britain not only had a huge active fleet but in the shipyards around the country there were new warships in all stages of construction. It would inevitably be some time before the requirements of the postwar navy could be determined. Indeed there were those who wondered whether the advent of rockets and atomic weapons would spell the virtual end of the surface ship as a viable unit.

Many ships taken up for war service were returned to their peacetime occupations, many more were earmarked for sale or scrapping, whilst others were placed in reserve pending a decision. Of the warships under construction there was an immediate cessation of work on all battleships, cruisers and aircraft carriers. On the other hand work on destroyers (the *Battle* and *Weapon* classes) was allowed to continue and it was agreed that the new *Daring* class, which had been ordered but not yet laid down, should also go ahead. Two new batches of submarines, the T and A classes, were to be completed.

By the beginning of the 1950s, a number of factors had become clear. The days of the battleship were over, and of the 15 which had survived the war, 10 had already been scrapped and 4 more placed in reserve from which they never re-emerged. Only the *Vanguard* was still in commission whilst pride of place in the Fleet had passed to the aircraft carrier. Two Fleet and three Light Fleet carriers, on which work had been suspended at the end of the war, were taken in hand once more whilst a sixth carrier, the *Hermes*,[46] which had been laid down in 1944, was added towards the end of the decade. Following the war in Korea there was again talk of rearmament and of strengthening the Reserve Fleet, although the mournful procession of older ships to the breaker's yard continued for several years.

Above all, however, it was the great Russian naval awakening, particularly in the field of submarines, which was to have the greatest influence on shaping the future fleet and it was the new concept of a fast frigate submarine-killer on which the Navy would mainly concentrate. At the same time the dangers of mine warfare, with new and more sophisticated mines, also loomed large and the next five years saw the completion of over 200 new coastal and inshore minesweepers. With their comprehensive degaussing system these ships placed a heavy load on the Compass Department and additional swinging officers were loaned from the Navigation School to assist.

Although cruisers remained with the fleet for some years,[47] from 1951 onwards it was to be primarily a small-ship navy with air cover. A new frigate building programme was rapidly put in hand and many of the wartime destroyers were converted to fast antisubmarine frigates with low profiles, enclosed bridges and greatly improved antisubmarine weapons, which later included helicopters. By 1958, in addition to its 1 battleship, 7 carriers and 12 cruisers the Navy had 56 destroyers and 105 modern frigates, with many more under construction.

Finally the concept of the true submarine, which could remain submerged for weeks on end, was taking shape and would require a drastic reappraisal of submarine navigation equipment. This more than any other factor was to control the destiny of the ACO over the years ahead. In January 1954 Mrs Dwight D. Eisenhower launched the first nuclear-powered submarine, the USS *Nautilus* which, four years later, excited the world with the first submerged transit of the North Pole from the Pacific to the Atlantic Ocean. But Great Britain was not far behind. In 1957 the Admiralty also announced its intention of entering the nuclear age with HMS *Dreadnought*, the first ship to bear the name since Lord Fisher's *Dreadnought* at the turn of the century. Here surely was a milestone in naval history as revolutionary as that of 1906.

New compasses for HM ships

When Captain Wynne-Edwards took over as director in 1951 the pattern of the future fleet was becoming clearer. Generally the requirements of navigation could still be adequately met by the current range of Admiralty gyro-compasses, despite their limited performance in high latitudes. For weapons systems and radar, however, the policy was to move towards self-aligning transmission. In addition certain modern weapons also required roll and pitch information, for which special weapon-stabilizers were provided. Although these stabilizers were not the responsibility of the director, he already foresaw the advantages if all these needs could be satisfied by one instrument.

By 1951 the Sperry Company in New York was well advanced with the design of a new gyro-compass which, in addition to giving a very accurate heading and a good high-latitude performance, would also define the vertical with an accuracy which was expected to rival that of the ship's main weapon-stabilizers. The company had already developed a compass in which electrical sensing devices, computers and torque motors, replaced the conventional mechanical control arrangements. This was the Sperry Mark 23 gyro-compass, which was introduced into the US Navy in 1952 and into the Royal Navy in 1964. (see p. 348). With their new compass Sperry now planned to take the further step, already ventured by the ACO in their prototype gyro-compass, of combining two gyroscopes, with their spin axes mounted at right angles, to produce a gyro-compass-stabilizer. This compass (later to become the Sperry Mark 19), when fully developed, promised to meet the future needs of the Royal Navy.

Accordingly as money and effort for work on the advanced ACO compass were scarce, it was decided to cease work on it and simply to modify the well-proven Admiralty gyro-compass to enable it to met the navy's immediate requirements over the next decade. Thus was born the 5005 series.

The basic Admiralty master unit, founded on the original Sperry and now over thirty years old, was given a modern facelift to raise it into the second half of the twentieth century. Synchronous transmission replaced the old M-type and the cosine ring and speed corrector were removed from the gyro-unit, the necessary correctons being injected into a bulkhead-mounted Master Transmission Unit (MTU). Further Compass Retransmission Units (CRU) could be added to increase the number of outputs, as required. In 1952 a new gyro laboratory was built onto the north-west corner of the mansion to handle this work. Meanwhile for those ships in which the gyro-compass was required for navigational purposes alone, the basic Admiralty gyro, Type 1005, was still entirely adequate.

GYRO-MAGNETIC COMPASS DEVELOPMENT

In parallel with the modernization of the Admiralty gyro-compass came a new development programme on gyro-magnetic compasses. The capabilities of the transmitting magnetic compass had been amply demonstrated by the AMTC2, which was widely fitted in destroyers, yet in 1951 the considerable additional benefits which could result from using a gyro-control to smooth out the random perturbations of the magnetic system had still only been tried in aircraft. An experimental rig was therefore constructed, using the ATMC2 with the addition of a gyro-unit (making it the ATMC2G) and this was tried at sea in the destroyer *Vigilant*. By February 1952 it had been developed into the Admiralty gyro-magnetic compass,

Type 5 (AGM5), with a completely redesigned master unit and binnacle and a new control console which, by adding variation and deviation, enabled true course to be transmitted to the repeaters. The compass became an immediate success and showed that a well placed and closely corrected magnetic compass could provide an accuracy comparable with or better than the gyro-compass itself. It had the additional advantage that in the event of power failure the instrument was still available as a simple magnetic compass.

The AGM5 was widely fitted as the Standard Compass, in place of the ATMC2, in the wheelhouse of destroyers and frigates, also in fast patrol boats and in inshore minesweepers. During the summer of 1954 one was fitted for trial in the Canadian ice-breaking patrol vessel, HMCS *Labrador*, during a voyage in which she became the first warship ever to complete a transit of the North-West Passage. This trial, which was conducted by Commander E. M. Penton from the Compass Department, showed that such a compass can be made to work, even when navigating in the vicinity of the magnetic pole, where the horizontal component of the earth's field is extremely small. Although the period of swing of the compass becomes long and its behaviour sluggish, it is still adequate to monitor the output from the gyro element, so enabling the compass to transmit a steady heading to the repeaters.[48]

It was now apparent that the magnetic compass in its modern form could, with the gyro-compass, provide a partnership of complementary instruments of comparable accuracy, capable of meeting the needs of modern warships. However, while the AGM5 made a suitable partner for the Admiralty gyro-compass Type 1005, it could not provide self-synchronous transmission and was thus not suitable to partner the new 5005 series. Accordingly the Admiralty gyro-magnetic compass, Type 6 was developed during 1953–54 to meet this need.

Either compass, the gyro or the AGM, could be switched to drive the ship's entire outfit of compass-repeaters, including those in the weapon system. Because of its importance as the equal partner of the gyro-compass, the AGM6 was always afforded a Grade 1 compass position and in frigates was generally fitted on a special platform amidships, which also acted as the emergency conning position. When gas-turbine propulsion was introduced, enabling ships to get underway at very short notice without having first to raise steam, the AGM6 provided an accurate compass which was immediately available for navigation, whereas the gyro-compass would take several hours to run up and settle. After a gradual decline in importance over almost half a century, the magnetic compass was back in business.

OTHER TRANSMITTING MAGNETIC COMPASSES

A brief attempt was made to extend the advantages of the gyro-magnetic system to large ships by fitting a magnetic element (a saturable inductor) on a spur up the mast, clear of magnetic interference, on the same principle as placing it in the wing of an aircraft. This was the Admiralty gyro-magnetic compass, Type 7 (AGM7). It saw trials, along with the Type 5005 gyro-compass and the AGM6, in the navy's trials' cruiser, HMS *Cumberland*, during 1954–55, and caused much friendly rivalry between the gyro- and magnetic compass sections. The AGM7 was fitted in the cruiser *Tiger* and in the carriers *Eagle* and *Hermes* (where it worked very well) but by this time modern and more accurate gyro-compasses were being introduced, and the idea was not pursued. Meanwhile, to reduce the weight of the AGM5, for use in fast patrol boats, a truncated version, the AGM10, was designed in 1956 and fitted in the Brave and later classes where it served well until the introduction of the small Arma-Brown gyro-compass during the 1960s.

A COMPASS FOR SUBMARINES

For many years the requirement for a projector binnacle, which needed a sizeable hole in the pressure hull, had been regarded unfavourably by the submariners, and in 1960 the problem was overcome by providing a transmitting magnetic compass, the ATMC8, with a watertight binnacle fitted in the fin. An inductor was used to sense the movement of the magnetic compass itself and transmit it to a repeater at the helmsman's position in the control room. This compass is still (1984) fitted in conventional submarines. One was initially fitted in HMS *Dreadnought* and a modified version, the ATMC11, with degaussing correction, was installed in HMS *Valiant*, but magnetic compasses proved unsuitable for nuclear submarines and they were later withdrawn.

The family of transmitting magnetic compasses, together with the 5005 series of gyro-compasses, constituted what the Director of the Compass Department regarded as phase 1 in his modernization plan, i.e. applying new techniques to well-established gyro and

magnetic equipment. Phase 2, the introduction of the next generation of navigational aids, including inertial navigation equipment,
will be covered in the next chapter. A 'family tree' of Admiralty
transmitting magnetic compasses, which served the Navy well for
two decades is given in appendix 11.

PERISCOPE SEXTANTS

The concept of a true submarine implies that the boat should no
longer have to surface in order to fix its position. Accordingly, in
1952 an investigation was started, at the request of Flag Officer,
Submarines, into the possibility of taking sights through the periscope. Early trials in the submarines *Aeneas* and *Thermopyle*, using
a modification of the normal marine sextant[49], showed that satisfactory sun sights were possible up to 20° altitude (the limit of the
field of view) but that the use of a bubble and averager, as in a
bubble-sextant, to enable star sights to be taken at anytime of night,
could not produce the accuracy required. At the end of 1953 it was
decided to go for a gyro-stabilized artificial horizon and this was
designed at the ACO, a development contract being placed with
Messrs Barr & Stroud of Glasgow, who made the periscopes.

Sights had to be taken through the attack periscope, as it was
considered undesirable to divert the search periscope from its proper
function of keeping a look-out, and a special optical window was
introduced near the top of the tube which allowed a view of the
sky up to 75°. Amongst the many problems to be solved were those
introduced by the bending of the periscope itself, particularly when
the submarine was rolling, and the fact that the stable platform,
which controlled the artificial horizon by means of a gyro and a
damped pendulum, was too bulky to fit into the periscope base.
Initially this unit was clamped on underneath and removed when
not required. However, a much neater arrangement emerged in
1958 when the lower casting of the periscope was redesigned and a
slimming down of the sextant enabled all its units (stable platform,
power-pack and averager) to be accommodated within the periscope
itself.

Trials continued through the 1950s, both in the periscope tower
at the Barr & Stroud works (finding a star in the skies over Glasgow
in February was a challenge in itself) and at sea, and retrospective
ship-fitting in all except the oldest submarines began in 1963. Close
co-operation was maintained with the Royal Netherlands Navy,

who were also working on the problem, and some models of their 'multi-facet' natural horizon solar sextant were fitted in RN submarines. Later the ACO's Artificial Horizon Periscope Sextant (AHPS) was sold to the Dutch, Italian and Israeli navies.

Although the AHPS was popular and successful at sea, the narrow top of the attack periscope severly restricted the size of the prism that could be used to collect starlight, so limiting its use to stars of the first magnitude. When, however, in 1965, it was agreed that the larger search periscope could be employed, the optics were redesigned and a greatly improved instrument, the AHPS Mark III, was developed. This was fitted in the second batch of nuclear submarines, the Swiftsures, from 1970 onwards. However, competition for space in the base of the periscope was always intense and it was not long before the continued inclusion of the AHPS was again seriously threatened. The problem was ovecome by the development of a radical new design, the AHPS Mark IV, in which the artificial horizon is controlled by the submarine's own stabilizer equipment, either SINS or the gyro-compass-stabilizer, so eliminating all the bulky items. This has now become the standard equipment for all new submarines and has considerably increased the accuracy of fixing through the periscope.

MINOR PROJECTS

Of the many minor projects which were undertaken during the mid-1950s, two deserve particular mention – remote-reading sextants and compasses for landing craft.

The requirement for mine counter-measures vessels to be able to navigate with great precision, both when sweeping and, more particularly, when required to return to an exact position to deal with a mine, could not at that time be satisfied by any radio navigational aid. Recourse was therefore made to the time-honoured method of using horizontal sextant angles (HSA), and the ACO was asked to design a remote-reading sextant to facilitate the rapid plotting of positions using this method. Although a system was developed and tried out at sea, it was never put into production and was finally overtaken by the introduction of more accurate radio navigation aids such as Decca Hi-fix.

The second project was more fruitful. The requirement for a flexible amphibious landing capability was growing and eventually led to the introduction of assault ships and the conversion of the

Light fleet carriers *Bulwark* and *Albion* to commando carriers. To meet the needs of the new landing craft (LCA and LCM) to be carried in these ships a periscopic binnacle based on the *Giraffe* tank compass, was designed, which enabled the compass to be raised above the magnetic influence of the load embarked. This compass outfit (Pattern 51) was still in general use in the 1980s.

Before embarking on an account of the momentous developments which were to influence the destiny of the Compass Department from 1956 onwards, three happy events deserve a brief mention.

In 1952 the ACO sports and social club members themselves completed the building of a new pavilion more suitable for social functions than the original wooden building that had stood since 1927. The club had built up strongly since the war and in the summer of 1950 had won the Admiralty cricket cup. Now new activities were introduced, including an archery section,[50] while the bowling green, which was becoming more important as the average age of the workforce increased, was extended to six rinks. It was later given the accolade of 'county standard' and in due course two members of the ACO, Mr R. Wickenden and Mr J. Lovegrove, were to serve as presidents of the Bucks County Bowling Association.

To mark the coronation of Her Majesty Queen Elizabeth II, the ACO was visited, on 26 October 1954, by His Royal Highness the Duke of Edinburgh, who toured the establishment and discussed its latest projects (which, at the time, included the AGM6 and the AHPS). He had lunch with the director (who had had the forethought to borrow the Commander-in-Chief's chef for the occasion) and after unveiling a sundial and planting a suitably non-magnetic tree (a Copper Beech) close to the Verdun oak planted by King George V, he departed from the south lawn by helicopter.

Two years later, at the request of the Royal Yachting Association, Captain Wynne-Edwards undertook the onerous task of managing Britain's sailing team for the Olympic Games in Melbourne, where they won a silver and two bronze medals. Although the visit was not sponsored by the Admiralty, the Director was invited by the Australian naval authorities to address them on the Royal Navy's plans to introduce the modern generation of compass equipment. He returned to England on 14 December 1956, to be met with dire news.

The 'way ahead' committee

A fortnight before Christmas 1956 the Director received a letter which might well have spelt the end of the ACO as a separate entity. It informed him that 'Their Lordships have decided, in principle, that the Admiralty Compass Observatory should be closed down and its work absorbed by other establishments'. The letter went on, 'I am to request, therefore, that you will examine and report how much of the work of this establishment is essential to the support of the Fleet of the future and how this might be absorbed by other establishments'.[51]

For some years it had been realized that the magnitude of the Navy's shore organization was disproportionately large in relation to the reduced size of the postwar fleet. Accordingly, in the summer of 1955 the First Sea Lord, Admiral Lord Louis Mountbatten had set up the 'way ahead' committee to spearhead his drive to reduce the number of shore establishments. The interim report of this committee had been placed before the Board and each recommendation had now to be reviewed in detail before any decision was taken.

The first few months of 1957 were hectic, even by Wynne-Edwards's standards. Meetings were held with the Directors of Navigation and Direction, of Stores, of Air Warfare, with the Ministry of Supply and representatives of the Army and the Royal Air Force, also with the heads of the Navy's main R & D establishments at Portsmouth and Portland who might be required to take over the duties of the ACO. A visit to the Admiralty at Bath on 9 January revealed that the Controller, Vice-Admiral Sir Peter Reid, had rather surprisingly, not been informed that one of his establishments might be due to close. A week later he told the Director that he was not convinced that it should! On 23 January the shop stewards' committee were informed of the situation and by the 25th news of a possible closure was carried in the local press.

Once the news became public knowledge the two Members of Parliament for the area naturally took a great interest in the progress of the enquiry and it is a pleasure to place on record the wholehearted support given to the establishment by Mr Fenner-Brockway, the member for Slough. After separate meetings in the House of Commons with the Director and with the shop stewards' committee, headed by Jock Steen, he visited the establishment and then, on 29

May, posed a question to the Minister of Defence, Mr Duncan Sandys, about the work of the ACO for the three services. This was followed by a clever 'supplementary' which elicited the brief reply that 'There is no present intention to close the establishment'. Although the Director warned the shop stewards' committee that nothing was yet settled and there was still a long way to go, this reply did much to take the heat out of the local debate.

Meanwhile a full and detailed investigation into ways of implementing this recommendation had to be carried out, as instructed by the Board. It showed that whilst the majority of the R & D and production work could be satisfactorily (but not necessarily more economically) transferred to the Admiralty Signal and Radar Establishment at Portsdown, certain facilities would need to be provided at other establishments, notably at HMS *Dryad* in Southwick Park (for such items as the geomagnetic recording equipment) and at suitable naval store depots (for storage and test facilities). The 'headquarters' and instructional commitments would need to be similarly dispersed. Whilst it was feasible for the very considerable amount of compass repair work undertaken at Slough to be put out to industry, this would mean disbanding the expert pool of skilled mechanics (instrument-makers) built up over many years, who were still required to meet the fluctuating demands for bench work of the highest order for R & D projects.

Two factors appeared to have a crucial bearing on the outcome of this investigation. The first was that to meet the needs of the true submarine the ACO had recently embarked on the development of the Ship's Intertial Navigation System (SINS), an instrument requiring very high-grade engineering techniques and using gyroscopes of an accuracy hitherto unknown in the navigation field. The second was that the 'way ahead' committee had already recommended that the Admiralty Gunnery Establishment (AGE) at Portland should be amalgamated with the Signal and Radar Establishment at Portsmouth, to form the Admiralty Surface Weapons Establishment (ASWE).[52] Very accurate gyroscopes were also required by AGE for stabilization projects and at first sight it appeared logical and attractive to co-ordinate all high-grade gyro work under one roof. In the event, however, it soon became evident that any commonality between the projects was more apparent than real, while from the point of view of space, the transfer of ACO in addition to AGE would cause serious embarrassment at ASWE.

Other factors also affected the outcome. It seemed probable that in undertaking the development of SINS and its complementary equipment, the Artificial Horizon Periscope Sextant, the Navy stood a better chance of making worthwhile progress if it could continue to draw upon the great store of knowledge and experience available at the ACO, and on the manual skills of the excellent workforce. It was also recognized that in the fields of compasses and navigational instruments the ACO had a worldwide reputation and that help and advice were constantly being sought by other government departments and by authorities in many parts of the world. Further, it appeared likely that the department's considerable contributions to the other branches of the fighting services might well be in jeopardy if there were to be any large disruption and reorganization such as might result from the ACO's absorption into 'surface weapons'. Gradually the feeling was shifting from a decision to close the ACO to the view that it might pay to keep it open.

On the matter of running a 'headquarters department', the Director's answer to a question from the 'way ahead' committee merits reproduction in full:

Headquarters Department. It might be argued with some modicum of truth that the Admiralty gets its headquarters Compass Department for nothing. This is at least true in the sense that no person in the establishment is employed on headquarters duties exclusively, and that any member of the non-industrial staff may be called upon as necessary, to contribute to headquarters business. I am quite unable to say who, on my staff, is 'headquarters' staff, and who 'outport' staff. This arrangement is extremely economical of effort and paper work, and is highly efficient. It ensures that technical questions are answered with minimum delay, and that Admiralty dockets are not held up for weeks or even months while advice is being sought from an outport technical establishment. It ensures that all papers belonging to and concerning the department are filed in the establishment and that they can be referred to without delay. It obviates all the clerical work involved in correspondence between headquarters department and outport.

This is a form of organisation which might with great advantage be put to more extensive use in the Admiralty.

By having so many functions under one director and one roof, this economy had always been a feature of the way the Compass Department ran its business. Some ten years later, when headquarters status was also given to the Surface and Underwater Weapons establishments, as a result of the recommendations of the Caldecote committee, they adopted very similar organizations.

After looking at these considerations and taking into account the views of all interested departments, the executive working party of the 'way ahead' committee accepted that the work of the ACO was essential to the support of the Fleet. When considering where it could best be carried out, they noted that absorption of the ACO elsewhere would involve transferring functions to the Director of Radio Equipment, to the Director of Navigation and Direction, to one or more stores depots, to an air station and, at Portsmouth, to ASWE and two instructional establishments, HMS *Dryad* and HMS *Collingwood*. In addition, much work would have to go to industry. Such a solution would simply fragment a compact organization in which all these functions were concentrated and would disband a highly skilled workforce, most of whom would be unwilling to move elsewhere.

Accordingly, on 28 October 1957 the Board's committee on the way ahead 'Approved that the Admiralty Compass Observatory should remain a separate Establishment at Slough'.[53] Further paragraphs followed, directing that the ACO's capacity and staff should be reduced to the minimum compatible with its R & D projects and that repair work undertaken by the workshops should be competitive with industry. These caveats were entirely reasonable and the establishment could breathe again. It had, however, been a very long ten-month struggle.

The ACO had had a good case, which stood up to scrutiny. Nevertheless, there can be little doubt that but for the firm, resolute and cogent way in which the director, Captain Wynne-Edwards, conducted the negotiations, the establishment would almost certainly have been closed. It was his brilliant and determined advocacy which prevented what, in the light of future developments, would have been a most unfortunate decision. Events have shown how right was his judgement, and the Navy has a great deal to thank him for.

In order not to be repetitive it would be worth recording at this juncture that although the ACO had survived a very thorough scrutiny and lived to tell the tale, there will always be other planners prepared to try again. The establishment was still small by most standards and as such was vulnerable. On no less than four occasions during the 1960s, working parties or committees proposed that the ACO should either be closed or amalgamated with some other establishment. Time and again the management was called upon to justify its work and much time and effort was wasted in dealing with what were sometimes ill-informed enquiries. When amalgamation with the Admiralty Surface Weapons Establishment eventually took place in 1971, following the 'Rayner Report', it was in changed circumstances and came about logically and without undue pain, albeit as the result of somewhat unprincipled tactics. But in the 1950s that lay a long way in the future.

The Nihil committee and the formation of the weapons department

In parallel with the work of the 'way ahead' committee, another enquiry, under Sir Barclay Nihil, examined the organization for handling the Admiralty's requirements in material. It was to a large extent a review of the organization under the Controller of the Navy.

For many years new Admiralty material departments had come into being as a consequence of the Navy's interest in new scientific or technical developments and, as in the case of the Compass Department, these had often grown up from small beginnings. As a result no less than fifteen separate autonomous departments now reported directly to the Controller, each concentrating on its own particular subject, equipment or technique, rather than on the wider functions which affected the Navy as a whole. The Nihil committee recommended that these departments should be grouped under four separate Directors-General, responsible to the Controller, for Ships (the hull, machinery and electrics), Weapons (including communications), Air (both aircraft and air material) and Dockyards and Fleet Maintenance. There was some debate in the committee as to whether 'compasses' should be regarded as part of the ship or part of the weapon system but, in the event, the decision in favour of the latter was clearly logical.

The Weapons Department came into being at Bath on 15 July 1958, with Rear Admiral Michael Le Fanu DSC, as the first Director-General, and was largely an amalgam of the old weapons headquarters departments.[54] The Compass Department thus became the Compass Division of the Weapons Department and the director assumed the title of Director of Weapons (Compass) (DWC). Also under the control of the Director-General Weapons (DGW), came the three R & D establishments, dealing with surface weapons, communications and radar (ASWE), underwater weapons (AUWE) and, providing a service to both, the Admiralty Compass Observatory.

Traditionally the Director of the Compass Department had, in addition to his headquarters function, acted as superintendent of his own R & D establishment, the ACO. However, such an anomalous situation, although it had existed since 1917 and was both efficient and economical, did not fit into the otherwise neat organizational pattern created by the Nihil committee. They were unhappy about it and would have preferred to see the headquarters function transferred to one of the directors in Bath, leaving the ACO as an 'outport' establishment, on the same footing as the surface and underwater establishments at Portsdown and Portland. Their deliberations had, surprisingly, not included an interview with the Director of the Compass Department nor a visit to the ACO. In the event the matter was left in abeyance for subsequent report by the Director-General (Weapons) after experience with the new orgainzation (see p. 319).

The Ship's Inertial Navigation System (SINS)

By the mid-1950s the Western countries were starting to rearm, the United States Navy had embarked on its Polaris programme and Britain had decided to build nuclear submarines. By its very nature a nuclear submarine is designed to remain submerged for long periods free from detection. It must therefore have a navigation system which, as far as possible, is independent of outside sources which would require it to surface. This requirement is, to a considerable extent, satisfied by the Ship's Inertial Navigation System (SINS).[55]

The purpose of SINS, in the simplest terms, is to tell the Navigator where he is at all times, within an acceptable accuracy. It is an entirely self-contained navigational system, giving continuous outputs of the ship's position, heading and velocity. It is not susceptible to jamming or outside interference. Although the principles of inertial navigation had been well understood for over a century, it was only in the decade following World War II that technology reached the stage where it might be possible in a ship to achieve an accuracy that was superior to conventional methods of navigation. However, no system can be made perfect and certain errors will inevitably accumulate with time. Whereas an inertial system in a missile or an aircraft may be required to operate accurately for a few hours, that in a submarine may need to provide useable outputs for days or even weeks. The degree of precision required is thus of an altogether higher order.

The first inertial navigation system for aircraft use was produced in the United States in the late 1940s, but it was a comparatively crude system by modern standards, and it was not until 1953, when Dr Draper at the Massachusetts Institute of Technology (MIT) developed the so-called 'Rate-integrating floated gyro' that worthwhile results appeared likely. In the following year a ship's inertial navigation system, using this type of gyro, made its 30 mile maiden voyage in a van, followed shortly afterwards by a sea trial in USS *Canisteo*.

The Admiralty watched these developments with interest. Both navigation and gunnery were interested in high-precision gyroscopes and in 1954 Dr Rawlinson of ACO and Mr Henry Heal of the Admiralty Gunnery Establishment were sent over to America together, to study these modern gyro techniques. Work had already started on the design of Britain's first nuclear submarine and, on 20 December 1954, Wynne-Edwards broached the subject of inertial navigation with the Controller. A month later he prepared a paper to acquaint the Board of Admiralty of its possibilities, the opening paragraph of which gave the essence of the system:

The purpose of this paper is to draw the attention of the Board to certain possibilities which exist for developing a new method for finding position at sea based upon the fact that in any given position on earth the direction of the force of gravity differs from that in any other position. For example, if an instrument could be made whose axis defined the true vertical at a known point of departure with sufficient accuracy, and if this instrument were capable of maintaining this definition over a period of time during which the ship in which it was mounted steamed over the earth's surface, the apparent movement of the axis in relation to the zenith and the true north would give a measure of the course and distance steamed.

The paper outlined the progress already made in America and in particular their success in developing the high-precision gyroscopes required. It emphasized that here lay probably the only hope of achieving the navigational accuracy required in a true submarine and requested that twelve of the new gyros should be purchased from the United States without delay so that development work on the system could start at once. In a concluding paragraph Wynne-Edwards wrote:

> Although these systems are still in the comparatively early stage of development it is thought that the results obtained are sufficiently impressive to underline the importance of the principle, and to show that its development may well lead to very worthwhile improvements in the art of navigation without placing any reliance upon either clear skies or radio aids. This may indeed, in future years, be ranked in navigational annals with such great developments as Harrison's chronometer and the gyro-compass, and from this viewpoint alone it is DCD's strong conviction that no time should be lost in starting development in this country.

The proposal received enthusiastic support from the Director of Navigation and Direction and a Staff Requirement for SINS was quickly raised. During the early part of 1955 a mild tug of war took place between the Director of Naval Ordnance and DCD as to who would be responsible for such a system which, by its very nature, would indicate the vertical with an accuracy far surpassing that of the normal weapons stabilizers. However, it was primarily an instrument for navigation and the matter was quickly resolved in favour of DCD.[56]

The Staff Requirement for SINS, which was approved in May 1956, stated two clear aims: (1) to develop a British inertial navigation system, using American gyros as a basis; and (2) to evaluate US gyros with a view to their production in the United Kingdom.

In 1957 a start was made at the ACO on the development of a British SINS. A new laboratory was created out of what had originally been a store for aircraft equipment, with a clean-room facility alongside it, for assembly. Two additional scientists, W. P. Anderson and Dr A. Lee, were appointed to handle the electronics and computer aspects. However, money was tight and these were meagre resources with which to tackle so ambitious a project. Techniques were new and there was inevitably a long learning curve. When, in December 1958, Dr Rawlinson, the Chief Scientist reached retirement age, little progress of significance had been made.

Rawlinson was succeeded by H. J. Elwertowski and it was really from this point that the establishment embarked on a decade of almost continual progress and expansion. Elwertowski had been leading the stabilization section at the Admiralty Gunnery Establishment (AGE) and had met Wynne-Edwards during the discussions over gyros. The two men saw eye to eye at once. Words were said in the right place and, when AGE transferred to Portsdown, Elwertowski found himself appointed as Chief Scientist and Assistant Director (R & D) at the ACO. The timing was perfect.

In parenthesis it is interesting to look briefly at the early career of this remarkable man. Born in Poland in 1911, Henry Elwertowski was educated at Warsaw University and worked on the design of army fire-control equipment. When the German invasion of Poland appeared imminent he enlisted in the Polish artillery but in September 1939 he was captured and interned in Hungary. Within months he had escaped and eventually reached France via Yugoslavia and Italy. A brief period with the Polish forces in exile in Paris was cut short by the German occupation but he again made his escape to the unoccupied south and eventually, via Spain and Portugal, by sea to Gibraltar. In 1942 he reached England in a troopship and was shortly afterwards engaged as a Senior Experimental Officer to work on Army anti-aircraft gunnery at the Admiralty Research Laboratory (later AGE), at Teddington. Promotion followed quickly and when AGE moved to Portland in 1954, Elwertowski became head of the stabilization group. He was promoted to Senior Principal Scientific Officer the following year.

In March 1959 Elwertowski was joined at the ACO by H. T. Heal, his number two at Portland, who later looked back on this appointment with some amusement. He had been sent to America with Dr Rawlinson in 1954 and, having learnt about SINS, he decided that it sounded an interesting job and applied for a transfer to the ACO. This was refused. He recalled, however, that he quickly got over his disappointment after deciding that 'the SINS job was an almost impossible one'. It was therefore with mixed feelings that in 1959 he found that he had got, as a pressed man, what he had earlier been refused as a volunteer!

Although the British Joint Staff in Washington had kept the Admiralty informed of progress on the American scene and further scientific visits had been made to study the latest developments in gyro manufacture, adjustment and testing, in January 1959 the government decided it was time to send a senior mission to look at developments at first hand. As it was still the aim, if possible, to co-ordinate all government work in the inertial gyro field, the team consisted of the Director and the Chief Scientist from the ACO, with officers from the Ministry of Supply and the Royal Aircraft Establishment. Together they carried out a four-week tour of the main laboratories, including MIT, and of the several firms which had shown themselves capable of building Draper-type gyros. The aim of the mission was to assess the respective products and the capabilities of the firms in order to advise on how best the limited development and manufacturing resources of the United Kingdom should be deployed. As Wynne-Edwards put it, 'We were picking the Americans' brains. Later they were to pick ours'.

Following the visit it became clear that it would be impracticable to develop a gyro to suit the requirements of both the ACO and the RAE and that the Navy would have to go its own way with SINS gyro development and production. The problems of deciding which firm in the United Kingdom should be given the chance to produce British SINS gyros had already been given careful study and discussions had been held with a number of possible candidates. Elliott's were in the field with an inertial system for *Blue Steel* and Sperry with one for *Blue Streak*, although neither required the same high-precision gyros as those now being considered. Ferranti, who were opening a new factory for high-grade gyros in Edinburgh, were also interested. Finally, however, it was English Electric Aviation of Stevenage[57] which was chosen. In 1961 a licence agreement was signed with Northrop Nortronics of Massachusetts which would allow English Electric Aviation to manufacture their particular design of gyro, known as the V6, in the United Kingdom. The progress of this outstandingly successful venture is further described in the next chapter.

Meanwhile Heal's team at the ACO had taken a fresh look at the problem. It was decided to base the design on the newly developed ETAS (Heal's experimental three-axis stabilizer)[58] which used simpler gyros of the rate-integrating type. The first British SINS was a three-axis stabilizer with a fourth gimbal added, and due to limitations in both the gyros and computers of the day the system had to be analogue. Additional staff were asked for and, pending recruitment, were borrowed from existing ACO projects. A new Electrical Officer, Lieutenant Commander J. Boyton, who had just completed a year's postgraduate study at MIT, was also appointed. In the remarkably short period of two years the team progressed from a blank sheet of paper to that magic moment on 4 July 1961 (British SINS 'Independence Day') when the first laboratory model, built in the ACO workshops, was switched on. A month later, when the Controller of the Navy visited the ACO, he was able to see SINS running.

Gyros for the early models of SINS had, of course, to be brought over from America and this presented some unusual logistic problems. SINS Gyros are filled with a flotation liquid called fluorolube which has to be kept permanently above a critical temperature of 40°C (104°F). When not in operation they have therefore to be kept heated to prevent the fluorolube from solidifying and damaging the very expensive mechanism. Specially heated boxes were designed for transport and storage purposes and the first two shipments of gyros were accompanied across the Atlantic by a responsible scientist to ensure that they did not cool. This man also witnessed the final tests on the gyros and accepted them from the manufacturers. It was a popular assignment and was undertaken by Dr J. Preston, who became the leading gyro specialist at the ACO and later the officer-in-charge.

In September 1961 the laboratory model of SINS was installed for sea trials in a converted mine-layer at Portsmouth, ironically named *Steady* (formerly *Miner VII*), and a number of short excursions were made along the south coast, giving some of the young scientists their first opportunity to acquire their sea legs. Apart from its violent motion, the vessel was far from ideal, offering few facilities for a scientific trial. Nevertheless SINS was shown to function satisfactorily at sea, albeit with an accuracy which fell far short of expectations, and demonstrated that the system was basically sound. Development, however, was still at a very early stage with, as yet, no opportunity to undertake final engineering or even tidying the job up. For example, changing 'modes' required plugs to be pulled out by hand and reinserted into other sockets, while testing a circuit could involve holding avometer probes onto terminals which might be carrying up to 300 volts. To form a true picture of the conditions one must imagine these operations being conducted by seasick scientists in a cramped compartment with the ship rolling 30° either way, apparently on a diet of curry, the Master's favourite fare. It was remarkable that so much was achieved and so many valuable lessons learnt.

Although the laboratory model of SINS remained in *Steady* and trials continued until the following summer, by the early autumn 1961 the project was already moving on to the next stage. It was now a race against time – hardly the ideal circumstances under which to develop an extremely advanced and sophisticated system – to get the next equipment, the first of three experimental models, ready in time for its installation in HMS *Dreadnought* during 1962.

Retirement of Captain Wynne-Edwards

In September 1961, shortly after the start of the *Steady* trials. Captain Wynne-Edwards retired after thirteen momentous years at the Admiralty Compass Observatory. When he joined in 1948 there was much uncertainty about the future, and he will be remembered particularly for the insight and prudent planning with which he placed the compass policy for the Navy on a firm basis, with its future plans well laid. He left nothing to chance. On taking over as director he found that the latest 'Instructions to the Director of the Compass Department' were those dated July 1935,[59] although much had changed in the interval. New equipments had been introduced and wider responsibilities accepted; working agreements had been reached with the Ministry of Aviation and the Board of Trade; the department had assumed sponsorship of the British nautical instrument industry; the production pool had been established. After prolonged negotiations with other departments revised 'Instructions' were issued in May 1954[60] and these needed only slight amendment and updating when, five years later, 'compasses' were incorporated into the Weapons Department.

At the ACO he had fought many battles on behalf of his staff. In 1956 when a pay award to the compass mechanics left the chargehands with no differential, he took up their case and pressed it right through to the First Lord of the Admiralty to achieve a just decision. Another case concerned the Naval Assistants who, although their naval pension was stopped under their terms of service, were nevertheless paid a mere pittance by a grateful Admiralty. Again he championed their cause and eventually achieved for them the proper rate for the job, tied to an equivalent civil service scale so that rises would come automatically. Many similar examples could be quoted.

However, Wynne-Edwards was essentially a practical sailor and navigator whose early achievements had twice earned him the Distinguished Service Cross to add to the Royal Humane Society's Bronze Medal he had been awarded before the war. He served on the council of the Royal Yachting Association and on many of its committees; he was also a council member of the Royal Institute of Navigation and winner of their Bronze Medal, being selected by them to serve as a member of the British delegation on the international working party on the 'prevention of collisions at sea'. In 1980 the Institute elected him into Honorary Membership, their highest honour.

Above all, however, Captain Wynne-Edwards will be remembered at the ACO for his shrewd and determined stand when negotiating with the 'way ahead' committee, which prevented it taking what, in the light of later developments, would have been a most unfortunate decision. Before retiring he saw the British SINS programme, which he himself had inspired, progress to the stage of a successful sea trial. His wide experience of navigational problems and his imaginative grasp of how to solve them were to continue to bear fruit for many years.[61]

Most appropriately his successor, Captain T. D. Ross, was the great grandson of Admiral Sir James Ross, chairman of the original Admiralty Compass Committee of 1837, which had brought the Compass Department into being. He had already held many important appointments in the navigation field, including that of Director of Navigation and Direction, and was the ideal person to guide the establishment through the next decade, which was to be one of almost continual growth and progress.

NOTES

CHAPTER 11

1 Reports on a number of German transmitting compasses are contained in Compass Department, 'R & D Report', 1946.

2 By the end of World War II Dr Gievers already had quite advanced ideas about the development of a type of inertial navigation system (known as *Obergrund Kompass*), although he realized that many fundamental problems remained to be solved. Technology could not provide the required mechanism for another ten years. Dr Gievers had managed to escape from the Russians and later from the Czechs before giving himself up to the British North Germany Mission.

3 Dr Ing. B. Stieler, 'Contributions of the late Dr Gievers to inertial technology', presented at the Gyro Symposium, Stuttgart, 25 September 1979.

4 Designed by Dr P. J. Kaiser, adviseur verificateur van's Rijks Zee-Instrumenten to the Dutch navy, 1890–1903.

5 During World War II this became the Admiralty Signal Establishment (ASE) at Haslemere, from which developed the Admiralty Surface Weapons Establishment.

6 The ACO gyro-compass is described in Compass Department, 'R & D Report', 1949, Item 1.

7 The principles involved are described in Compass Department, 'R & D Report', 1947, Item 19.

8 A description of the *Proteus* mounting is given in Compass Department 'R & D Report', 1946, Item 11.

9 Admiralty Fleet Order, 3605/49.

10 Compass Department, 'R & D Report', 1949, Item 5.

11 During the 1950s coastal-forces craft were designated as fast patrol boats (FPBs) and were designed to be interchangeable as MTBs or MGBs.

12 Compass Department, 'R & D Report', 1947, Item 10.

13 A description of the ATMC4 is contained in Compass Department, 'R & D Report', 1948, Item 9.

14 Ibid., Item 15.

15 In its simplest form a saturable inductor consists of two energized coils mounted at right angles to one another, both of which detect components of the earth's magnetic field. Combining their outputs gives the direction, relative to the aircraft, of magnetic north.

16 The terms 'flux valve' and 'fluxgate' both refer to earth-inductor or saturable-inductor systems made by different manufacturers, the former by Sperry, the latter by Pioneer Bendix. A simple description of the Sperry gyrosyn compass is given in Compass Department, 'R & D Report', 1946, Item 12.

17 Compass Department, 'R & D Report', 1947, Item 5; also 1948, Item 4, 1949, Item 7.

18 Compass Department, 'R & D Report', 1946, Item 15. See also A. Hine, *Magnetic Compasses and Magnetometers*, Adam Hilger, Bristol 1968, p.72.

[19] ACO Historical Section, (AA EE/Inst/66, Item R27(4)).

[20] ACO Historical Section, Item R42A (2), (NASWDU, Report No. 500/50).

[21] Rumour has it that despite the modern computerized aids carried, on at least one occasion the Captain of Concorde has been very grateful to have his little E2 compass.

[22] ACO Historical Section, Item R20 (2), (EANS, Report No. 45/2, Part 2).

[23] The dip pole was located in position 76°N 102°W (compare p. 42).

[24] Compass Department, 'R & D Report', 1948, Item 2, (this matter was also reported in *The Times*, 10 January 1948.)

[25] ACO Historical Section. Items R27(18), (19), (20), (AAEE/Inst/95, 96, 97).

[26] Admiralty Fleet Order, 2934/58.

[27] ACO Archives. (CA Notice No. Orgn. 5, 1 June 1955.)

[28] Ibid. (CD A/13/102/58, 28 October 1958).

[29] Ibid. (CA Notice No. Orgn. 5, 21 March 1963.)

[30] Public Records Office, ADM 1/18425.

[31] The Hydrographer introduced a similar change in the compass roses printed on charts, but agreed to retain points on certain charts for the benefit of fishermen.

[32] The marine compass test stands, designed by Messrs Barr & Stroud of Glasgow in 1967 to meet the exacting ISO standards, incorporate certain techniques which were then in advance of any British or foreign equivalent.

[33] A description of this sonobuoy compass is contained in Compass Department, 'R & D Report', 1948, Item 18.

[34] Compass Department, 'R & D Report', 1946, Item 17, 1947, Item 15.

[35] Compass Department, 'R & D Report' 1947, Item 15, and *Journal of the Institute of Navigation*, Vol. 1, No. 3.

[36] Compass Department, 'R & D Report', 1947, Item 16. Commander Raynes was at this time in charge of the Magnetic compass test rooms at the ACO.

[37] HMSO, BR101 (48). This publication had been reissued on a number of occasions (see also p. 66). An extensive revision by Creak appeared in 1901 (6th edn) and was republished by Chetwynd with only minor amendments in 1912 (7td edn). This was reprinted under Creagh-Osborne in 1920. In 1936 a new edition entitled *The Theory of the Deviation of the Magnetic Compass in Iron Ships*, was writted by Instructor Commander H. V. Rumsey, the instructor officer at the ACO. With only thirty-eight pages, plus examples, this is a masterpiece of succinct mathematical theory.

[38] Twenty-five years later a similar requirement, which arose in connection with exploratory bore holes for North Sea Oil, was solved by Messrs Ferranti, using a miniature inertial navigation system.

[39] Admiralty docket, CD 28/52.

40 J. C. Cordle, '100 years of sextant testing', included in NPL memoir, 'The National Physical Laboratory 1900–1970'.

41 Admiralty Fleet Order, No. 1708/48.

42 'Compass policy', paper dated 2 September 1946, ACO archives.

43 It was argued that it would be impossible to lose power to all three gyro-compasses simultaneously. However, in 1947, HMS *Vanguard* (the first large ship to be built without a magnetic compass), whilst on passage to Cape Town with King George VI embarked, had to steer by the stars for several hours due to a complete power failure.

44 Admiralty Fleet Orders, 2846/47, 2040/50. The rules are now contained in CD Pamphlet 11.

45 In a Grade I position the residual deviations of a compass, after adjustment, should remain steady within 2° over a period of several months. In a Grade II position the equivalent figure is 5°.

46 The *Hermes* later achieved fame as the flagship of the task force which fought the Falkland Islands campaign in 1982.

47 The three cruisers of the *Tiger* class, laid down in 1941, finally emerged towards the end of the 1950s, with an automatic gun armament of very advanced design.

48 *Journal of the Institute of Navigation*, Vol. VIII (1955). p.60.

49 This was designed by Mr D. W. Payn of the ACO and known locally as the Payn sextant attachment.

50 This was inspired by Mr Roy Laker, a compass mechanic at the ACO, who shot for England in the Olympic Games of 1948.

51 ACO Archives. (Admiralty letter, M 50/60/56/14, 10 December 1956).

52 Initially this was to have been called the Radar and Above-water Weapons Establishment (RAWE).

53 ACO Archives. (Admiralty military branch acquaint, No. M 50/43/57 (Serial No. 4785), 11 November 1957.)

54 The oldest of these was DNO, which was formed in 1830. As head of a department, the title of DCD went back to 1917.

55 An explanation of the principles of the Ship's Inertial Navigation System is contained in the *Journal of Institute of Navigation*, Vol. 12 (November 1959).

56 Captain Wynne-Edwards later recalled that he had suggested to DNO that, with the impending introduction of SINS and the Sperry Mark 19 gyro-compass, which also indicated the vertical (see p. 294), the gyro-stabilization section at the Admiralty Gunnery Establishment should be transferred to the ACO. Although the idea was not received with much enthusiasm at the time, it was the logical outcome and the transfer eventually took place in 1964 (see p. 349).

57 Later to form part of the British Aircraft Corporation and eventually British Aerospace.

58 Designed at the Admiralty Gunnery Establishment at Portland. The successful Type 12 weapons stabilizer was developed from this equipment.

59 ACO Archives. (Admiralty memorandum, CE 219/35. July 1935.)

60 Ibid. (Admiralty memorandum O and M 5125/52, 18 May 1954.)

61 Captain Wynne-Edwards died on 12 April 1982 at his home in Hayling Island, having remained briskly active in the fields of local government, education and sailing to the end. In 1981 he received the Royal Yachting Association's special award for services to yachting.

'SINS,' Polaris and the last Naval Director, 1961-71

'Great Oaks from little ACOrns grow'.

The gradual expansion of the ACO, which began with the start of the SINS project, continued for almost ten years. This chapter covers the period up to 1971, when the ACO became administratively integrated with the Admiralty Surface Weapons Establishment at Portsmouth and the Director of Weapons (Navigation), the natural successor of the original Compass Department, ceased to exist as a separate authority. It was a period of great activity which saw the start of a number of new projects, some of which were continued into the 1970s. Where appropriate, therefore, their story has been told without interruption.

It will be recalled that when, in 1959, the Nihil committee placed 'compasses' under the Director-General (Weapons), they had reservations about the Director's 'headquarters' function. It was 'untidy' and they would have preferred to see the ACO as an outpost, administered by the director of one of the divisions in Bath. The matter was, however, left to the Director-General to report on after experience with the new organization.

In 1961, shortly after Captain Ross became Director, Rear Admiral R. E. Washbourne wrote to the Admiralty as follows:

It is inconceivable that the 'Headquarters' function at present carried out at the Compass Observatory should be transferred to DGW at Bath or London. This could only result in an increase in staff, travelling and telephone calls, and a decrease in efficiency with nothing on the profit side of the ledger bar a tidy organisation chart.

The present arrangement works admirably.

This was a very satisfactory outcome and it was only a few years later that headquarters functions were also given to the heads of the Surface and Underwater Weapons establishments, thus bringing them into line with compasses. Although the justification for the ACO was further questioned on a number of occasions, generally when cuts in service expenditure were under discussion, the establishment stood up well to investigation and the next decade was one of almost continual growth.

Retirement of Commander A. V. Thomas

On 9 March 1962, having allowed the new Director six months to settle in, the Deputy Director, Commander Thomas, retired. During twenty-four eventful years at the ACO his tall, distinguished figure, his pungent pen, his sometimes sardonic sense of humour and his immense knowledge of gyro- and magnetic compass matters had an influence on almost every aspect of the establishment's life and work, while his wide experience of the vicissitudes of Admiralty procedures enabled him to guide the Compass Department during a period of considerable activity and expansion.

Anthony Vyvyan Thomas joined the Royal Naval College, Osborne, in 1919. He specialized in submarines but had to leave the branch in 1929 because of asthma. Two years later he qualified in Navigation but ill health continued to dog him and he was eventually invalided from the service, joining the ACO as a Naval Assistant in 1938. In the following year he had a fortunate escape from the submarine *Thetis* when she sank off Liverpool on her initial sea trials (see p. 239).

Thomas continued travelling throughout the war, inspecting and adjusting magnetic compasses and sometimes performing great feats of endurance. One evening, having just returned from a job in a northern yard, he was called to the Combined Operations base at Hythe where a new flotilla of landing craft had arrived that afternoon. None of their compasses had been adjusted. With one assistant he worked throughout the night to complete the heeling-error corrections. At first light they started the swings and by evening the flotilla was ready to sail for a raid on the Channel Islands. In 1944, when Combined Operations Headquarters at last appreciated the importance of swinging officers, Thomas was given the task of organizing their training. He was also deeply involved, during the

1940s, in the task providing reliable compasses for tanks and, during their trials, insisted on driving every type of tank which visited Ditton Park.

Commander Thomas became the Deputy Director in 1954 and from then until his retirement in 1962 he was actively concerned with every detail of life at the ACO, setting and demanding the highest standards, particularly in the department's relationships with the outside world. He took a close personal interest in everything that went on during a period which covered the postwar renaissance of the Navy, the 'way ahead' investigation, the formation of the Weapons Department, and the beginning of the SINS project, which started the great expansion. However, Thomas was a heart a 'magnetics man'. When, in 1952, the ACO became responsible for testing magnetic compasses on behalf of the Board of Trade, it was largely his initiative[1] which led to the production of a set of internationally agreed standards for magnetic compasses. He was invited by the British Nautical Instrument Trade Association (BNITA) to lead the British delegation at the meetings of the International Standards Organization and so helped again to focus world attention on the pre-eminent position of the ACO in this field.

Throughout the 24 years that he lived at Datchet, near Slough, Thomas took an active part in local affairs as Parish and District Councillor and as a Justice of the Peace, a task he continued in retirement to the age of 70.[2] Commander Thomas's position as Deputy Director was taken by the author in March 1962. It was a difficult act to follow.

New facilities

By the end of 1961, SINS had had its first unsteady trip to sea and had shown itself to be capable of keeping its equilibrium. The concept was sound. Meanwhile the scientific team that would be needed as the project gained momentum was beginning to build up, and at the ACO the R & D department was reorganized into five sections. Inertial navigation (under H. T. Heal) had been separated from Instruments (H. C. Wassell); Compasses (A. Hine) now covered all gyro and magnetic work; the Drawing Office (W. Watterson) was beginning to expand, while the fifth section, Electronics (W. P. Anderson) was to provide a service to all the

other sections as required. The Production department under M. P.
Wooller, who had relieved Akehurst as Assistant Director (Production) in 1958, was also strengthened to compete with the weighty
procurement and documentation problems which would arise.

New facilities were now urgently needed and spaces in the
mansion and outbuildings which had been left vacant since the run-
down after the war were pressed into service as offices, test rooms
and even laboratories. In the workshops modern machines were
installed and a temperature-controlled measurements room was
established to check the work they turned out. The lift between the
upper and lower halves of No.3 workshop was strengthened to take
heavier components. SINS began to take over the establishment.

It had been appreciated that a new laboratory block would soon
be required and the advent of Polaris in 1963 further emphasized
the need. However, as all too often happens in government affairs,
the administrative and financial aspects of such an undertaking took
far longer than the construction process itself. It was not, therefore,
until 1966 that a fine new building was ready for occupation,
replacing the old Montgomery block, erected in 1942 to last ten
years. Until that time much vital work had to be carried out in a
complex of mobile caravan units, referred to by the Chief Scientist
as 'the village'.

As this was the first purpose-designed laboratory building to be
provided at the ACO since the move to Ditton Park in 1917, a brief
description of its facilities is appropriate. Built largely of glass and
concrete, in contemporary style, it contained ten laboratories with
associated office accommodation for some forty scientists and engineers. In addition to laboratories for SINS, it provided a gyro test
facility more advanced than any then existing outside the United
States[3] and a large rolling-table where systems could be subjected
to the roll, pitch and yaw motions which they would encounter at
sea. Other laboratories catered for electronics, optics, computer
programming and standardization. Finally a completely non-magnetic laboratory was provided, separated from the remainder of the
building by a large glazed entrance hall containing a wooden
staircase of unusual design. The whole building was both functional
and aesthetically pleasing.

The new laboratory block was formally opened on 14 July 1967,
by Vice Admiral Sir Horace Law, the Controller of the Navy, in
the presence of Rear Admiral H. R. B. Janvrin, Deputy Chief of

Naval Staff, and Mr Basil Lythall, Chief Scientist (Royal Navy). This was the Compass Department's golden jubilee year in Ditton Park, an occasion that was marked by an official garden party and an open day for families.

Experimental models of SINS

The 'breadboard' model of SINS had worked at sea in *Steady* but at the end of 1961 the development of the first experimental model (X-1) was still at an early stage. Meanwhile, the first nuclear submarine, *Dreadnought*, in which it was to be installed for evaluation, was due to be completed during 1962. As manufacture was likely to take up to two years, the engineering design work on the X-1 equipment was begun even before the laboratory model had been switched on and the ACO workshops began its construction in parallel with the development and trials. Manufacturing drawings had, of necessity, frequently to be amended and much excellent work was done from sketches and even from word of mouth, as the lessons learnt were turned into modifications to the design. It was a desperate case of telescoping the basic design work, development and manufacture into one continual, overlapping process and was spurred on by the desire to get the British SINS to sea at the very beginning of the nuclear submarine era. In retrospect, this may not have been altogether wise.

In the event *Dreadnought* herself was delayed and SINS was duly completed and installed at Barrow-in-Furness early in 1963. Within weeks an error on the part of a shipyard technician caused a massive over-volt surge which wrecked a large number of components in the electronics and strained many more. After so much effort it seemed a cruel blow. However, all the electronic trays were immediately removed from the cabinets and returned to the ACO where hundreds of components were laboriously tested and, where necessary, replaced. At the same time the submarine's own electrical staff made a remarkable job of renewing the charred wiring in the SINS cabinets themselves. With little time to spare, the trays were replaced and the task of setting the system to work and testing and tuning it were undertaken by ACO staff. With the first model of so complex an equipment this phase had been planned to last six weeks. It was now completed in six days. Although, after what it had suffered, this equipment was never entirely satisfactory, *Dreadnought* was able to go to sea for her first commission, with SINS running.

Admiralty approval had been given for the construction of three experimental models, the first two of which would be sent to sea for evaluation. These were to be made in the ACO workshops and would use American gyros. The third equipment was to be made by the firm selected for SINS manufacture, and would be regarded as a pre-production prototype to give them experience before starting the main production run. It was hoped that this would be the first equipment to have British-made gyros and it was the intention that it should be installed at the Electrical School, HMS *Collingwood*, in order that training on the new equipment could start at the earliest possible date.

The firm chosen for this important task was the Sperry Gyroscope Company which, it will be remembered, had been associated with Admiralty compass equipment for half a century. The firm had recently built a new factory at Bracknell in Berkshire, primarily for the development and production of inertial systems for Britain's missile-launcher *Blue Streak*. The cancellation of this project late in 1959 made available a factory, only 12 miles from the ACO, which was ideally suited to the manufacture of SINS.[4] Furthermore, the firm still had a workforce fully capable of the task. The third experimental equipment was successfully completed by Sperry and was launched with a fine burst of publicity on 5 December 1963.

It was perhaps one of the more remarkable facets of the SINS project that the development and production of these three experimental models were completed on time and within the cost budget allowed, surely a boast that can be made for very few postwar projects of such a revolutionary nature.

SHIP-FITTING POLICY FOR SINS

A year after SINS was fitted in *Dreadnought*, the second experimental model was installed for evaluation in the aircraft carrier *Eagle*, a decision which deserves some explanation. At the time the Naval Staff foresaw a need for SINS in surface ships to provide an accurate, up-to-date position for 'picture compilation' via a long-range data link that was then under development. Data exchange between ships in a widely dispersed force requires each ship to know its position accurately and, in the absence (in the early 1960s) of any global radio position system, the fitting of SINS appeared to be the only solution. Plans were accordingly made to install SINS in all ships of frigate size and above, a very ambitious programme which can hardly have looked realistic, even in 1960!

In the event the long-range data link took many years to develop and, although SINS was installed in the second batch of guided-missile destroyers, most of this extensive programme never took place. It would nevertheless have been fitted in the aircraft-carriers had the decision not been taken in 1966 to phase them out of service.[5] When they were reintroduced into the Navy early in the 1980s, SINS was again fitted. It was also installed in certain survey vessels where it proved to be of great value for deep-ocean work. However, the main purpose of SINS has remained essentially for nuclear submarines – for which, of course, it had originally been designed.

SINS Mark 1

The late 1950s saw the beginning of the modern explosion in electronic devices. It was thus largely an accident of timing which dictated that whilst the experimental models of SINS were built with valves, in the follow-on equipments these would be to a large extent superseded by the more reliable transistors. A rapid redesign of the main electronic components had therefore to be undertaken and this, coupled with certain important changes suggested by the continuing trials in *Steady*, meant that the production version (SINS Mark 1) would differ considerably from the pre-production proto-type (X-3) on which the Sperry factory would be cutting its manufacturing teeth. Furthermore the latter (X-3) would no longer be suitable for instructional purposes at HMS *Collingwood* and it was therefore decided that it should be installed in the second nuclear submarine, *Valiant*,[6] for which SINS Mark 1 would have been late. As matters turned out this decision had unfortunate repercussions.

For several years these three experimental models caused the ACO considerable embarrassment. With outdated electronics and early American gyros.[7] both their accuracy and their reliability were low. They had been intended primarily as test vehicles and although, as such, their performance was encouraging, this consideration was all too readily lost sight of by those at sea who, understandably, were hoping for a proven operational equipment. As a result SINS acquired a bad name which took some years to correct, despite the excellent equipments which followed. At the same time, because of their limitations, few useful lessons could be learnt from these experimental models, whilst the need to support them placed heavy demands on the already stretched ACO resources. In retrospect, it would have been more sensible to have put them in moth balls until SINS Mark 1 was ready.

In 1962, whilst the first experimental model of SINS was still under construction in the ACO workshops, the redesign of the new production version was begun in earnest. The original laboratory model was removed from *Steady* and revamped as a test vehicle for SINS Mark 1. It was given a new gimbal configuration and, most important of all, was fitted with British made gyros incorporating gas bearings (see p. 331). Early in 1964, at the invitation of the Hydrographer, the equipment was sent to sea for trials in the Survey vessel *Vidal*, engaged at the time on special surveys which took it continuously to and fro across the Atlantic. It was ideal employment for proving the SINS system. For the first time an acceptable performance was achieved and it was possible, with greater confidence, to draw conclusions about its behaviour. Some unexpected lessons were learnt, the results of which were signalled back to the design team at the ACO for action. The scientist in charge of these trials was William L. Thomson who, during the years ahead, was to spend a great deal of time at sea in ships and submarines in support of SINS, instructing and trouble-shooting, and rightly earning a very high reputation with the Royal Navy.

It would have been desirable at this point to pause for an evaluation of SINS, but the project was committed to a ship-fitting programme which required the first production order to be placed with Sperry in 1963. The basic design was ready but there were still many details to be worked out. Once again the separate processes of development, proving, drawing and handing over to manufacture had to be severely telescoped. It was a situation in which the ACO was to be caught for the first ten years of the SINS project. Over-optimism at management level and the desire to provide the Navy with what it wanted, when it wanted it, no doubt played their part but, more than anything, the situation reflected the establishment's inexperience in handling so large and complex a project. Crises were frequent. Having joined the big league, the ACO had much to learn.

However, the team was being gradually strengthened and, under the determined leadership of Henry Elwertowski, the programme somehow always managed to struggle back onto the rails and in the end a first-class equipment was provided.

One problem which was identified at sea early in the ife of the project was the need for a stable and reliable power supply. Even a momentary break or surge was sufficient to cause a change in gyro performance after which it would take a minimum of 24 hours before SINS outputs could again be relied upon. Ship's power supplies did not provide such stability and a special motor-generator with a heavy flywheel was therefore introduced, capable of protecting SINS from all but the worst fluctuations. This proved very successful but added considerably to the size and weight of the installation, a very serious matter in submarines.

Manufacturing the first SINS Mark 1 began at the Sperry factory early in 1964 and although the firm had already built the third experimental model, it still faced a major challenge. It should not, therefore, in any way detract from their triumph to say that the successful completion of certain aspects of this task became very much a joint venture between Sperry and the ACO. The firm still had much to learn about the system and it was necessary for scientific staff to provide considerable support and technical assistance, particularly during the final assembly and testing stage and sometimes, it must be admitted, in lieu of detailed drawings and specifications which were not yet complete. Meanwhile changes to the drawings continued to emanate from the ACO design team as final details were worked out and these, too, were incorporated, sometimes by ACO scientists themselves. Such procedures were unorthodox but were the inevitable result of the telescoped programme. However, Sperry's co-operated well and this collaborative effort undoubtedly paid dividends as later models came forward.

The first production model of SINS Mark 1 was installed by Sperry engineers in the guided-missile destroyer *Fife* during the summer of 1966, with the second following a few months later in *Warspite*, the third of Britain's nuclear submarines. Not surprisingly in view of the rushed development, both outfits suffered severe teething troubles and ACO staff logged a considerable amount of sea time whilst diagnosing problems. The first official sea trial in *Fife* was interrupted when the ship was diverted to Gibraltar to act as guardship during the talks between the Prime Minister, Harold

Wilson, and Ian Smith of Rhodesia aboard the cruiser *Tiger*, but by this time it was already clear than SINS was exhibiting abnormal symptoms.[8] Eventually the equipment was removed for laboratory investigation at the ACO and much midnight oil was burnt before the trouble was located.

Warspite, too, had her crop of teething troubles which took several months to clear, but the ship's company were aware that the project was in its early days and gave every assistance. It was *Warspite* which achieved the first successful SINS start-up and resettle at sea in the Royal Navy. As reliability and operating techniques improved the ACO continued to monitor performance, with ships making regular reports of their results and experience. It is a pleasure to recall the occasion in 1968 when a signal was received from *Warspite* which read 'Request permission to switch off SINS. Ship's Company going on leave'. It had then been running successfully for over six weeks. Things were looking up.

The next opportunity to install SINS in *Fife* did not occur until late in 1969, shortly before the ship sailed on an operational cruise which took her round the world. She would be crossing the equator twice and here was an excellent chance for a thorough test of SINS performance. This was shown to be generally better than that required by its specification and the extensive experience gained in operating techniques was invaluable. When, in November 1970, the ship was required to follow a very intricate evasive path during a Fleet exercise in the Mediterranean, the Navigating Officer relied on his SINS with complete confidence, reporting that the operation would have been impossible with it.

By the early 1970s the fitting of SINS had become a matter of routine in all nuclear submarines and in the later guided-missile destroyers,[9] and very satisfactory results were being achieved, despite a number of self-inflicted setbacks. The over-volting experienced by the original SINS in *Dreadnought* was repeated in a very similar fashion in *Eagle*, while the ship was in dockyard hands. *Warspite*'s equipment suffered from a serious fire on board whilst that being delivered to *Glamorgan* was inexcusably allowed to fall off a lorry in Devonport. Two more nuclear submarines managed to flood their outfits. Finding replacements for all these damaged equipments placed a serious added burden on the hard-pressed supply lines during those early days.

OPERATING AND SUPPORTING SINS

SINS Mark 1, the most expensive and sophisticated navigation equipment ever produced, was capable of extreme accuracy but the Navy still had to learn how to use it effectively. Even SINS gyros are not perfect and any flaw in gyro performance causes an error in SINS outputs which builds up with time, following a twenty-four-hour sine wave. The navigator's prime concern is therefore to determine and ultimately to correct these errors which he does by comparing SINS position with the ship's true position obtained by some other means. Plainly it is advantageous initially to do this in harbour, where the ship's position is accurately known, so that errors can be established and SINS corrected before sailing.

Once settled, SINS will remain stable but any change in gyro performance will cause further errors to build up, the pattern of which will again have to be determined from further fixes. The process is thus one of continually monitoring SINS performance whenever fix information is available, in order that its errors may be accurately predicted once the submarine is submerged and no longer able to check its position. The more precise the initial assessment, the more accurate and reliable will be the subsequent information SINS can give.

The operating procedures for using SINS and the techniques for assessing its errors had to be worked out from scratch. At sea assessment often has to be based on fix information that is far from perfect and requires an understanding of just how inaccurate it might be. (Claims of extreme accuracy for some standard radio fixing systems have been shown to be highly suspect!) A serving navigating officer was therefore appointed to the ACO in the summer of 1966 to work with the project staff in formulating and trying out the most practical procedures for use under different operating conditions. It was a task which was greatly simplified once desk-top calculators and digital computers became readily available but at first it had to be done by hand-plotting and the use of a simple analogue SINS error-computer. Like navigation itself, navigating SINS was both a science and an art.

Due to the priority given to meeting ship-fitting dates it was some while before an equipment could be made available for the Electrical School, HMS *Collingwood*, and technical training had at first to be carried out at the ACO, imposing a considerable additional burden. However, the job was admirably undertaken by the naval electrical officers with help from the project staff, giving students the great advantage of being able to discuss problems with the designers. Producing a handbook for this very complex equipment also raised problems as the ACO had no formal book-writing organization, designers having hitherto written the handbooks for their own comparatively simple equipments themselves. In 1964 a senior technical author was recruited from one of the larger establishments to set up a handbook section so that the writing of all the necessary supporting documentation could in future be undertaken by contract. It was late in the day but the ACO was still learning!

Meanwhile it was clear that with the small number of SINS equipments which would be at sea during the first few years, the normal channels of help and diagnostic support through the Fleet Maintenance Units and dockyards might prove ineffective as experience would be too thinly spread. Approval was therefore given for two senior chief electrical artificers to be appointed to the ACO as SINS-travellers, on whom ships could call for assistance. The ACO was thus able to provide a direct service to the Fleet, as it had done so often in the past, and with the added advantage of back-up support from the project staff. This quickly built up an excellent two-way exchange of information and reliance on the system grew with it.

GAS-BEARING GYROS FOR SINS

We have already noted that at the heart of SINS are three very high-precision gyroscopes which, in the first instance, it had been necessary to purchase from the United States. However, in 1961 a licence agreement was negotiated with the US government which permitted these gyros to be manufactured in the United Kingdom, and a contract was placed with the firm of English Electric Aviation at Stevenage. A special beryllium[10] facility was set up specifically for this purpose, requiring very tightly controlled processes and constant health-checking.

American experience had shown that the early ball-bearing gyros were unlikely ever to meet the high performance required from SINS, also that their life expectancy was short and would make them extremely expensive for continuous running. Work was therefore begun at the ACO in 1959 on the study of gas-bearing technology[11] in the hope that by applying this technique to the gyros these deficiencies could be surmounted. The first British (and, it is believed, the first world) gas-bearing gyro-rotor assembly was designed at the ACO and built by Premier Precision Ltd of Bracknell in the same year.

The Navy had settled on a type of gyro called the V6, manufactured by Northrop Nortronics of Massachusetts, and in 1962 the ACO exhibited a gas-bearing assembly suitable for this type of gyro at the Physical Societies' Exhibition. English Electric Aviation were keen to co-operate in this work and made some useful contributions to the programme. Although it was decided that their first batch of V6 gyros made under licence should be of the conventional ball-bearing pattern, thereafter these were built exclusively with UK-designed gas bearings.

The most immediate effect was on the performance of the gyros themselves which showed an increase in accuracy more than one order better than that obtained from similar ball-bearing gyros. Indeed it would be no exaggeration to say that the improvement in the accuracy of the original American-designed gyros which followed the introduction of the ACO-designed gas bearings gave SINS a performance considerably better than either its designers or the Naval Staff had dared to hope for. It was a remarkable breakthrough which undoubtedly contributed largely to the viability of SINS itself.

As Nortronics were running their own gas-bearing programme in parallel with that of the UK, they were informed of the improvement and were given the technical data. Subsequently the firm produced their own gas-bearing version of their gyro which was very similar to the UK gyro and was designated V7. It was widely fitted in the navigational SINS of the US Navy.

Meanwhile, although the introduction of gas bearings would increase gyro life since, once running, there is negligible friction, they had introduced a new problem. The gyros were now very difficult to start. A further lengthy period of research was needed, both at the ACO and elsewhere, before the problem was solved. It was eventually shown that the very sophisticated cleaning methods used had the effect of increasing rather than decreasing the starting friction, but that this could be overcome by the subsequent application of monomolecular layers of boundary lubricant. (i.e. having made them super-clean, they had then to be slightly contaminated

in a precisely controlled manner). Once this procedure was introduced into gyro manufacture a life expectancy of 10,000 hours and
upwards was regularly achieved.

The man chiefly responsible for this pioneering work was A.
Graham Patterson[12] of the ACO and in this field both he and
Elwertowski were held in high regard on both sides of the Atlantic.
Since 1958 the exchange of information on precision gyros had been
conducted through the Inter-service Gyro Panel but early in the
project the ACO had taken the lead in founding and sponsoring a
separate British Gas-Bearing Panel for the free interchange of
technical information amongst research institutes, universities and
industry. In 1966 the ACO was invited to become a member of the
equivalent American body, the American Gas Bearing Committee,
sponsored by the Office of Naval Research, and in subsequent years
fruitful joint meetings were held between these organizations, both
in America and at the ACO.

Finally a word must be said about the excellent work done
by English Electric Aviation (later part of the British Aircraft
Corporation) in the development and manufacture of SINS gyros,
upon which the whole success of the SINS project ultimately rested.
The technical problems to be overcome were formidable, much of
the high-precision mechanical work being on the fringe of what
was technologically possible. From the start, however, the firm was
keen to get involved and to commit their top men to the task. In
particular the contributions of Roy Hurrell and Pat Boyer were of
great significance. Despite often fierce arguments, very friendly
relations were maintained throughout this multimillion-pound contract and great credit must go to the Director, Captain Ross, who
chaired the regular project meetings, to Mr Elwertowski and to Sir
John Carroll, the Deputy Controller, who backed this pioneering
project all the way. This was without doubt one of the success
stories of government/industrial co-operation.

ALTERNATIVES TO THE SINS GYRO

Despite the notable increase in the life of the SINS gyros which
resulted from the introduction of gas bearings, the inevitable escala-
tion in the cost of their manufacture and repair still made SINS a
very expensive equipment to run. The ACO has therefore remained
constantly on the look-out for a cheaper alternative. During the
1960s work on ring lasers at the Services Electronic Research

Laboratory at Baldock was showing promise as a means of detecting rotation[13] and in 1968 this work was accordingly passed over to the ACO to ascertain whether it could be developed to the stage where it could usefully be applied to SINS. Although some progress was made by a small team, led initially by A. F. H. Thomson[14] and later by D. Bromley, it was soon apparent that there were a number of fundamental problems in physics and applied optics still be to solved, and that this technique was as yet too young to achieve the accuracy required. Contracts to build three ring-laser outfits, working in the infra-red, were placed with the firm of Electrical and Musical Industries Ltd (EMI) and research continued for about five years, but the resources available were limited and progress disappointing. The work was later taken up by the RAE at Farnborough which devoted considerable effort to the problem.

In retrospect it seems clear that the fundamental difficulties were greater than expected. Even in America, where millions of dollars were invested in the enterprise, progress was slow. Whilst ring-laser inertial systems, with an accuracy suitable for aircraft use, appeared in America during the 1970s, it was another ten years before a breakthrough to anything approaching SINS performance was achieved.

The ACO has kept in touch with advances on any front which appeared likely to offer a cheaper alternative to the SINS gyro. A device called a dry-tuned gyro (DTG) at one time showed promise for naval applications, while the Americans did much work on various forms of mini-SINS, using a development of the much smaller aircraft inertial gyro. Although these devices seem unlikely ever to approach the extreme accuracy attainable with SINS gyros, they may well prove adequate for some form of Medium Accuracy Inertial Navigation System (MAINS). In the long term, however, the solution may well lie with something more sophisticated. The miniature electrostatic gyro (ESG) and the improved ring-laser gyro are already (1984) realities whilst, to anticipate the next chapter, a fibre-optic gyro (FOG) is under development and research is already proceeding at the ACO into a Cryogenic nuclear magnetic resonance gyroscope, using the atomic nucleus which, under certain circumstances, appears to behave like a spinning mass. The future seems to be full of interesting possibilities.

ASSESSMENT OF SINS MARK 1

SINS Mark 1, the first large project that the ACO had ever tackled, was designed entirely intramurally. It had required a bold decision in 1955 to go for a British SINS at a time when national experience in the new technology barely existed, but it had come off. The project had undoubtedly taken over the establishment which, during the 1960s, had grown out of all recognition. The number of non-industrial staff had doubled and, by 1966, over a hundred were employed in the R & D department alone. SINS had more than met the performance requirements set for it and the design team under Henry Heal could be rightly proud of their achievements. By the 1970s SINS was in regular service and fully supported; the traumas of the experimental models were forgotten and confidence restored. Certainly there had been stumblings along the way, largely through over-confidence and inexperience in the management of so large an undertaking. Although the gyro-development contract with the British Aircraft Corporation was an outstanding success, it would probably have been prudent also to have involved the high-grade engineering skills of Sperry by giving them a partial development contract instead of one only for manufacture. Nevertheless the concept of SINS was brilliant, its basic design was sound and its performance was improving from year to year. The nuclear submarine fleet would have been in a poor way without it.

SINS Mark 2

Although the limited analogue computing capacity of SINS Mark 1 meant that it was not suitable for protracted operations in the vicinity of the North Pole, Elwertowski was determined that the possibility should be fully investigated. Accordingly, as soon as the *Steady* trials came to an end in the summer of 1962, E. Hoy was given the task. His calculations showed that theoretically the provision of a polar mode of operation was perfectly feasible, but it was also quickly apparent that, with the current state of the art, the additional electronics needed would make the equipment far too large for submarine use. The idea of incorporating it into SINS Mark 1 was therefore dropped. Nevertheless the requirement that submarines be able to operate freely in extreme northern latitudes remained and when, in 1964, Elliott Automation introduced their Type 920 digital computer, which occupied a mere half-cabinet of electronics,[15] it was time to look at the problem again. The characteristics required of SINS were accordingly rewritten by the Naval Staff to include a full navigation capability under ice in polar regions. By the summer of 1965 the Admiralty Board and the Treasury had endorsed the requirement and the SINS Mark 2 project was born.

This was a busy period at the ACO. Staff were already committed to Polaris, to SINS Mark 1 and to the introduction of the new generation of gyro-compasses and stabilizers. There were few spare resources for a major new task. A survey was therefore made of firms who might be technically capable of undertaking this development, but although two possibilities emerged both were already too heavily loaded. It was therefore decided that the work should be undertaken as another intramural project at the ACO and early in 1966 a small team under Heal began work on the problem. Their number was frequently reduced by urgent calls for unprogrammed work, generally for SINS Mark 1, which was still having teething troubles, or by arbitrary cuts in the establishment staff to comply with some Treasury ruling. However, by the autumn of 1967 a test vehicle, with a stable platform based on the original gimbal set already used in *Steady* and *Vidal*, was ready for its first trip to sea in the frigate *Penelope*. Although, as a breadboard model, the system worked satisfactorily, it was shown to be extremely sensitive both to temperature changes and to fluctuations in the ship's power supply, factors which had an important influence on subsequent design.

As the amount of work needed on Polaris and SINS Mark 1 declined during the late 1960s it became possible to build up the team for Mark 2. Good progress was made with the design of components although rapid developments in the electronics field during the first five years of the project guaranteed a constantly changing situation. By 1969 work had reached the stage where a further sea trial was desirable and, again with the co-operation of the Hydrographer, this took place in the survey vessel *Hecate*. Several significant changes had been introduced since the first trial, making full use of the digital computing capacity of the Elliott 920B in order to simplify hardware in favour of software. The stable platform was supported by a heater and a refrigerator, forerunners of the sophisticated environment-control arrangements that were eventually employed, and the equipment now had its own battery-supported power supply. Also, a start had been made on the introduction of integrated circuits.

The trial itself was successful and full of interest. After a courtesy visit to Hamburg, which provided a welcome bonus for the scientists, *Hecate* was employed on a routine survey off the west coast of Ireland. Her first break, after several weeks at sea, was to have been a visit to Londonderry where she would have arrived just as the first shots of the troubles were fired. Her diversion to Belfast offered little improvement. Cafés and bars were all closed and only in the Chinese restaurants was it business as usual.

On the project, too, life was becoming exciting and by the time SINS was ready for its next sea trial in 1971, again in *Hecate*, two major advances had been introduced. The 920B computer had been replaced by the 920M which was faster, more powerful, and no bigger than a sandwich box. Further, control of SINS could now be exercised through a simple keyboard and display which it was planned would be duplicated to enable the navigator to 'talk' to SINS from a remote position in the vicinity of the bridge.

Once again in addition to normal survey work in the south-western approaches to the British Isles the trials party came in for some special entertainment. During an interesting passage to the Firth of Forth, via the English Channel and North Sea, SINS functioned so satisfactorily that it was possible to say with some assurance that the accuracy claims made for certain radio navigational aids were decidedly optimistic. On arrival in Leith *Hecate* acted as a floating exhibition, for the centenary celebrations of *Challenger*'s historic voyage of exploration (1871–76) (see p. 129), and this interlude was followed by a trip to Gibraltar which offered an excellent chance to test SINS over a substantial change of latitude. From all points of view it had been a very satisfactory trial, and the Hydrographer was already finding SINS a most useful adjunct to very accurate off-shore surveying. It would become essential as the work moved out into the Atlantic.

By the autumn of 1971 the SINS team was ready to start on the construction of a fully engineered prototype, using integrated circuits and micro-miniature techniques. The advantages expected from SINS Mark 2 over the Mark 1 equipment could now be briefly summarized as follows:

1. Accuracy would be increased and errors would build up more slowly. Fewer fixes would therefore be needed, giving the submarine greater freedom of operation. (A semi-technical note explaining the main reason for the increase in accuracy is given in appendix 12.)

2. Operation would be more flexible and would include the ability to operate in 'polar mode'.

3. The digital computer, keyboard and CRT display would enable the navigating officer to 'talk' to SINS, calling up programmes for 'starting up' and 'shutting down', for positional calculation, for error assessment and forecasting, for resets and for many other operations.

4. Programmes would also be provided for automatic fault diagnosis and for a variety of supporting functions.

5. With modern electronics the equipment would be more reliable and would require less maintenance, while the battery-supported power supply obviated the need for the large motor generator.

6. The equipment would be smaller and lighter and would cost no more than SINS Mark 1.

Two other facilities had originally been included in the specification for SINS Mark 2 which, although eventually dropped from the final version, absorbed considerable scientific effort. These were a dual SINS operation and the alignment of Aircraft Inertial Navigation Systems (AINS). Both were interesting concepts, which might well be needed in the future, and should be briefly described here.

Because of the reduced size of SINS Mark 2 there was the possibility that two linked equipments could be accommodated in the space previously required for one SINS and a gyro-compass. The advantages would be manifold. In the event of failure the operation of restarting and settling a single SINS at sea presents many problems and the navigational outputs are unlikely to be useable for at least twenty-four hours. However, with two digital SINS it would be possible to 'slave' one from the other, so restoring availability in a few hours. The likelihood of ever being without SINS information would then be almost negligible, whilst to have two SINS in agreement would greatly improve the level of confidence in their navigational outputs and make the submarine still less dependent on external fixing.

The idea of a dual SINS fit was therefore most attractive and considerable work was done on its development. In the event, however, space became even more critical in the new generation of nuclear submarine, and this desirable, though not essential improvement had to be dropped.

The other interesting but nugatory research project was the alignment of Aircraft Inertial Navigation Systems (AINS). The problems involved in settling a SINS at sea, where it is subject to the motion of the ship, apply equally to an inertial system in an aircraft on the flight deck. There is therefore a need for some form of stable frame of reference with which the AINS can be compared and this can most readily be provided by SINS. The Staff Requirement for SINS Mark 2 had specified the ability to align AINS by 'slaving' and considerable experimental work was carried out by George Gulland in conjunction with the British Aircraft Corporation and the Fleet Air Arm, to develop the appropriate techniques. Eventually, however, the Admiralty decided against fitting AINS in naval aircraft and the requirement was deleted.

THE STROMNESS TRIALS

Early in 1975, after three years of intense activity, SINS Mark 2 was ready for a full-scale sea trial. It was installed in a trials hut measuring 20 feet by 12 feet of which the equipment occupied one half and all the necessary recorders and test gear the other. It was then completely groomed and set to work at the ACO. This was to be the crucial test of the system, requiring a long sea voyage, and preferably one that crossed the equator. The ship allocated was the 16,000 ton Royal Fleet Auxiliary *Stromness* and preparations were made for fitting the trials hut on board, protected between decks, and for the provision of the necessary power supplies and facilities.

Stromness was to take part in a Fleet deployment to the Far East in January 1975, with the return passage due in April and May. This offered an ideal opportunity for the trial. With the co-operation of the RAF the trials hut was flown out to Singapore in two halves by Hercules aircraft, a total lift of some 13 tons. The gyros were flown separately, in their 'hot boxes' and, due to the excellence of the trials-hut arrangement, SINS was switched on and operating within hours of their arrival on board.

The conditions in this large new stores support ship were almost ideal for the trial. Two satellite navigation (SatNav) receivers, against which the performance of SINS could be monitored, were installed by ACO representatives, and there was ample working space and plenty of comfortable accommodation. The trials party included representatives of the Hydrographer and of the Flag Officer, Submarines, the two operating authorities primarily interested in the outcome, whilst the ACO contingent included four scientists, R. H. Stretton, D. Gardiner, M. W. Willcocks and W. L. Thomson, who had been with the SINS project since the *Steady* trials in 1961. How very different it must have seemed.

The Fleet sailed from Singapore on 4 April 1975 and, after a brief call at the Seychelles, proceeded via the Cape of Good Hope to Rio de Janeiro, carrying out extensive exercises en route. The performance of SINS during this passage can only be described as remarkable, and far exceeded expectations. Although a constant check was kept on its accuracy throughout the trip, the equipment was never once reset. At the end of a voyage of 10,000 miles and lasting 33 days the errors were such that, had there been no fix information at all (i.e. as in a submarine remaining deep the whole way) the ship would still comfortably have found Rio relying on SINS alone. During very rough weather experienced when rounding the Cape, the wide 'scatter' in the SatNav positions was clearly shown up by the consistency of SINS.

The trials crews changed over at Rio enabling both teams to enjoy the South American hospitality. After a week in harbour, during which the equipment was reset, the Fleet sailed for home via Gibraltar, a further 8000 miles, and SINS Mark 2 obliged with a repeat performance. It was all extremely satisfactory.

BRINGING SINS MARK 2 INTO SERVICE

Although the introduction of SINS Mark 2 into the Royal Navy falls outside the period of this narrative, it deserves special mention in order to round off the account of this successful project. To meet the Hydrographer's requirement for SINS Mark 2 in the survey vessels *Hecate* and *Hecla* in 1976–77, it was essential that a production contract should be placed with Sperry early in 1973, two years before development was complete. Despite the daunting experience with SINS Mark 1, it was thus again necessary to telescope development and production, although this time the risks were slight and the possible effects could be more readily assessed. Nevertheless a heavy load was again placed on the project team as scientific staff were required to provide back-up to the firm during the crucial 'setting to work and testing' period, also during the installation and proving phases on board the two ships. At the same time training for the crews had also to be arranged at the ACO.

With flexibility on both sides the installations were successfully completed on time and before long the Hydrographer was conducting deep-ocean surveying to an accuracy never before achieved. Thereafter manufacture at Sperry was changed over from SINS Mark 1 to SINS Mark 2. The new equipment was fitted into the next generation of nuclear submarines[16] as well as retrospectively into the earlier boats to replace SINS Mark 1. It also went into the new generation of aircraft carriers.[17] As, however, it was now primarily a submarine equipment (and was no longer to be fitted in guided-missile destroyers), in 1977 responsibility for all training in SINS was transferred from HMS *Collingwood* to HMS *Dolphin* at Gosport, the true *alma mater* of all submariners.

Although man's dream of having an instrument that would make navigation wholly automatic was still some way off, SINS Mark 2 represented a tremendous advance over earlier equipments. In the opinion of one of the submarine navigating officers who took part in the *Stromness* trial, 'it is more accurate that the Polaris SINS'.[18] Nevertheless refinements to its software, which would further increase its performance, continued to be introduced for a number of years.

This was certainly the largest intramural project ever to be undertaken at the ACO and, in the changed climate of the times, in which development work is almost exclusively contracted to industry, it is unlikely to be surpassed. Sadly Elwertowski did not live to see the Navy enjoy the benefits of this remarkable development. When, in 1971, he became Head of the ACO, responsibility for the management of the project fell to George Gulland, who kept a very tight control over its progress for the next seven years. He, with Heal, Hoy, Alan Lee and the many leading contributors to the project, both on the scientific and production sides of the ACO, could be justifiably proud of their achievements.

To the North Pole

It had been done before. In 1958 the USS *Nautilus* had become the first submarine to transit from the Pacific to the Atlantic oceans 'over the top'. A year later the USS *Skate* became the first to surface at the Pole. In 1971 it was the turn of the Royal Navy, when HMS

Dreadnought made the trip, with assistance from the ACO to modify her standard navigational equipments.

In addition to her normal outfit of SINS Mark 1, Sperry Mark 23 and Arma-Brown gyro-compasses, *Dreadnought* was given a Sperry Mark 19, which was installed in the radar office from which much of the equipment had been removed. Her Loran was supplemented with an aircraft Omega receiver, the only type that could then be acquired.

The main navigational problem in Artic regions stems from the fact that neither SINS Mark 1 nor any gyro-compass can operate in its normal mode in the vicinity of the pole and it becomes necessary to employ different techniques. In the case of the gyro-compasses, by switching off the controls which make the compass north-seeking, it is possible to operate in what is called the directional-gyro (DG) mode. A heading can then be obtained based on the direction of the North Pole at the time the changeover is made, and allowing for the 'drift' of the gyro since that time. This heading can be kept up to date by feeding the compass with 'earth-rate'.

A special modification was also made to the SINS equipment to enable it to operate in a type of DG mode. This was designed at the ACO especially for this trip and, when it is brought into operation, SINS ceases to navigate normally but will still give accurate heading and latitude. Switchover to DG mode is made when about 150 miles from the Pole. As, however, the drift errors of the SINS gyros are minute compared with those of the gyro-compasses, SINS can safely be used as a datum against which the other compasses can be compared. In this way, with the help of the log, it is possible to navigate with fair accuracy in the vicinity of the Pole for a considerable period.

On 20 February 1971 *Dreadnought*, under the command of Commander A. G. Kennedy, sailed from Faslane and, after surfacing off the coast of Spitzbergen, dived and set course for the Pole which she reached at 0800 on 3 March. Due to the very heavy ice conditions it was not until that afternoon that she was able to find a polynya (ice window) through which she could surface. After remaining at the North Pole for twelve hours, during which many tasks had to be accomplished, including obtaining the magnetic variation, the ship headed south along the Greenwich meridian and so home. It was a fine effort.

Watching over the performance of the navigation equipment during this voyage was a member of the ACO SINS team, Mr W. L. Thomson, a direct descendant of the gentleman who had so dramatically entered the compass field almost a hundred years before. His contribution to the success of the mission, although difficult to quantify, was undoubtedly significant.

The next trip to the pole, by HMS *Sovereign* in 1976, was on a more ambitious scale. Instead of a straightforward 'there and back' the submarine had first to surface off the northern tip of Greenland in position 85°N 70°W, to mark the 'farthest north' achievement of Captain Nares, in 1876 (see p. 129). She was then to sail along the meridian of 70°W to the North Pole and out again along 15°E, carrying out a survey in the Spitzbergen Greenland gap before returning home.

Once again the ACO undertook the preparation of the submarine's navigation equipment for the trip. Although the prototype of SINS Mark 2 had been completed it was not yet ready for ship-fitting. SINS Mark 1 was therefore modified as before, to enable it to operate in DG mode and an Arma-Brown gyro-compass was added to the Sperry Mark 19 and Mark 23 already fitted. In addition an Omega and a SatNav receiver were supplied to supplement the ship's radio navigation aids (at that time only Loran C and Decca). All these equipments were specially checked out by ACO staff in conjunction with the ship. Once again Bill Thomson volunteered to make the trip.

Sovereign sailed from Plymouth on 1 October 1971 and surfaced at the Pole on the 23rd after the now familiar lengthy search for a polynya. To quote from Thomson's account of the operation:[19]

> Once surfaced the work load is enormous because naturally at the North Pole all Navigational Aids are used to determine position for posterity, and manufacturers always want to know how their equipment worked. Also everyone wants to do his particular 'little bit' at the North Pole, play football, golf, cricket, snowball fight, race round the world, etc., etc. After completing their designated task, I believe everybody achieved his ambition.

Sovereign returned to Plymouth on 5 November after a round trip of almost 7000 miles, of which 2200 had been under the ice. Bill Thomson is believed to be the only man to have been to the Pole twice by submarine. He was deservedly awarded the MBE in the following year's Birthday honours.

Polaris

Shortly before Christmas 1962 the Prime Minister, Mr Harold Macmillan, and his defence chiefs flew to Nassau in the Bahamas to meet President Kennedy. The American air-launched missile *Skybolt*, on which Britain had pinned its hopes for the next-generation nuclear deterrent, had failed on trials and the project had been cancelled. They were therefore negotiating the 'Polaris agreement' under which the United Kingdom would build Polaris submarines for which the United States would sell them the missiles and the weapon-control and navigation systems.

During the early months of 1963 many technical missions crossed the Atlantic to study the problems involved, among them a Navigation mission headed by the Director of Navigation, Captain J. G. B. Bennett. This included the Director, Chief Scientist and Electrical Officer from the ACO and the Navigation Officer attached to the Chief Polaris Executive (CPE), Vice-Admiral Sir Hugh Mackenzie. Their instructions were to assess the effectiveness of the very expensive American Polaris navigation system and to look at the possibility of reducing its cost. The mission reported its findings to CPE on 15 February and within a week its recommendations had been broadly accepted.

At that time the American system was extremely elaborate and costly, containing a high degree of redundancy, including three SINS. When the first Polaris submarine, the USS *George Washington*, had gone to sea, towards the end of 1960, this was considered essential in order to guarantee total availability, but by 1963 equipment reliability had greatly improved. Accordingly the Navigation mission confidently recommended two important changes: first to fit only two SINS instead of three and second to dispense with the very expensive star-tracking periscope, designed to check the SINS azimuth, an instrument which had given the Americans considerable trouble. In any case the type of SINS which the mission had recommended for the UK Polaris boats was fitted with a 'monitor gyro' which would make heading checks at sea unnecessary. These changes saved the Navy several million dollars on each boat and were later adopted by the Americans themselves. In 1963 the ACO was the only centre of advanced knowledge of SINS and precision gyroscopes in the country and on 1 April Captain Ross and Mr Elwertowski, this time accompanied by Mr Heal, were again invited to go to the United States to report on certain technical aspects, including their choice of SINS to be used and the overall management of the navigation system.

On his return from Nassau the Prime Minister had announced to the world that Britain's Polaris nuclear deterrent would be a sea in 1968. This allowed just sufficient time to build the submarines themselves but would certainly not permit any major redesign of the weapons or navigation systems. It was essential, therefore, that the principal American packages in the strategic area should be adopted with the minimum of change. The two main recommendations of the Navigation mission, fitting two SINS instead of three and dropping the star-tracking periscope, would be implemented, but that was all. Although both the mission and the subsequent ACO visit to the United States had also made a positive recommendation, on both technical and financial grounds, to use an alternative type of American SINS, and had even proposed that minor modifications should be made to allow the excellent British gyros to be employed, these were firmly vetoed. After several frustrating months, during which there appeared to be a possibility that some form of Polaris Navigation Centre might be established at the ACO, it was finally decided that the Compass Division would be responsible only for those items of navigational equipment which were of British origin. It would not be directly involved in the development and support of the main Polaris navigation system itself – except in one all-important area.

Having recommended the omission of the American star-tracking periscope it was essential that during the initial 'setting to work' in harbour, there should be an alternative means of checking the azimuth from SINS, upon which the whole success of any firing would ultimately depend. It was therefore necessary for the Royal Navy to develop its own procedure for conveying very precise alignment data from the outside world into the heart of the Polaris weapon system, and responsibility for the operation, which became known as the Heading Transfer Test (HTT), was placed with the ACO.

To handle these tasks a Polaris section was formed, headed by a Principal Scientific Officer, Geoffrey Hebditch, who acted as the link man between the ACO and the Polaris Executive, to whom he was ultimately responsible. Whilst his brief included certain aspects of the main Polaris navigational problem, he was specifically charged with the co-ordination and timely procurement of all the essentially British navigational items, amounting to quite a substantial list. As only two American SINS would be fitted in each submarine it was decided to provide a Mark 19 gyro-compass for ship control and as a third heading reference.[20] There was also the compass transmission system for distributing data throughout the submarine, the Synchronous Clock System, the Artifical Horizon Periscope Sextant, the Decca Navigator and the plotting tables. All these were standard RN equipments which would form part of the tactical weapons system of any normal submarine. Responsibility for developing the necessary interface between this area and the Polaris strategic centre also rested with the ACO. Although the establishment had no direct responsibility for the American strategic package itself, it was nevertheless able to provide considerable scientific back-up in the navigation field to Admiral Mackenzie's staff in the Polaris executive office, and over the next few years a very good working relationship was built up.

The one item above all others for which the ACO Polaris section deserves special recognition was the successful and timely development of a workable Heading Transfer procedure. It was a matter over which the American Special Projects Office (responsible for Polaris) felt some concern since its success was essential to the ultimate efficiency of Britain's deterrent. Progress was therefore closely monitored. In essence the scheme involved the optical transfer of the bearing of an accurately surveyed distant mark from the dockside to the submarine and then vertically down the conning tower to the weapon system, where it could be compared with the heading shown by SINS. A means had therefore to be found of making the vertical transfer without losing the essential supreme accuracy.

It was fortuitous that during the early 1960s the US Navy had been developing an instrument called the Azimuth Comparator, as part of an overall system for checking the accuracy of their own star-tracker. This instrument, resembling an additional periscope, could be dropped into the boat when in harbour and used to compare the readings at the top and bottom of the periscope. It seemed possible that it could also be adapted to handle the transfer problem. A contract was therefore placed with the designers, Perkin Elmer Inc. of New York, and in due course a successful and practicable modification was developed.

Meanwhile Hebditch had begun the task of planning the shore facilities and developing the necessary techniques and programmes for the whole operation, keeping in touch with the Azimuth Comparator developments through E. (Ted) Hoy, who was then working in America with the Special Projects Office. Because of the significant differences in the proposed UK fit and the extensive interface with the UK tactical navigation equipment, Hoy had been lent to the CPE to advise on these aspects. Towards the end of his time in the United States and later, on his return to the United Kingdom, he also played a major part in the design of the navigation area of the RN Polaris School at Faslane, on the Gare Loch. He returned to the ACO in July 1964 where he joined Hebditch in the Polaris section, eventually taking over from him the following year, and it was he who saw the project through to fruition. It is interesting to note that as a measure of the trust and confidence that had been built up, the United Kingdom was permitted to reprogram a section of the Polaris navigation computer for the Heading Transfer Test without US involvement.

Shore installations for the azimuth transfer operation were established at the operating base at Falane, at Barrow-in-Furness and Birkenhead, where the boats were built, and at Rosyth, where they would be refitted; also at Cape Canaveral for use during demonstration firings.[21] At each place the bearing of an accurately surveyed distant mark had to be transferred from the dockside to the top of the Azimuth Comparator mast by means of a very accurate theodolite. For missile firing, Azimuth is needed to an accuracy of seconds of arc, perhaps two orders better than is normally achieved by conventional alignment techniques, and this check had initially to be done before every Polaris patrol. A magnificent theodolite of 8 inches aperture was therefore developed by Messrs Hilger and Watts for use at Faslane itself, with portable (but very accurate) surveyor's theodolites for use at other bases.

In the summer of 1968 the effectiveness of these arrangements was put to the ultimate test off Cape Canaveral when, after final checks by the ACO alignment team, the first British Polaris submarine, HMS *Resolution*, fired her first two missiles straight and true down the Atlantic range within a few milliseconds of the date and time fixed five years before. This was a remarkable demonstration of the power of modern project-control methods.

At this point Hoy was transferred back to work on the UK SINS programme and leadership of the Polaris section and the ACO alignment team was taken over by C. Vernon Hardy. Further firings followed as each submarine became operational, and it was he who saw the task through to completion when the fourth submarine, HMS *Revenge*, fired her two missiles to complete a remarkable 100 per cent record of successes. In July 1969 the Royal Navy officially took over responsibility for the nation's contribution to the western strategic nuclear deterrent from the Royal Air Force.

Although the Azimuth Comparator was an extremely accurate instrument, it was delicate and difficult to use, requiring a large number of calibration checks and a very high level of operator expertise. It was also expensive. Only two were purchased as, from the outset, it had been envisaged that a British instrument could eventually be provided for the vertical transfer operation. The ACO first discussed the problem with Messrs Barr & Stroud of Glasgow in 1964 but it was another three years before a Naval Staff Requirement was authorized and a development contract placed. By this time Barr & Stroud had already, on their own initiative, evolved a scheme that was almost ready for trial. It was a brilliantly simple device called the Azimuth Transfer Mast (ATM), which achieved the same object as the Azimuth Comparator, with the same degree of accuracy and employing the same shore facilities, but was very much easier to use, more robust and considerably cheaper. After several years of further development and trial the Azimuth Transfer Mast was introduced into service early in the 1970s, to replace the Azimuth Comparator, and from then on played a vital role in maintaining the operational efficiency of Britain's Polaris fleet.

Thereafter, until 1982, when the introduction of an updated Polaris navigation system rendered the Heading Transfer Test no longer necessary, a team from the ACO attended every British Polaris missile firing – and *all were successful*.

Modern gyro-compasses

Early in 1963, with the development of SINS Mark 1 well advanced, it was time to look again at the overall gyro-compass policy for the Fleet, as a number of new compasses were now on the market. The Sperry Mark 19 compass-stabilizer, developed during the previous decade, had been at sea in the US Navy for a number of years. There was also the Sperry Mark 23, which had been widely fitted in the US and Canadian navies since 1952 and was now being manufactured exclusively in Canada. Meanwhile, when, in 1959, S. G. Brown had been sold by the Admiralty to become a member of the Hawker Siddley Dynamics group, the firm had also entered into a co-operative venture with the American Arma Company and was now marketing the small Arma-Brown gyro-compass, in place of the original Brown 'A' and 'B', the basic design of which has been little changed over forty years.

These compasses all used modern electronics with a form of electro-level or equivalent control. The Sperry Mark 19 was very accurate but it was large and expensive and at first it was introduced purely as a back-up to SINS. Although it also indicated the vertical and was therefore capable of acting as a weapon-stabilizer as well, at this stage the stabilization of weapons was not the Compass Division's responsibility. The Mark 23 and the Arma-Brown both had performances similar to the Admiralty gyro-compasses then fitted in the Fleet, but were better in high latitudes. They were considerably smaller and, where necessary, two could be fitted into the space required by one Admiralty compass. After comparative trials the Mark 23 was preferred, mainly because of its proven performance as a military equipment, its better shock protection and the fact that its transmission arrangements were compatible with other naval compasses.

WEAPON STABILIZATION

With SINS and the Sperry Mark 19 gyro-compass both capable of providing extremely accurate heading and a first-class vertical (roll and pitch) reference for stabilization purposes, the time was ripe for a rationalization of the stabilizer policy for the Fleet, as had been proposed by Captain Wynne-Edwards in 1956. For many years it had been the policy for each weapon system needing roll-and-pitch information to be provided with its own dedicated stabilizer, with the gyro-compass providing stabilization in azimuth. There now appeared to be a case for providing a central source of all stabilization data in the form of a single equipment, either SINS or the Mark 19 gyro-compass, to replace all the individual weapon and radar stabilizers. In 1964 the Director General (Weapons) ruled that the Compass Division should assume responsibility for all weapon stabilization and that the small Stabilization section which had, to some extent, been without a parent division since the setting up of the Weapons Department, should move from Bath to the ACO. This section would have the task of planning a rationalized system of stabilization, based entirely on SINS and the Mark 19 compass, for fitting in new ships and those undergoing modernization. The Stabilization section was quickly integrated into the Compass Division, which thus became responsible for providing data not only in azimuth, which it has done for 120 years, but for all ship movements.

A telling example of the economy effected by the new policy occurred shortly afterwards when the aircraft carrier *Ark Royal* was refitted. Her compass outfit was due for updating. By replacing the three Admiralty Type 5005 gyro-compasses with three Sperry Mark 19s it was possible to remove nineteen separate dedicated weapon and radar stabilizers.

COMPASS MODERNIZATION POLICY

The introduction of SINS and new gyro-compasses during the late 1960s made it necessary for the Compass Division, in conjunction with the Naval Staff, to produce a comprehensive compass-stabilizer fitting policy which could be stated in a few simple rules:

1. SINS would be fitted in nuclear submarines and where required in support of long-range data links. (It might also be needed for aligning aircraft inertial systems.)
2. The Mark 19 gyro-compass would be fitted in support of SINS and if the weapon system required roll and pitch data (e.g. for a guided missile).
3. In other cases the Mark 23 gyro-compass would be the standard gyro-compass unless considerations of space and weight dictated the even smaller Arma-Brown (e.g. in fast patrol boats or as the third compass in early nuclear submarines).
4. Where the gyro-compass was required for weapon-control or stabilization purposes, at least two should be fitted in order to ensure 100 per cent availability (SINS to count as a gyro-compass).

5. All ships should carry a magnetic compass unless equipped with three gyro-compasses (as in nuclear submarines).

These rules would apply to all new ships and to those undergoing a major modernization. For the first time there would be room to fit two gyro-compasses (Mark 23) into conventional (non-nuclear) submarines, in the space previously occupied by one Admiralty gyro-compass. In frigates two Mark 23s would replace the Admiralty gyro- and gyro-magnetic compasses. It was thus immediately apparent that a large number of these compasses would be needed for this programme, and the Sperry Company decided to start manufacture in England, with a view to extending their market into Europe. This was not, however, done for the larger Mark 19s as it at first appeared that the number of compasses likely to be needed would never justify such a step. All Mark 19 compasses had therefore to be imported from America. In the event, a later decision to introduce two foreign missile equipments, which could be bought practically off the shelf,[22] meant that a very large number of Mark 19s were required for stabilizer purposes at comparatively short notice, all of which had to be paid for in dollars.[23]

Naval Compass-Stabilizer Mark 1 (NCS 1)

The success of the central stable reference concept and the large number of Mark 19 gyro-compasses that would be needed made a clear case for the development of a British gyro-compass-stabilizer. Early in 1969 a detailed technical specification was prepared at the ACO by C. K. (George) Gulland, the Head of the gyro section and, J. M. Redwood, the Project Manager, and seven of the leading firms in the compass and inertial navigation field were invited to submit their broad proposals as to how it could best be met. Tenders, giving estimated development and production costs, were received from five firms, two of which gave alternate solutions using marine or aero-space gyros.

Analysis of these proposals and discussions with the individual firms showed that the two most promising contributors were the Sperry Gyroscope Company of Bracknell and Elliott Flight Automation of Rochester. Both planned to use gyros of well-proven design, a factor which had a marked bearing on the 'through-life' cost of the equipment; both offered sound technical solutions and a strong and capable management. Eventually, after the two firms had been invited to re-submit their porposals in greater depth, it was Elliotts which was chosen. The firm celebrated by recalling that it had held the first gyro-compass agency ever to be granted in England, from Anschütz, in 1911 (see p. 177).

A fixed-price, package deal contract for some four million pounds was placed early in 1971, to cover both the development and proving of the new system as well as the manufacture of the first fifty production equipments. It was a type of contract which offered incentive to the firm but it was a relatively new approach for the Navy and would require very careful monitoring. The programme called for four prototype equipments, one of which would be used for sea trials at the beginning of 1975 with the other three available for maintainer trials and environmental testing. Two of these would subsequently go to HMS *Collingwood* for technical training. Development was to be completed by mid-1976 and the first production equipment delivered nine months later. It was essential that these dates should be met as the Sperry Company of America had announced their intention of closing their production line of Mark 19 compasses, while offering the Navy a chance to buy a final fifty equipments on advantageous terms, to cover the gap.

The contract with Elliott's was to cause the ACO project management considerable anxiety as it soon became clear that, despite persistent pressure, the build-up of effort by the firm fell far short of that required to achieve the agreed programme. As slippages increased and the likelihood of recovery appeared to be receding, it eventually became necessary to call up the 'big guns'. In November 1972 the naval Director of Surface Weapon Projects[24] requested a meeting with the firm's top management at which he drew their attention to the serious situation that had developed. Their reaction was immediate. Project management was reorganized, the team was considerably strengthened and, after a long and hard struggle over the next two years, the situation was gradually retrieved. The Navy agreed to accept a four-month delay in sea trials, to the spring of 1975, and the prototype equipment was delivered on time. This episode had shown good project management in action and moved the Director of Surface Weapon Projects to comment, 'This example seems to be a classic in monitoring and detecting a shortfall in performance, then initiating the necessary correcting action.' The ACO had learnt a lot.

In service the Naval Compass Stabilizer Mark 1 has fulfilled every promise. It is a very sophisticated instrument in which a stable platform, carrying two Arma-Brown gyroscopes, is mounted on a special shock-mount to give it complete protection from underwater shock while still accurately maintaining its orientation. A separate bulkhead-mounted cabinet contains the solid-state electronics, the controlling keyboard and the computer which also operates the automatic fault-diagnosis programme or built-in test equipment (BITE). Sea trials of the NCS1 were carried out in the guided missile destroyer *Antrim* during 1975, using SINS as a reference as that was the only equipment in existence likely to have a higher performance than the system under test. In every respect it passed with flying colours, comfortably meeting all the performance standards laid down for it in the original specification. It was soon to become widely fitted in all new HM ships of frigate size and above, in all new submarines and in a number of 'modernizations'. In addition it showed a promising sales potential and was purchased by a large number of foreign navies.

After the initial alarms this project turned out to be a model, both in its management and in its excellent end product, and credit for its success must go primarily to John Redwood who, with George Gulland, helped to prepare the original specification, recommended the selection of the firm and oversaw its management. From 1969 he was responsible for the day to day project control and had the difficult task of getting the show on the road and drawing the firm's attention to its early shortcomings. In 1974 Derek Kitch took over in midstream and saw the project through to its successful sea trials. Great credit must also be given to Marconi Elliott Automation for designing and producing, on time, an equipment of the very highest order, fully proved, documented and supported.

Other activities

The three major undertakings, SINS, Polaris and modern gyro-compasses, took up the greater part of the ACO's effort during the 1960s. There were, however, a host of smaller activities going on in parallel, some of which (e.g. sonobuoy compasses and the Artificial Horizon Periscope Sextant) have already been discused. Of the others, four deserve special mention, magnetic anomaly detection, synchronous clock systems and the use of radio navigational aids and integrated navigation systems.

MAGNETIC ANOMALY DETECTION (MAD)

The purpose of MAD, as its name implies, is to find small irregularities in the general pattern of the earth's magnetic field. The technique employs a very sensitive stabilized magnetic element, either fixed to an aircraft or towed behind in a streamlined body known as a 'bird', and can be used to show up ferromagnetic rock deposits or oil-bearing strata. It has been successfully employed in area surveys since the mid-1950s.

The same procedure can also be applied to the detection of submerged submarines and is used by maritime reconnaissance aircraft and naval anti-submarine helicopters. As the anomaly concerned is small (depending, of course, on the height of the aircraft and the depth of the submarine) it is of paramount importance to ensure that the magnetic effect of the aircraft should not interfere with the sensor and, with their experience in conducting magnetic surveys on aircraft, this project fell naturally to the ACO. Whilst a submarine threat remains, efforts to improve the sensitivity of this system are likely to continue, with the ACO also providing scientific support for the operational equipment in the field.

SYNCHRONOUS CLOCK SYSTEM (SCS)

Shortly after World War II, as part of the exercise to keep the workshops loaded, the ACO undertook the repair of domestic and operational clocks and watches for the Navy, the Compass Department later assuming responsibility for their design and procurement. The provision of accurate, synchronized time in operational compartments had long been a requirement at sea, particularly for record keeping, but it had been difficult to satisfy economically using mechanical clocks. When, therefore, in 1960 the development of the experimental SINS provided a very accurate time source in the form of a crystal oscillator, it was decided to tap the output to provide synchronous time throughout the ship. An electronic chronometer was provided as a back-up for those periods when SINS was not running, and the first system was installed in HMS *Dreadnought*. With SINS Mark 1, however, provision of this output proved inconvenient and a Staff Requirement was accordingly raised to develop a separate master control unit for a clock system which would also incorporate facilities for central zone-time changing. Initially this unit used mechanical clocks with electrical transmission but it was soon redesigned with solid-state electronics and crystal-controlled clocks (making it SCS Mark 2) and was widely fitted in the operational spaces of all frigates and major units. When, in 1968, the Hydrographer took over all domestic and navigational clocks, the Compass Division retained responsibility for synchronous electric clocks but the system was discontinued early in the 1980s, as by then accurate time was readily and cheaply available to all.

RADIO NAVIGATIONAL AIDS (NAVAIDS) AND INTEGRATED NAVIGATION SYSTEMS

At the start of the 1960s the Compass Division was responsible, with a few minor exceptions, for all naval navigational equipment other than that concerned with radio, which belonged to the Admiralty Surface Weapons Establishment. The exceptions were plotting tables, on which no development work had been done for many years, and logs, which counted as hull-fittings. Both were handled by the Ship Department and both were to some extent to come the way of the ACO during the 1970s.[25]

As already discussed, accurate positional (fix) information is essential in order to assess and correct SINS performance and this can often be most readily obtained from radio navigational aids. The division's responsibility for SINS thus gave it a particular interest in the use and performance of these aids. In 1967, with the backing of the Director of Navigation and Tactical Control (DNTC), a study was started at the ACO into the possibility of developing an integrated navigation system in which navigational information from all sources, including SINS where fitted, would be automatically processed, assessed and co-ordinated in order to produce the best available navigational position at any time.

Such a co-ordinating task would further broaden the activities of the ACO, and it was abundantly clear that the name Compass Division no longer adequately described the widening range of equipments and functions for which the Director was responsible. Accordingly, in August 1967, the Director-General (Weapons) decided that the title Director of Weapons (Compasses) should be changed to the Director of Weapons (Navigation) – DW (Nav) – and at the same time he specifically gave the division responsibility for the operational use of all navigational aids, including radio aids, and for the development of integrated navigation systems.

The idea of an integrated navigation system was sound and well within the state of the art at the time. It was unfortunate therefore that with this concept the ACO appeared to have been too far ahead of conventional naval thinking and, with a limited budget, the Naval Staff were reluctant to be led too quickly into the realms of expensive computerized navigation. Although research continued at a low level and two experimental systems were built, approval for full development was withheld and it was to be another ten years before the project was given whole-hearted support.[26] Nevertheless DW Nav's involvement in radio navigational aids continued to grow and in 1969 he became the design authority for all future aids, concentrating initially on Omega which was then under development in the United States. Of the other aids, Decca was well established and Loran C was just coming into service. Although the satellite navigation system (Transit) was also operational, receivers were still very expensive and were only fitted for special purposes. During the years which followed this new responsibility was to become a major branch of the ACO's activities.

Off with the old . . .

During the early 1960s the ACO's tradition of long service was highlighted by the retirement of three senior members of staff all of whom had served in the establishment since before the war. As already discussed, Commander A. V. Thomas, the Deputy Director, was relieved by the author, then serving as a Naval Assistant, and Alfred Hine, the head of the compass section, was succeeded by his two deputies, J. L. Howard (who was promoted to Chief Experimental Officer) for magnetics and H. B. Hewitson for gyros, both also prewar veterans. When, however, gyro work was expanded to include the range of new equipments, the section was taken over by C. K. (George) Gulland. The third retirement was Horace C. Wassell who, with the arrival of Henry Heal to lead the SINS team, had taken charge of a new cell to handle the greatly increased R & D budget and to oversee the new building projects, while still running his instrument section. By far the longest-serving member, however, was Connie Gaskill who had been in charge of the registry throughout the war and who retired in August 1967, after a remarkable fifty years at the ACO.

Throughout the 1960s the number of scientists, draughtsmen, production engineers and supporting staff continued to grow and an Establishment Officer was appointed to assist the Deputy Director with administration. In 1959 there had been exactly one hundred non-industrials, of whom 35 belonged to the Royal Naval Scientific Service. By 1967 the equivalent figures were 217 and 118, the latter including 28 draughtsmen, and the average age of the staff, which had risen steadily since the war, dropped dramatically. In the following year Henry Elwertowski was fittingly promoted to Deputy Chief Scientific Officer (DCSO) and appointed to the upgraded post of Deputy Director (R & D), the Deputy Director being reappointed as the Naval Deputy.

Such a rapid expansion placed a considerable strain on the establishment's facilities, many of which had not been updated since before the war, and a wide-ranging programme of modernization had to be put in hand at once. As already described, a complex of portacabins was needed to absorb the overflow of staff while a new laboratory block was being built for them behind the mansion. For several years roads, paths, flowerbeds and floorboards were being continually dug up. An automatic telephone exchange replaced the manual switchboard which had been installed in the early 1930s and a new oil-fired central heating plant took the place of the twenty-two coke boilers, some of which predated the Admiralty's occupation of 1917. From car parks to drainage, from fire precautions to security, all facilities were examined and where necessary extended or renewed. Even the kitchen arrangements enjoyed a facelift.

In the workshops and laboratories, clean areas, air conditioning and modern precision machines were installed to compete with the increasing high-grade work (giving impetus to the removal of the coke dumps). Mr Wooller recalled how, during his early years at the ACO, he was frequently shown examples of the excellent work being turned out by the workshops, despite outdated equipment. After a detailed assessment of the existing machines he drew up a scheme for a radical modernization of the workshop facilities, to be spread over five years. In the event it was completed in three, giving the ACO a greatly improved capability for the high-grade precision work that would be needed.

In the naval stores compound, where huge Nissen huts, erected during the war, were still in use, modern storerooms sprang up to house the valuable and in some cases secret equipment. To add to the general upheaval, in 1963 it was discovered that much of the area around No. 4 workshop was contaminated with radio active material, a legacy of the wartime luminizing work at a time when the hazards were not fully understood and, by modern standards, safety measures were minimal.[27] Many lorry loads of earth had to be excavated and removed to safety while twenty-eight sealed concrete drums of the most active soil had to be dumped at sea before the factory inspector was satisfied. When, in 1966, 21 years after the war, a Home Office circular authorized government establishments to dispense with their air-raid shelters, these were quickly removed and the oval in front of the mansion was restored to its pristine turf. An Admiralty Order a few weeks later saying that the Home Office ruling did not apply to naval establishments was fortunately just too late!

The 1960s was thus a period of great turmoil, but it was also a time when the establishment's scientific programme was probably more extensive and varied than at any previous period in its history. It was therefore essential that, despite the bulldozers, business should continue as usual and to this end Captain Ross used personally to chair the regular liaison meetings with the men from the Ministry of Public Buildings and Works. Although the momentum was well-maintained, it must sometimes have saddened him that he hardly ever saw the place when its pleasant surroundings were not being dug up for one very good reason or another, but from this future generations would greatly benefit.

Service to the Fleet

Since 1842 the proper installation of magnetic compasses in ships had been one of the principal duties of the department and when, shortly before World War I, gyro-compasses appeared they were given equal care and attention.

During the early 1950s all ACO activities concerned with installation, inspection and acceptance trials of gyro-compasses in ships were concentrated in one Gyro section which had wide-ranging responsibilities. It vetted the installation plans prepared by the ship-designers at Bath and it arranged the allocation of equipments to

individual ships. In commercial shipyards gyro-travellers belonging
to the section supervised the installation, set the compasses to work
and, after conducting the acceptance trials, handed the equipment
over to the ship's officers. In HM dockyards these tasks were
undertaken for the department by the Superintendents of Gyro-
compasses (SGCs) who also reported to the head of the Gyro
section. When ships experienced compass trouble, it was the SGCs
who diagnosed faults and supervised repairs. It was a tidy organization and it had worked admirably for many years.

By the 1960s, however, the Compass Division had become part
of the Naval Weapons Department and changes were necessary to
conform with the latter's organization and procedures. Gradually
the ACO began to take the lead in the planning of compass
installations, passing 'guidance information' to the Ship Department
to be processed into detailed ship's drawings. When the stabilization
section moved to the ACO in 1964, guidance information concerning stabilization (roll and pitch) was at first provided separately
from compass (azimuth) information, but it was not long before
the two were integrated and handled by one Installation Planning
Section. In 1971, when the ACO was administratively absorbed by
ASWE, this section became the navigation part of the wider Ship-
Weapons System Engineering organization and covered all ACO
sponsored equipments.[28]

Meanwhile, with the increasing variety and complexity of equipments, opinion was hardening (outside the ACO) that the traditional
special arrangements for compasses made by DWC ought no longer
to be necessary. The compass was increasingly becoming an integral
part of the overall weapons system and it was felt that it should be
treated in the same way as all other weapons equipment. No other
department gave the same special service to its customers. All other
weapons systems in new ships were installed by the ship-builders
and set to work by a specially trained team known as the Weapon
Systems Tuning Group (WSTG). It looked as if the gyro-travellers
at the ACO might soon be out of a job.

In the same way it was apparent that the division's representatives
in the naval dockyards, the SGCs, were something of an anachronism
and it was decided that their duties should be undertaken by
dockyard personnel, Inspectors of Electrical Fitters who would be
responsible to a newly appointed dockyard officer, the Weapon and
Radio Engineering Co-ordinating Officer. Special courses were

therefore arranged at the ACO to train these inspectors (although they could hardly expect ever to achieve the experience of the men they replaced) and in 1966–67 the SGCs were gradually withdrawn as their terms of appointment came to an end. It was not the first penalty of co-ordination but it was sad to have to end so fine a force.[29] Fortunately it was possible to find billets for most of these men at the ACO where their great experience in gyro-compass work could still be put to good use.

Under the new arrangements outlined above, two important functions still remained to be covered, those of Inspections and Acceptance, and there was a strong feeling that these should be undertaken by a completely independent authority who had no responsibility for supplying, installing or setting the equipment to work. As a start, in 1965 a Naval Weapons Trials Co-ordinator was appointed to organize the activities of the several separate trials teams which covered the different weapons equipments. These parties represented the various R & D establishments and specialist schools and were responsible to the heads of their respective organizations. After a number of hybrid, transitional arrangements, in 1970 a Captain Weapons Trials (CWT) was appointed to head the Naval Weapons Trials Organization, with his headquarters at HMS *Excellent* at Portsmouth. From this date all trial parties came under his orders and all reported direct to him, and through him to the Director-General (Weapons).

At the ACO the new organization was brought into being very simply. The gyro-travellers were transferred 'on paper' to CWT, and their work and reports were co-ordinated by one of the ex-SGCs[30] who was also attached to his staff. Instead of inspecting and accepting gyro-compass equipment which they themselves had installed and set to work, the travellers would now, as representatives of an independent CWT, inspect and conduct acceptance trials on equipment installed by the yards and set to work by the WSTG (or their dockyard counterparts). As new equipments (e.g. SINS, new gyro-compasses, AHPS, SCS) came into service, these too were taken on. The Naval Assistants also wore a 'CWT hat' when inspecting and adjusting magnetic compasses while, to save employing other, less qualified staff, the (N) and (L) Application Officers did the same thing when carrying out similar CWT functions (e.g. SINS navigational trials). Finally, the Deputy Director also acquired a CWT hat as the Trial's Commander at the ACO. It all added up to a neat, independant CWT unit within the ACO, without requiring any additional staff.

Initially there was some pressure from CWT for the gyro-travellers, as the only full-time ACO members of the new trials organization, to move to Portsmouth to join the other trial teams. This would have achieved a tidy paper organization but it would have separated them from the very useful back-up they enjoyed from the ACO scientists and the installation section. It would also have involved additional travelling when visiting northern shipyards, and would have been very unpopular domestically. However the idea was eventually dropped and this somewhat unusual organization continued to work extremely well for many years.

Thus by the 1970s the original Gyro section had been split into many parts, responsible to no less than four separate authorities in different places. At working level, however, the parts were all still under one roof and so the rather special ACO tradition of service to the Fleet has been maintained.

The end of independance

At the beginning of the 1970s the Navigation Division and the ACO, still firmly integrated as one unit, could look back over the past decade with satisfaction. The establishment had grown considerably in size and importance and its international reputation, particularly in America, was high. New responsibilities had been accepted and all projects were going well. The build-up of staff had been achieved without undue disruption, and establishment facilities has been extended to cope. The peak numbers, reached in 1967, had remained roughly steady for two years but by 1970 had begun to fall, partly as a result of government pressure to cut the Civil Service[31] and partly because the effort needed on some projects was tapering off. Nevertheless augories for the future were still bright and there was as yet no indication of the changes that lay ahead.

On a number of occasions in the past, starting with the 'way ahead' investigation of 1957, there had been suggestions that the ACO should be merged with ASWE, and it was known that the director of ASWE, H. W. Pout, favoured the idea. Two factors now conspired to create a suitable climate for a takeover bid, the most obvious of which was the fact that Captain Ross would reach the age of 60 in 1971. Although his terms of service might have allowed him to continue in post to the age of 65, it was known that he was contemplating retirement.

The second factor was the Rayner report. In October 1970 Mr (later Sir) Derek Rayner, a director of Marks & Spencer, was invited by the government to head an investigation into 'how best to organise the integration of all defence research and development and procurement activities under the responsibility of the Secretary of State for Defence'. (i.e. to rationalize the procurement, in its widest sense, of defence equipment for the three services). Recommendations were required in time for them to be implemented by 1 April 1972.

The main proposals of this report[32] will be discussed briefly in the next chapter. However, it was evident at once that they would have a marked impact on R & D establishments (some of which might even be closed or amalgamated) and that considerable reorganization would be inevitable. It might well be logical to integrate the ACO with ASWE during this reorganization. The impending retirement of the Director was fortuitous while the fact that the two Admirals concerned, the Controller of the Navy and the Director General (Weapons), were both about to be replaced, added to the instability of the moment.

The news broke early in 1971 when, during a visit to the ACO, DGW informed the Director that he had decided to place the Establishment administratively under ASWE. The matter had clearly been discussed at length between the Director of ASWE and DGW's staff but until that moment there had been no consultation with the ACO whatsoever. To Captain Ross the decision came as a complete surprise and a most unpleasant shock. If however, he felt aggrieved, as indeed he might, he was careful to say nothing which might create dissension in the future. Rather, he spent his last few months at the ACO working to ensure that the handover, when it came would take place smoothly and with the least possible disruption.

Initially the ACO was to form the Navigational Department of ASWE, Elwertowski remaining as Head of ACO, with the title XN as head of an ASWE department, and incorporating the Civil Marine division at Eastney. Commander Fanning, the Naval Deputy, would be the Senior Naval Officer and Navigation Application Commander, and Mr Wooller would continue as Head of Production.

The effect of any further reorganization as a result of the implement-
ation of Rayner would take time to work out and would not be
known for some months.

In many ways the amalgamation was logical as so much ACO
equipment was closely integrated with the weapons systems. On
the other hand, Navigation information was needed as much by
submarines as by surface ships, while stabilization applied equally
to underwater and surface weapons. Would the system not have
worked just as well, and equally logically, if the ACO had been left
as it was, providing its traditional service to both surface and
underwater alike, without the traumas of a takeover? The answer,
of course, will never be known, and the matter was never discussed
with the ACO management before the die was cast.

In other ways the establishment would have much to gain from
the many excellent resources and services at ASWE to which it
would now have access. Career prospects, too, could well benefit
from the wider environment. Apart from the loss of independence,
the most obvious penalty that would result from the merger was
the fragmentation of a closely knit organization into a number of
groups, responsible to Heads of Dapartments in remote places such
as Portsmouth and Bath, instead of all ultimately owing allegiance
to one man, one accessible leader, the Director. Under these circumstances, maintaining the *esprit de corps* of the establishment, which
had been its strength through two wars and many ups and downs,
would be an important challenge to the head of the establishment
in the years to come.

It was under these circumstances that the ACO said good-bye to
the twelfth and last Naval Director of the Compass Department,
after 129 years. Captain Ross had led the establishment and the
department through yet another remarkable phase in its history
which had witnessed the successful development of SINS, the arrival
of Polaris, the rationalization of compasses and stabilizers and the
considerable broadening of its navigational responsibilities, resulting
finally in the change of title to Director of Weapons, Navigation.
Through all this activity his personal contribution, although often
intangible, had been immense. With so many new programmes,
running to tight time-scales, resources were fully stretched and it
was inevitable that crises would be frequent. It was Captain Ross's
calm counsel that so often averted calamity and pointed the right
course. It was he who told outside authorities truthfully just what

and when the ACO could deliver, earning their trust and respect while ensuring maximum co-ordinated effort within the establishment. There is little doubt that during the Polaris project the USN's acceptance of the part played by the ACO owed much to their confidence in its Director.

When reading the draft of this chapter and agreeing to the account of the often traumatic events during his 10 years in office, Captain Ross remarked 'it does seem to have gone smoothly. I wonder why I sometimes got so worried'. He, of course, had known where the final responsibility lay.

What ever the future might hold, the departure of Captain Ross marked the end of an era which had seen the department grow in size and stature from one man alone, dealing with simple magnetic compasses, to an internationally recognized authority responsible for virtually all Navigational equipment for the Navy and with design responsibilities for the compasses used by the Army, the Royal Air Force and Civil Aviation. It was fitting that the great-grandson of Sir James Ross, chairman of the original Admiralty Compass Committee which had first put the show on the road, should be the one to hand the organization on, in such excellent shape, to face its new horizons.

NOTES

CHAPTER 12

[1] Working with Captain Hugh Topley of the Board of Trade.

[2] Commander A. V. Thomas OBE, OSJ, JP, DL, died at his home in Powys on 8 August 1981.

[3] This was the Ultra-precision Test Equipment (UPTE), which was set up on a 30-ton concrete block extending 6 feet below ground level and completely isolated from the building.

[4] A second consideration which resulted from the demise of *Blue Streak* concerned the gyros. Mainly for reasons of cost it had been the original intention to develop a common British gyro for SINS and *Blue Streak*, based on a US Air Force design and to accept the fact that this would be something of a compromise. It was now possible to select a gyro with considerably greater potential for SINS alone and this led to the choice of the Nortronics V6, with most gratifying results (see p. 331).

[5] It was the original intention that SINS should be used for the alignment of aircraft inertial systems. In the event

the defence estimates for 1966–67 announced the cancellation by the Wilson government of the Navy's new aircraft-carrier, which had been approved three years earlier, and the phasing out of existing carriers. The experimental SINS was removed from *Eagle* in 1967 but the ship was never fitted with SINS Mark 1.

6 The X-3 model (ex-*Valiant*) may now be seen in the National Maritime Museum at Greenwich. In 1967 *Valiant* made a record submerged passage from Singapore to the United Kingdom, a distance of some 11,000 miles.

7 The X-3 model also used American gyros and not the new British gyros, as had been originally planned.

8 It was oscillating with a period of 19-hours instead of 24, something which should not have been possible since the earth rotates once every 24 hours.

9 Only HM Ships *Fife*, *Glamorgan*, *Norfolk*, *Antrim* and *Bristol* were fitted. This was in anticipation of their receiving the long-range data link but, in the event, this was never installed and SINS was later removed.

10 Beryllium is a very light, strong, stable metal which is widely used in SINS gyros.

11 In a gas-lubricated bearing the hydrodynamic effect is used to build up a gas pressure between the surfaces which prevents them touching. Once running, there is therefore no friction and no wear.

12 In 1974 A. G. Patterson was given an 'individual merit promotion' to Senior Principal Scientific Officer for his work on gas bearings, on which he was recognized as a world authority.

13 This effect was first demonstrated in 1913 by Sagnac long before lasers appeared. In simple terms two light beams travel in opposite directions round a path defined by mirrors and rotation of the system leads to a shift of interference fringes.

14 Thomson had been transferred from Baldock. He had achieved fame during World War II as the man chiefly responsible for the development of the proximity fuse.

15 Five years earlier, when the design of SINS was started, a computer with the same capacity would have occupied a whole compartment and would have had quite inadequate reliability.

16 HMS *Trafalgar* class. It was, in fact, just in time to catch the last of the previous class, HMS *Splendid*, on building.

17 HM Ships *Invincible*, *Illustrious* and *Ark Royal*.

18 This American equipment was, of course, already almost 10 years old.

19 *Journal of Naval Science*, Vol. 4, No. 2.

20 Although this equipment was manufactured by Sperry (USA) it was not initially fitted in the US Polaris boats and was therefore regarded as a British addition.

21 These took place during what was termed a demonstration and shakedown operation (DASO). The importance of the ACO contribution was recognized when the establishment received a visit from the Minister of Defence, Mr Roy Mason MP, in November 1967, just a few months before the first DASO firing.

22 These were the Australian anti-submarine missile *Ikara* and the French anti-ship missile *Exocet*.

23 Nevertheless Sperry (USA) were very co-operative. On two occasions they offered Mark 19 compasses at a reduced rate provided fifty were ordered at a time – considerably more than a year's supply. The Treasury agreed to break their own rules and allowed these deals to go through, thus saving many thousands of dollars.

24 Captain G. W. Bridle, later Rear Admiral and Assistant Controller of the Navy.

25 A third exception was the echo-sounder. As this instrument depends on the speed of sound in water, it fell logically into the province of the Admiralty Undewater Weapons Establishment at Portland.

26 As a result of this decision when, in the mid-1970s, the off-shore patrol vessels were built, to a very short time-scale, to cover the North Sea oil rigs, it was necessary to purchase an expensive commercial system to meet their requirements.

27 It appeared that most of this radiation originated from the residue of luminous compound which was frequently emptied into the coke-heating stoves, the ashes of which were later scattered over the paths!

28 In 1977 John A. White was appointed head of the installation planning section. Apart from three years service in the RAF, he had served at the ACO since 1944 and, having joined the Gyro section in 1952, had had a unique record of experience through all its changes and reorganization.

29 The Fleet's regret was well expressed in a letter to the Director from the Commander-in-Chief, Far East Fleet, at Singapore: 'There is no doubt that it is to a great extend due to the Superintendents of Gyro-compasses of the past and present, and their independent position, that the gyro-compass equipment has been so reliable in the Fleet. It is with misgivings . . .' The decision was probably inevitable but it appeared to many as yet another sacrifice on the alter of 'progress and uniformity'.

30 This was Roy C. Dairy, the last SGC at Singapore, who efficiently organized an amorphous amalgam of travellers for some sixteen years.

31 Two of the posts cut, both coincident with the retirement of their incumbents, were those of a Naval Assistant (leaving only one to handle all magnetic work with the Fleet) and of the Instructor Officer. By 1971 all instruction except that of swinging officers had been transferred to HMS *Collingwood*.

32 Cmnd 4641. The report also covered civil aircraft and aerospace activities.

Into the future

'History is the essence of innumerable biographies'. (Thomas Carlyle)
'The best of Prophets of the future is the past'. (Lord Byron)

This final chapter looks briefly at how the ACO settled down under a new regime and how it was reorganized to meet the needs of the future. It deals in general terms with the new responsibilities which came to Ditton Park, in particular those concerned with radio navigational aids and the systematic processing of navigation data, but touches only lightly on the individual projects and equipments involved.

The Admiralty Compass Observatory had experienced a severe shock and life would never be quite the same again. The complete integration that had existed for so many years between the ACO, as an R & D establishment, and its parent headquarters department was a thing of the past. The Director of Weapons (Navigation), the natural successor of the Director of the Compass Department of 1842, had vanished, and although the ACO itself had survived, from 1 June 1971 it became no more than an out-station of the great Admiralty Surface Weapons Establishment, 60 miles away. The Rayner recommendations had not yet been implemented but when these took effect radical reorganization would inevitably follow. However, as in Captain Creak's time a century earlier, when high-level decisions had brought unwanted change, there was no point in regrets. The traditional responsibilities for providing navigational equipment for the Fleet remained and these were, if anything, likely to increase. The ACO must now accept the challenge and look to the future.

For ten months Henry Elwertowski remained as Head of the ACO and in charge of the Navigation Department of ASWE, before he, too, retired. It was in many ways an excellent thing that he should have continued for this period, as it allowed the staff to adjust gradually to the new situation. Although they still all worked in the same establishment it was already clear that certain individuals and sections would shortly find themselves owing allegiance to remote bosses whom they seldom saw. They would acquire tallies which fitted them into other organizational charts whose members mainly worked elsewhere. Meanwhile the Navigation Department acquired an important new section, the Civil Marine Navigation Aid Division, based at Eastney in Portsmouth, which was responsible for overseeing the development of electronic systems for the safety of navigation at sea and for testing and approving commercial marine radar and radio aid equipment on behalf of the Department of Trade.

On 30 March 1972, before Rayner really took effect, Elwertowski retired after an exhilarating fourteen years at the ACO, which had seen immense progress. Joining in 1958, he had picked his team carefully, guiding its build-up to tackle SINS, Polaris and the many other projects already discussed. His keen interest in collaboration with other authorities had resulted in the ring-laser and MAD work coming to the ACO whilst his interest in information exchange with the United States, particularly on gas-bearing technology and later on Omega, led to many fruitful meetings. He was on the technical committee of the Royal Institute of Navigation and also attended a number of NATO navigation meetings, leading the UK delegation on behalf of the Ministry of Defence when dealing with long-term studies. With all these activities and the many successes he achieved at the ACO he had done much to enhance the establishment's reputation, both at home and abroad. Official recognition came with the well-deserved award of a CBE in the 1972 Birthday honours.[1]

Co-incident with Elwertowski's retirement the reorganization for Rayner within ASWE was getting under way. 'Navigation' became a division of the new department of Communications and Navigation under Ben Craven, who also became Head of the ACO although based at Portsdown. For six months G. J. R. Rosevear, who had been deputy Head, remained at the ACO as the local Officer-in-Charge and head of the Navigation Division before giving way, on retirement, to Heal, the leader of the SINS project. This became the pattern for the future and since that time each head of the ACO in turn has endeavoured to ensure that the gap separating his office in ASWE from the ACO should always be kept as narrow as possible.[2]

The Rayner recommendations

The principal aim of the Rayner recommendations was to combine all the existing procurement activities of the Ministries of Defence and Aviation Supply under one Chief Executive, who would become an additional member of the Defence Council. Responsible to him would be nine Controllers, of whom the most important would be the Controller of Research and Development Establishments and Research (CER) and the Controllers of Sea, Land and Air Systems, who would handle the specific needs of the three services.[3]

CER would be responsible for the management of all defence research and development establishments, and was particularly charged with their rationalization to avoid duplication of effort. Directors of R & D establishments were to be allowed the maximum delegated authority for the work of their establishments, and particularly for its research programme, but should not normally take responsibility for project management. The report particularly stressed the importance of adequate research before staff targets were raised and of the careful selection of 'research objectives', to ensure the most effective use of available resources.

The systems controllers would be responsible for seeing that their services got the equipment they required, within the approved development and production programmes. Project managers, grouped appropriately under wider project-management organizations, should be given full executive responsibility and be supported by technical specialists allocated by the R & D establishments and attached to the project staff.

Prior to 1972 little distinction had been made between research and development, both being the responsibility of establishment directors, exercised as necessary to meet the Naval Staff Requirements. The Rayner reorganization drew a sharp line between the two, leaving responsibility for research with the establishment directors, under CER, and setting up new directorates to manage projects which covered development, production and introduction into service, under the system controllers. Thus a Director of Surface Weapons Projects (DSWP) appeared, with a staff of project managers, housed at ASWE but having no management link with the Director of the establishment.

This project organization had, of course, to be staffed largely from those already serving in the R & D establishments and this necessitated much reorganization, spread over many months. C. K. Gulland was appointed Head of Navigation Projects, to co-ordinate the work of a number of project managers, each of whom handled one or more projects. Although accommodated at the ACO, these men were no longer under the orders of the Director, ASWE, but worked for DSWP. On the other hand the scientists who were needed to support the individual projects did come under the Director, ASWE, and were allocated to projects by the Officer-in-Charge of the ACO. It could have been confusing, but with the Head of Navigation Projects and the Officer-in-Charge working closely together in adjacent offices, it worked very smoothly and many junior staff hardly noticed the change as they went steadily on with the same job. For others, however, matters were not so straightforward and initially there was considerable fragmentation of the scientific community. In addition to the Navigation Division and project staffs, the ACO found itself with 'bits' (some only one or two strong) of *eight* other divisions, all working for different bosses at ASWE. Fortunately over the years, common sense prevailed and the majority were gradually reabsorbed into the Navigation Division. The small Naval Staff, in particular, found themselves serving many masters. Primarily they were there to provide naval input to a number of projects, across a wide spectrum, but they also worked for the Captain Surface Weapons Acceptance (CSWA), a new authority responsible to the Director-General (Weapons), for accepting new equipments into service, for Captain Weapons Trials and occasionally for the head of the establishment.[4] Nevertheless, the new project organization quickly settled down and worked well. There is little doubt that project management at the ACO benefited very considerably from the tighter discipline it imposed.

The planning and execution of the research programme was also drastically changed by grouping research into 'major fields' and appointing headquarters directorates to administer them. Research on navigation at first found itself controlled by the Director of Research, Avionics, Space and Air Traffic Control (DRASA) in Whitehall. There were many teething troubles (and occasional frayed tempers) as the ACO's proposals were subjected to scrutiny by aviation specialists who knew little of the requirements of naval navigation. In 1978, however, the headquarters directorates were de-centralized. Control of the navigation research programme was then placed under the head of the Radio and Navigation Department at the Royal Aircraft Establishment at Farnborough, a far more satisfactory arrangement which helped to strengthen the already close links between the two establishments in this field. Under the new arrangement the Research Area leader controlled the extramural programme whilst intramural work remained the responsibility of the Director of ASWE. This at last restored to the head of the Navigation Division (who was also Officer-in-Charge, ACO) a considerable degree of freedom and flexibility to direct the research programme, as had been enjoyed by his predecessors prior to Rayner and the amalgamation.

Navigation policy

Navigation has always been an integral part of a warship's ability to fight or to carry out its task and, with the increased requirement for the exchange of tactical information between widely dispersed forces, the trend for the future appears to be towards an ever greater involvement of navigation in the functional roles of the Fleet. Although navigation can claim to be amongst the oldest of the sciences, the continual application of technology, particularly during the second half of the twentieth century, has resulted in a bewildering array of systems and aids designed to help the navigator and to improve accuracy. Radio navigational aids first appeared during World War II in the form of Gee, Decca, Loran and Consol, but all had limited coverage, and for some years astronomical navigation remained the only worldwide fixing system. Despite the recognized need for increased accuracy, the analysis of Fleet exercises often showed that, even in the 1960s, ships could differ in their estimates of position by many miles. It was, however, in that decade that the first global all-weather methods of fixing began to appear.

As new navigational aids were introduced they began to revolutionize the practice of navigation and it soon became practicable for the Naval Staff to lay down the navigation accuracies required by the Royal Navy under a variety of conditions and operational situations. There was also a need to forecast accuracy requirements for the years ahead as these might well be influenced by the introduction of future weapons systems or equipments, not yet at sea. A wide-ranging 'Navigation Accuracy Policy Paper' was therefore produced which aimed at establishing the maximum error that would be operationally acceptable for each activity and under different circumstances, both in peace and war. It was a paper which would inevitably need to be reviewed and updated at regular intervals.

Clearly such a document required a feasibility input from the ACO, based on an up-to-date knowledge of the systems and techniques available or expected, although the papers did not, of course, specify the actual equipments necessary to achieve the objectives. At a time of rapid development in the field of navigational aids the detailed requirements of the Fleet had to be kept under constant review and the equipments needed would be authorized by Naval Staff Requirements and procured through the normal project organization at the ACO, under DSWP, subject always to the harsh realities of the defence budget.

Whilst too many details of ship-fitting would be inappropriate in this narrative, a few remarks on the individual systems might help to demonstrate the ever widening scope of the ACO's responsibilities.

INTRODUCTION AND PERFORMANCE OF THE PRINCIPAL RADIO NAVIGATIONAL AIDS

After World War II the extension of Decca as a coastal navigational aid (Navaid) had been rapid and the system quickly proved entirely adequate for its purpose. During the 1950s, Decca receivers were gradually fitted throughout the Fleet. For ocean work there was Loran (later called Loran-A), which had begun operation in 1942, but this had limited coverage and, except in favoured areas, its accuracy was low. It was finally phased out of service during the 1970s. In 1958 the United States had introduced the greatly improved Loran-C system, to support the Polaris programme and to provide general navaid coverage over the northern half of the NATO sea area. This was later extended along the coastlines of Canada and North America, also to the Mediterranean and to certain other operational regions. Receivers were widely fitted in the Royal Navy from the late 1960s and were a great boon for updating SINS. In 1962 the US Navy launched the first of its Transit satellites, the start of the first worldwide all-weather navigational positioning system, SatNav, which became fully operational two years later. However, although this system had great potential, the receivers were at first bulky and expensive and it was not until well into the 1970s that it was adopted for general use in the Royal Navy.

Meanwhile, during the late 1960s another navigational system, Omega, had begun operation. Initially three very-low-frequency (VLF) transmitters provided limited coverage over the northern and central Atlantic but this was gradually extended during the following decade until eight transmitters were available, providing a fixing capability over all the generally accessible ocean areas.

With such an array of systems, navigational accuracy improved considerably. Loran-C and SatNav can, under favourable circumstances, produce fixes of an accuracy better than one mile and half a mile respectively, whilst Omega has an approximate accuracy of two miles by day and four miles by night. Although both Satnav and Omega may be adversely affected by ionospheric conditions, suitable monitoring and other techniques can do much to improve matters. Further, by using the accuracy of Satnav (which can give a fix every $1\frac{1}{2}$–3 hours) to improve the positions from Omega (which gives a continuous read-out) it was possible to have the best of both worlds. Thus, by the late 1970s a continuous worldwide all-weather positional accuracy of better than two miles was generally attainable with a fair degree of confidence. In ships fitted with SINS, the performance was probably as good as the non-uniformity of the earth's gravity would allow.

The next step began in the mid-1970s with a return to the concept of an integrated navigation system. Navigation data was now available from many sources, both new and traditional, some of which could give continuous information and others periodic spot fixes. Each source had its own probable error pattern. The rapid and reliable assimilation and analysis of such varied data is best done by a computer with a suitable display which can be used to give the best co-ordinated position. Not only can error modelling and optimum filtering improve the achievable accuracy, but the system is also able to offset the potential weaknesses of one aid by the strength of another.[5] In this way, and with the continuing advances in both equipments and techniques, it seems probable that still further improvements in navigational performance will be achieved in the future.

For coastal and in-shore survey work and for certain other operational requirements, particularly those connected with mine warfare, there is a requirement for very precise and repeatable navigation accuracy over a limited area. For these purposes specialized radio navigational equipment of the Hifix or Transponder types is essential and this, too, is best employed in conjunction with some form of computorized integrated navigation system.

Finally, when the American Navstar Global Positioning System (GPS), becomes operational about 1990, it will become the most accurate worldwide positioning system available. Navstar GPS is a satellite-based system, employing 18 satellites in 6 equally spaced orbital planes, each containing 3 satellites, at a height of about 11,000 miles. Two modes of operation will be available, a standard positioning service (SPS signal) and a precise positioning service (PPS Signal). The former will give a horizontal accuracy of approximately a 100 meters whilst with the PPS signal, which is likely to be available to authorized users only, accuracies of the order of a few metres in both the horizontal and vertical may be expected.

Meanwhile the task of the ACO will be to guide commercial manufacturers in the design and production of the necessary receivers to meet the requirements of the Navy, to organize appropriate evaluation trials and eventually to arrange for the introduction into service of this new and revolutionary radio navaid.

RESPONSIBILITY FOR NAVIGATION EQUIPMENT

From 1967, when the Director of Weapons (Navigation) (DW Nav) was given responsibility for the operational use of all navaids, thought at the ACO had been directed towards the whole navigational function. Two years later DW Nav had become the design authority for all future radio navaids, concentrating initially on *Omega* which was then under development. It was therefore natural that, following the amalgamation with ASWE in 1971, the ACO should also take over the management and procurement responsibilities for all the radio navaids already in service and hitherto looked after at Portsdown. These included Decca and Loran (A and C) but did not embrace navigational radar which had wider implications connected with the Action Information Organization. Radio navaids thus became one of the ACO's major activities, on a par with SINS and compasses. During the 1970s Omega, Satnav and Hifix-6, as well as many items of ancilliary equipment, were introduced into regular service.

In parallel with the project work on radio navaids came a number of interesting research items aimed at improving the reception or accuracy of the systems and extending their use. Two examples, both connected with Omega, are typical. Although the Americans had built up a theoretical propagation model for Omega and had prepared tables and formulae to allow for ionospheric changes, these needed to be checked and refined by actual observations. As part of a worldwide monitoring network, the ACO set up recording posts at the Butt of Lewis in the Outer Hebrides, in Malta and on the islands of St Helena and Ascension.[6] Results from these stations were passed to the appropriate branch of the US Coast Guard responsible for Omega navigational warnings (the Omega navigation system operations detail, ONSOD) and were used to modify or refine the theoretical models in order to increase the accuracy of the positions obtained. The second example concerned the use of Omega by submarines. Although it was well known that VLF reception was possible in submarines using submerged aerials, only limited information was available concerning the depth at which these signals could be used for navigation. Also the effects of their transition from air to water, of wave motion and of depth, all had a bearing on the accuracy of the position obtained. Considerable theoretical work was done at the ACO to determine the laws governing reception under these differing conditions and this was followed by extensive sea trials to prove the results. In this way the accuracy of submerged navigation using Omega was markedly improved.

Meanwhile, during the 1970s work in the 'compass' field continued as before. The development of SINS Mark 2 and the Naval Compass Stabilizer Mark 1 have already been described in chapter 12. The requirement to provide a gyro-compass with a very low magnetic signature for the new class of Mine-Countermeasures Vessel (MCMV), built mainly of glass-reinforced plastic, placed new and stringent demands on the department. After attempts to reduce the magnetic effect of the Sperry Mark 23 gyro-compass to an acceptable level had proved impracticable, S. G. Brown were asked to develop a non-magnetic version of their Arma-Brown. In the event a new and very neat commercial version of this compass, the Mark 10, was just appearing and, after modifications had been made to enable it to meet naval requirements, it was eventually introduced into the service in 1977 as the Arma-Brown Mark 12. This soon became the Navy's main general-purpose small-ship compass and, in a 'non-magnetic' version, it also met the needs of the MCMV.

Although the Department of Trade regulations had, for many years, required merchant vessels to carry a Standard Magnetic

Compass with either an ACO or an ISO certificate, no similar requirement had ever been stated for gyro-compasses. In 1979 a recommendation prepared by the ACO and published by the Intergovernmental Maritime Consultative Organization, (IMCO) laid down for the first time a performance specification for marine gyro-compasses. This was adopted by Britain and, at the request of the Department of Trade, the ACO agreed to provide the necessary testing facilities. Since 1981 a type-test certificate has been required for every gyro-compass to be fitted in a British ship. The Head of the ACO thus became responsible, on behalf of the Department of Trade, for the certification of all commercial gyro-compasses, in addition to his existing responsibilities for magnetic compasses, sextants and civil and marine radio aids and radar.

RESEARCH

The requirements for greater accuracy in navigation and for more cost-effective navigation systems were reflected in a research programme which was pursued at an increasingly active level during the 1970s and 1980s. In addition to items concerned with the introduction and use of radio navaids, already briefly discussed, investigations were conducted into ways of reducing the 'cost of ownership' of SINS and into the viability of low-cost medium accuracy inertial systems. Following the progress made with ring-laser gyros in the United States and at the RAE, Farnborough, interst was rekindled into their possible use in SINS, while work continued with potential alternatives for a gyroscope based on cryogenic nuclear magnetic resonance or fibre optics. From 1977, when the ACO was given responsibility for 'unconventional' logs, trials were conducted into the use of radar doppler logs for hovercraft and of sonar logs, particularly as part of a self-contained navigation system for mine-hunters and similar craft. A few years later the ACO became responsible for the management (including research) of all forms of log. The standard marine sextant, which had remained practically unaltered for some 200 years, was studied with a view to digitizing its output for direct processing into 'ship's position' and to providing a twenty-four hour capability by the use of low-light techniques for horizon viewing. These and many other items are being constantly investigated as research continues into ways in which new scientific principles can be applied to improving the practice of navigation. History will show which activities eventually lead to new projects and new equipments for the Fleet.

SHIP'S NAVIGATION PROCESSING SYSTEM (SNAPS)

Although the ACO had had responsibility for developing integrated navigation systems since 1967 and much research work had been carried out, there was as yet no Naval Staff Requirement for such a system. The go-ahead for the Ship's Navigation Processing System, one of the most imaginative and far-reaching projects to be started at the ACO during the 1970s, came about almost by chance, when an urgent requirement arose for a modern navigational plotting table.

The ARL plotting table (designed at the Admiralty Research Laboratory at Teddington) had been introduced into the Navy early in the 1930s and although many variations had appeared during and after the war to meet the requirements of the Action Information Organization (AIO), the basic design of the mechanism had remained virtually unchanged for over forty years. Navigationally the table could develop dead reckoning from the gyro-compass and log by means of a mechanical analogue system but it was in no way suitable for handling the great variety of additional navigation information that was becoming available.

Meanwhile at ASWE a number of automatic plotting systems had been developed for use in the AIO. These were designed to display a geographically stabilized radar picture, but were not intended for navigation and worked simply in dead reckoning. Nevertheless their introduction had gradually made the ARL table obsolescent and, except in submarines, it had been largely phased out of service. It had become more convenient to conduct operations from the face of a cathode-ray tube. When, during the 1970s, the importance of accurate navigation began to figure more prominently, there was a sudden and urgent need for a modern plotting table suitable for navigation. In particular, the satisfactory analysis of fleet exercises was proving almost impossible through the inability to correlate the tracks of individual ships due to the inaccuracy of their navigation plots. A new table was also required for the production of a long-range situation plot (the General Operations Plot, GOP) which in many frigates was kept entirely by hand – a condition that would not have been tolerated thirty years earlier.

While the ACO now had the prime responsibility for developing navigation equipment, it had no mandate for work on plotting tables. At the same time the Ship Department, which had handled the procurement of ARL tables since their inception, had no wish to become involved in the development of a new design. Approval was therefore given for the ACO to take over this task and in 1976 a Naval Staff Requirement was raised for a modern system which would facilitate the compilation of both the navigational plot and the GOP. In this simple manner the SNAPS project was born.

Modern technology could now provide fast and accurate processing of navigation data and its automatic display and recording in a form suitable for retrieval when required. SNAPS was designed as a digital, integrated system capable of taking inputs from all current Navaids and ship's sensors and co-ordinating the information in order to generate continuously the ship's best position, based on parameters decided by the operator. This can be displayed on a chart, together with much other information which is immediately available within the computer. Where SINS is fitted, this naturally constitutes a prime source of data.

It should be stressed, however, that the automatic co-ordination of navigational information in this manner in no way usurps the navigating officer's responsibility as the final arbiter. It is he who controls the selection of navigational aid(s) to be used and who decides on the weight to be given to each. He must always remain an essential link in the system, able to assess, accept, reject or modify whatever is offered, from his knowledge of the circumstances of the moment.

A ship's navigation processing system consists essentially of a computer which can accept and process inputs from all sources of Navigational data and can drive one or more semi-automatic plotting tables. There is also a magnetic tape recorder. Control of each table is exercised through a keyboard/display unit (KDU) which enables the operator to perform a wide range of functions such as the selection and 'weighting' of the navigation inputs to be used, inserting or recalling navigational or other data, and injecting information from other sources, in particular on enemy tracks which it is desired to keep up-to-date. In addition the computer may be instructed to carry out all the normal navigational and tactical calculations including relative velocity problems, passage details,

ETAs and so on. The best available navigational position is generated continuously for the navigation plot and is transferred automatically to the action information organization. At the same time the processor can also accept and record data passed from other plots and systems.

The design and development of SNAPS took some six years. In order to ensure that the system, which was urgently needed by the Fleet, could be fitted as soon as possible after development was completed, a series of purpose-built consoles was designed to house the individual units. These could be fitted in advance, either when a ship was being built or during a dockyard refit, and SNAPS could then be virtually 'plugged in' when it became available. Simple fits would involve only one plotting table while frigates would require two, one on the bridge as a navigation plot and the second in the operations room as GOP. Larger ships would have additional requirements. For the latest submarines a console was designed to accommodate the SNAPS, all-radio navigational receivers, and the SINS remote terminal. Modern submarines thus had, for the first time, a totally co-ordinated navigation centre.

In retrospect it may well have been to the Navy's advantage that in 1968 the Naval Staff declined to be led too quickly into the realms of computerized navigation, albeit possibly for the wrong reasons. Progress in electronics, in error modelling and in optimum filtering during the following decade all contributed to the advanced techniques required for the design of a truly integrated navigation system. SNAPS thus appeared as a thoroughly modern system in keeping with the operational requirements of the 1980s and 1990s.

Closure of the production workshops and the future of the ACO

Exactly twenty years after the 'way ahead' committee had scrutinized the ACO, the establishment was again under examination. This time, however, the reasons were mainly political. Early in 1976 the government was committed to making major reductions in civilian manpower within the Ministry of Defence, and the production workshops at the ACO represented a sizeable pool of manpower that might be cut.

An investigation showed that almost all the production functions of the workshops could, if necessary, be undertaken by industry.

The only exception appeared to be refurbishing the old Admiralty-type gyro-compasses, of which about 140 were still fitted in HM ships and Royal Fleet Auxiliaries, although many of these were already in reserve. Expertise on these elderly compasses was held entirely in the ACO and, as documentation was far from complete, it would not be possible to pass their support to an outside firm. The number of such compasses was, of course, likely to diminish considerably over the following decade.

The Ministry of Defence decision to close the production work-shops was announced on 12 November 1976 and occasioned little surprise. For several years something of the kind had been expected and there had been a gradual reduction in numbers as men due for retirement were not replaced. To handle the Admiralty gyro-compass work a small cell of craftsmen would be retained in addition to the highly skilled group who were still needed for work in support of research and development. The run-down of the remainder was achieved by offering voluntary-redundancy terms or early retire-ment, and was phased over three years. With the high average age of the workforce and the excellent industrial opportunities available in Slough, it caused few problems. Early in 1980, with little fanfare, the production workshops were formally closed, marking the end of an era going back more than sixty years.

However, it appeared that the rest of the ACO was not yet out of the wood as the Ministry's announcement contained the unexpected sentence: 'The R & D activities currently at Slough are not likely to change significantly during the next few years but a review of their longer term future (and of the associated RNSTS⁷ activities at Slough) will be carried out over the next six months.' To everyone's surprise the long term future of the establishment was apparently still in question and, after the axe had fallen on the workshops, another worrying period ensued. Once again the long-term objectives, responsibilities and planned activities of the estab-lishment were reviewed and scrutinized. Once again the manage-ment, now headed by Ted Hoy, was called upon to argue and justify its case, which it did with great skill and cogency. Amongst the considerations which undoubtedly weighed heavily in favour of retaining the ACO in Ditton Park were the excellent magnetic and seismic stabilities of the area which enabled work to be undertaken at Slough under conditions which could not have been provided at ASWE at Portsdown. Meanwhile, as the enquiry proceeded the action committee, the 'Save the ACO' campaign and a considerable amount of lobbying of MPs could have left the authorities in no doubt that the ACO was still a busy and contented unit which wanted only to be left alone to get on with its important job.

At last, on 14 October 1977, after eleven anxious months, the Ministry of Defence announced its findings. Referring to the very thorough investigation that had been carried out, it stated:

> As a result of this review, the conclusions reached are that on present Defence policies and planning:
> a. there is no reduction in the scope of the R & D programme in the foreseeable future which would permit abandonment of work currently done at ACO Slough;
> b. the R & D activities in Ditton Park could not be undertaken elsewhere without reproviding major capital facilities at a heavy cost and with some difficulties in siting;
> c. based on these considerations, the cost of rationalising the activities of the ACO into other Establishments would substantially exceed the benefits.
>
> In the light of these considerations the Department has confirmed the continuing need to retain ACO's R & D facilities for defence purposes for the foreseeable future and ACO Slough will therefore remain in operation.

It was an enormous relief and the establishment was once more able to get on with its work and look to the future.

'Per Stet'

After 140 years the ACO could surely face the morrow with a confidence based on experience, despite occasional mistakes or wrong turnings along the way. In the 1840s Captain Johnson sometimes erred as he grappled with the unknown, but he succeeded in establishing the Compass Department on firm foundations. Captain Evans further enhanced its reputation and, with the help of the brilliant Archibald Smith, contributed greatly to the advance of human knowledge, although his excessive caution undoubtedly delayed material progress. Such ups and downs have continued over the years. If in the course of a long history, hopes have not always been completely fulfilled, progress overall has undoubtedly been steady and continuous. Sometimes it has been spectacular. The second half of the twentieth century has witnessed an unparalleled explosion of new ideas and exciting possibilities, with the ACO expanding at an unprecedented rate into new fields of activity, with new obligations. All the most advanced technology known today is now being applied to navigation. Gyroscopic devices, inertial systems, radio aids, satellites and, above all, digital computers have produced a revolution in navigational thinking which has tended to change the whole subject from being 'largely an art' into 'basically a science' – although the author still tends to believe with Gibbon that 'The winds and waves will always be on the side of the ablest Navigators'.[8]

As it accepts the challenge of the future, the ACO still remains the only scientific compass authority in the country, with obligations covering land, sea and air. For the Royal Navy it is responsible for 'everything that matters' in navigation equipment. Although the successors to Captain Johnson now handle a variety of subjects and techniques undreamt of even a generation ago, their prime task nevertheless remains very much what it was in 1842, to provide the fleet with the navigation equipment it requires.

The future of the ACO will surely depend on the success with which it discharges this wide-ranging task and the best advice to the establishment must clearly be that contained in its motto, *Per stet* – 'Let it stand firm', or in a freer translation, 'Steady as she goes'.

NOTES

CHAPTER 13

[1] Sadly Elwertowski did not live to see the very successful SINS Mark 2, which he had started, go to sea. He died on 12 February 1973, less than a year after his retirement.

[2] Ben Craven was followed as head of the ACO by J. Peter Grantham while

in June 1976 Hoy took over as officer-in-charge from Heal. Having been associated with the ACO for twenty years, Hoy was the natural successor when Grantham retired in 1981.

[3] These were the Controller of the Navy, the Master General of the Ordnance and the Controller, Air,

respectively, who kept their traditional titles.

4 The Senior Naval Officer, ACO, who was also the Application Commander, was appointed to the co-ordinating directorate of DGW at Bath. He gave a service to DSWP, CSWA and the Director, all at ASWE, and to the Captain Weapons Trials, at HMS *Excellent*. He thus had five masters!

5 An example of this feature is the combined SatNav/Omega system which can produce better positional information than would be possible from the two working separately.

6 A monitoring station was also maintained at the RAE at Farnborough.

7 The naval stores organization.

8 Edward Gibbon, *The Decline and Fall of the Roman Empire* (1776–88).

Illustrations

1. Rose of the winds. c. 1521

2. 17th Century ornamental compass card.

3. Azimuth Compass, 1669. (Reproduction in National Maritime Museum)

4. Walker's Meridional Compass 1793.

5. Variation Chart of the World by Edmond Halley, 1702.

6. Dr Gowin Knight. c. 1750.

7. Card from Gowin Knight's compass. Late 18th Century.

8. Captain Matthew Flinders. c. 1812.

9. Barlow's correc
plate. c. 1830.

10. Binnacle of *HMS Victory*,
containing two compasses by
Gowin Knight and central lant

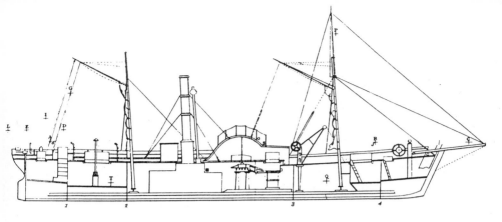

1.2.3.4. Four Watertight Bulk Heads of Wrought Iron ¼ in. thick.

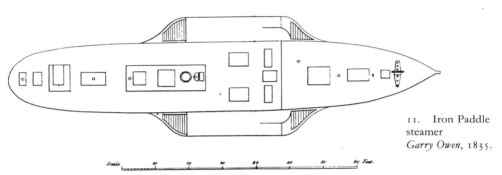

11. Iron Paddle steamer *Garry Owen*, 1835.

Scale [scale bar] 10 20 30 40 50 60 Feet.

12. Crow's Liquid Azimuth Compass, 1813.

13. Compass bowl on glass pillars.

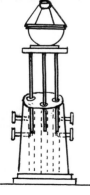

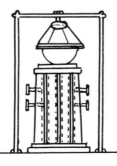

14. Retractable binnacle for use in brigs. (Sketch by Johnson)

389

15. Captain James Clark Ross, c. 1830.

16. Captain Edward John Johnson, c. 1850.

17. Capitain Francis Beaufort, 1838.

18. George Biddel Airy, c. 1835.

19. Staff Captain William Mayes. c. 1880.

20. Captain Frederick John Owen Evans, c.

21. Dry card compass by Snow Harris, made by Mrs Janet Taylor, with eddy current damping.

22. Dry card compass by Dent, with double-pivot and damping device.

23. Jennings Insulating Compass (Patent 1818).

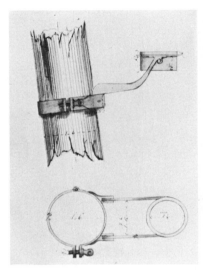

24. Mast compass (sketch by Johnson).

25. Admiralty Pattern One Standard Compass, 1840.

26. *HMS Birkenhead* (*HMS Trident* was similar)

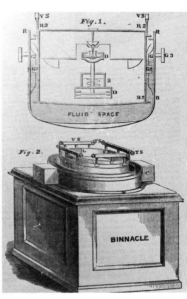

27. Gray's binnacle with correctors, 1854.

28. Kayser's binnacle, using small compasses for quadrantal correction c. 1895.

29. Evans's double binnacle, 1862.

30. *HMS Warrior*, 1870, showing uppe deck steering after Standard Compasses.

32.   Thomson's 4-inch compass, showing grommet suspension.

31.   Sir William Thomson. c.1840.

33.   Thomson's famous 10-inch dry card compass.

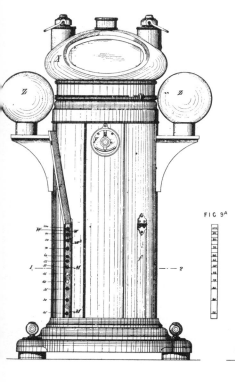

FIG 9ᴬ

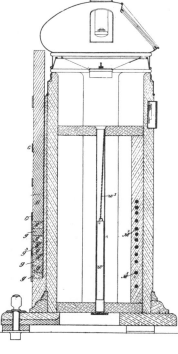

34.   Illustration from Thomson's Patent of 1879, showing corrector magnets, spheres and flinders bar.

35. Adjusting forward Standard Compass aboard HMS *Minataur*, 1870.

"Advance."

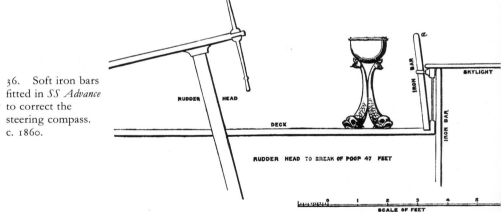

36. Soft iron bars fitted in *SS Advance* to correct the steering compass. c. 1860.

RUDDER HEAD

DECK

IRON BAR

IRON BAR

SKYLIGHT

RUDDER HEAD TO BREAK OF POOP 47 FEET

SCALE OF FEET

37. The bombardment of Alexandria, 188 HMS *Alexandra* the foreground with HMS *Inflexible* to the

38. (Far Left) Staff Captain James Henderson (1889–1904).

39. (Left) Captain Ettrick William Creak (1868–1901).

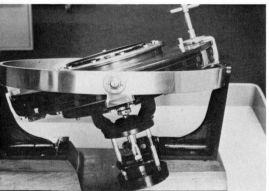

Piechl Compass, with radial soft iron rods. c. 1888.

41. Dent's Liquid Boats Compass. (1860–92)

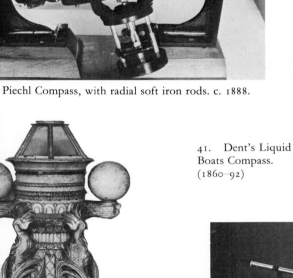

Binnacle from Royal :ht *Victoria and Albert.* 895.

43. Method of using Heeling Error instrument, Patt. 5.

44. Upper Deck steering position in *HMS Pylades*, 1897, with two Thomson compasses.

45. 1st Class Torpedo-
c. 1899.

46. Pillar binnacl
adapted for use in
Torpedo-boats.

47. Torpedo-boat Des
c. 1898.

Captain the Hon. Louis
tworth Packington
wynd. (1901–12)

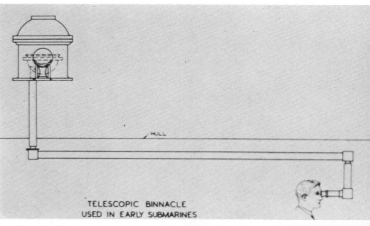

49.   Chetwynd's Patent liquid
compass with reduced-diameter card.

Telescopic binnacle used
' Class submarines.

TELESCOPIC BINNACLE
USED IN EARLY SUBMARINES

51.   Portable binnacle
for submarines.
(Faithful Freddie)

'A' Class Submarines,
ing binnacle on casing,
.o.

53. Colonel Cody and his aircraft, 1909.

54. First compass to operate in an aircraft, 1909.

55. First standardised airc compass, pattern 200, 1913.

56. Curtiss flying-boat *America*, the type used on anti-submarine patrol during WW1.

57. Compass, with sphere designed for *America*'s atter the North Atlantic crossing

58. Commander Creagh-Osborne operates a Sperry gyro-sight in a Curtiss aircraft.

Type 5/17 aircraft compass. (ay 1917)

60. Commander Geoffrey Brankner Harrison. (1914–28)

62. Clifford Chaffer. (1919–36)

Pattern 259 aircraft compass h vertical card, 1915.

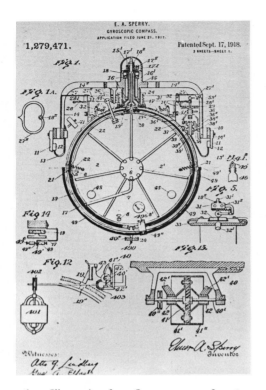

63.   Illustration from Sperry patent of 1918.

64.   Sperry gyro-compass with floating ballistic, 1914.

65.   Sperry gyro-compass with Harrison-Rawlings mercury control, 1919.

66.   SG Brown's gyro-compass, 1916.

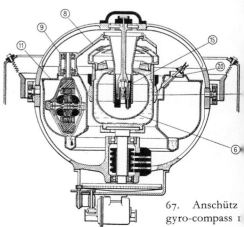

67.   Anschütz gyro-compass 1

68. (Left) Captain Frank Osborne Creagh-Osborne. (1904–26)

69. His Majesty, King George V visits the ACO. (26 August 1918) Prince Albert (later George VI) is behind the King and Commander S. B. Norfolk to the left.

Front of the Mansion, Ditton Park, 1918.

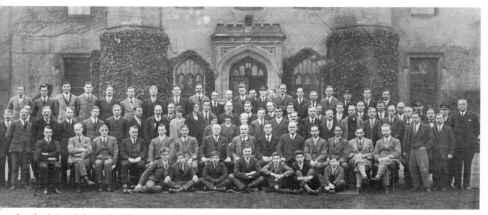

Staff of the Admiralty Compass Observatory, 1926.

72.   Air C
1915. Airc
hangar (no
Safe-distan
Laboratory
in the
backgroun

73.   Magnetic Test Room, 1917.

74.   Mr James Brunton. Teste
1842–1883.

75.   Lieutenant George H. Alexander,
1907–1929.

76.   Mr Thomas Foden, 1883–1907.

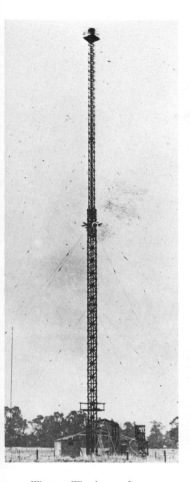

78. Ditton Park. North Park with radio aerials. c. 1926.

77. Watson Watt's 210 ft wooden radio mast.

79. Sad destruction of the 210 ft mast. c. 1927.

80. ACO fire-engine, which assisted at the fire.

81. Radio Research Station during the floods of 1947.

82. Captain Henry Luxmore Hitchins. (1928–48)

83. Captain Bertie Cecil Porter. (1926–51)

84. Aircraft P3 compass, 1926.

85. Aircraft P12 compass, with grid steering.

86. Hand-bearing compass. (Originally 06) 1935.

87. Master unit for RAF Distant Reading compass.

88.   Commander William Edward May.
(1929–51)

89.   Commander Anthony Vivian
Thomas. (1938–62)

91.   Dr W. F. Rawlinson.
(1945–58)

92.   Horrace Cyril Wassell.
(1939–67)

90.   W. George Heatley.
Chief Scientist. (1936–46)

93.   Alfred Hine. (1935–64)

94.   John L. Howard. (1937–71)

96. X-craft with side-cargo, 1944.

95. His Majesty
King Edward VIII
boarding a submarine.
Note 'Faithful
Freddie' on bridge.

97. *HM S/M Stubborn* returns
from patrol. Note gyro
repeater mounted on top of
projector binnacle.

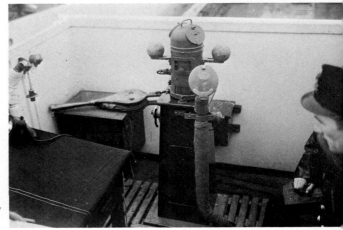

98. Bridge of Landing Craft
(Tank) with 'Faithful Freddie'
as Standard Compass. 1944.

406

99. Gas Drill at the ACO, 1940.

100. Blast protection for the Mansion during WW2.

101. Installing Air Raid Shelters on the oval at Ditton Park.

102. ACO Home Guard returning from an exercise, 1942.

103. Pattern 190 binnacle incorporating DG corrector coils (see 105).

104. Detector unit for GM4B aircraft compass.

105. Pattern 196S binnacle showing all 'add-on' DG corrector coils.

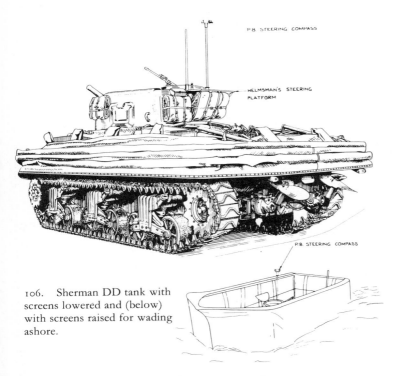

106. Sherman DD tank with screens lowered and (below) with screens raised for wading ashore.

107. Tank compass used by Sir Vivian Fuchs in snocat 'Rock'n roll'.

108. Crab Tank (Flail) negotiating Ditton Park mud, 1943.

109. Comet tank with PX3 compass.

110. 'Giraffe' tank compass.

111. Magnetic Compass Museum re-established in Main hall at Ditton Park after WW2.

112. Magnetic Test Room (Air), c. 1944.

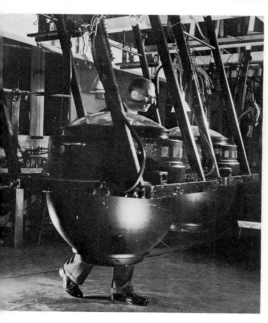

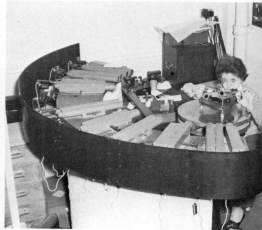

114. Sextant test bench.

113. (left) Admiralty gyro-compasses being tested in swings.

115. The Duke of Edinburgh's personal standard flying at the ACO. (26 October 1954)

116. The Duke with Captain Cecil John Wynne-Edwards, after unveiling a Sundial.

117. The Duke in discussion with 'Uncle' Wickham, in charge of workshops.

118. Aircraft E2B compass in the Duke's car.

119. Aircraft emergency compass, E2B.

120. Admiralty Transmitting Magnetic Compass, Mk 1, 1944.

121. ATMC Mark 2, 1945.

122. Admiralty Gyro Magnetic Compass, Mark 5, 1952.

124. Watertight binnacle for submarines. ATMC8, 1960.

Environ
tal testing
AGM5
he ACO.

HMCS
rador in the
th West
age, 1954.
ting
M5)

126. C. K. (George) Gulland.
(1963–76)

127. Admi
gyro-compas
Proteus mou

128. An Ele
Artificer maki
adjustment to
Admiralty gy
compass type

129. Trials of the Naval Compass Stabiliser Mark 1, (NCS1) aboard HMS Antrim.

130. Arma-Brown gyro-compass Mark 1, 1962.

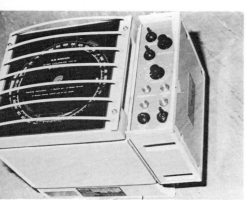

Arma-Brown gyro-compass Mark 12, 1977.

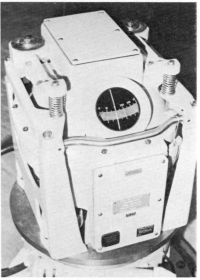

132. Sperry Mark 23 gyro-compass. Introduced into RN 1963.

133. (Left) Sperry Mark 19 gyro-compass-stabiliser in anti-shock mounting.

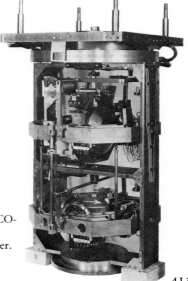

134. (Right) Prototype of ACO-designed gyro-compass-stabiliser. c. 1949.

135. SINS Trials Vessel *Steady*.

(Below) Some principle members of the SINS team:−

136. H. T. Heal.

137. E. Hoy.

138. W. P. Anderson.

139. Dr A. Lee.

140. A. G. Patterson.

141. Dr J. Preston.

142. E. J. Burton.

143. D. Gardne

144. R. H. Stretton.

145. M. W. Willcocks.

146. C. V. Hardy.

147. W. L. Tho

148. Magnificent Magnetic Test Room, to meet ISO standards. c. 1970.

149. L to R Captain T. D. Ross, W. P. Thurston, Mr Roy Mason (Defence Minister), Albert Barnes (Head Foreman), W. Bowley.

150. Magnetic Compass assembly workshop before modernisation. c. 1963.

151. Azimuth Transfer Mast for Polaris alignment. c. 1973.

152. The first British Polaris firing, 1968.

153. Expe
SINS on R(
Table at th(
factory, 19(

154. SINS Mark 1. Stable Platform
and transistorised electronics.

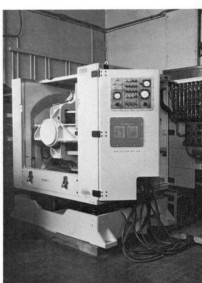

155. SINS Mark 2, with solid state
electronics.

156. Comparison of sizes of Elliott 920B
computer (1964) and 920M (Left) (1970).

157. HM Nuclear Submarine *Conqueror*

159. Captain T. Desmond Ross (1961–71) with Henry J. Elwertowski, (1958–72).

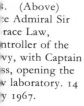

. (Above)
e Admiral Sir
race Law,
ntroller of the
vy, with Captain
ss, opening the
w laboratory. 14
y 1967.

. (Right) New
oratory block,
7.

. (Below) Staff
he Admiralty
npass
servatory, 1971.

417

162. (Above) Aerial
view of the ACO, 1971.

163. (Right) Admiral
Sir Anthony Griffin,
(Controller) Rear Admiral
P. A. Watson (DGW(N))
Mr Cyril Fogg (Director,
ASWE) and B. W. Craven
(Head of ACO), with
senior staff, 1972.

164. (Below) The
Typing
Pool join the protest.

165. Ships Navigation Processing
System (SNAPS), 1982.

418

Appendices

Deviation
A simple description

1. *Deviation* is the term used to denote the error of the magnetic compass caused by the attraction of the iron in the ship. The word seems first to have been used by Sir John Ross, the Arctic explorer, about 1820, the practice before that time being to refer to the effect as the local attraction (of the iron).

2. The *earth's magnetic field* behaves as if it were due to a bar magnet buried deep within the earth and inclined to the direction of the earth's rotational axis. The lines of force from this magnet will thus be vertical to the earth's surface at the magnetic poles (situated to the north of Canada and in Victoria Land, Antarctica) and parallel with the earth's surface at the magnetic equator. At any point in between, the lines of force will make varying angles with the earth's surface, known as the angle of dip. The angle of dip reverses its direction on crossing the magnetic equator, where there is no dip (figure 1).

3. These lines of magnetic force can be resolved into *horizontal* and *vertical* components. A magnetic compass gets its directive force only from the horizontal component of the earth's field, which is thus a maximum at the magnetic equator and nil at the magnetic poles. Similarly the vertical component of the earth's field is a maximum at the poles and nil at the equator.

4. From a magnetic point of view the iron in a ship may be categorized as either hard iron or soft iron. *Hard iron* (normally steel) is iron which cannot be easily magnetized but which, once magnetized, may be expected to retain its magnetism almost permanently. This effect is described as permanent magnetism. The ship's hull and structure consist largely of hard iron which becomes magnetized by the earth's magnetic field during the building process. The ship becomes, in effect, a permanent magnet and the character of its magnetism is a function of the direction in which the ship was lying when on the building-slip. (In practice this effect may be

considerably modified during the 'fitting out' period, after launching, when the ship may well lie on quite a different heading.)

5. *Soft iron* is iron which is easily magnetized when exposed to a magnetic field but which loses or changes its magnetism readily when the field is removed or changed. This effect is described as induced magnetism. Each piece of soft iron in the ship is magnetized by the earth's magnetic field, the direction of the magnetism induced depending on the orientation of the piece to the direction of the lines of force of the earth's field. Thus, when a ship alters course the magnetism induced in each piece of soft iron will change, as also will its situation relative to the direction of the compass needle. Both effects will alter the amount by which the compass needle is attracted or repelled by the magnetized soft iron, and hence the deviation caused.

6. The *induced magnetism* in the soft iron of a ship can be considered in two parts, that induced by the horizontal component of the earth's magnetic field and that due to the vertical component. Whilst the effect of horizontal induced magnetism always acts in the same direction, this is not true of that induced by the vertical component. The magnetism induced in vertical soft iron will vary according to the latitude of the ship. It will be a maximum in high latitudes, where the angle of dip is greatest, and will gradually reduce as the ship approaches the magnetic equator; it will be zero at the magnetic equator and will reverse its direction when the ship crosses into the other hemisphere. The direction of the deviation (i.e. either to the east or to the west) produced by this induced magnetism will thus also be reversed when the ship crosses the magnetic equator. The failure to appreciate the significance of this important effect (which had been pointed out by Captain Flinders in 1812) had a profound bearing on the safety of navigation during the middle decades of the nineteenth century.

7. *Factors causing deviation.* Although in practice most of the iron in a ship will display both hard and soft properties in varying degrees, the effect on the compass can be most easily understood if each type is considered separately. The deviating effect on the compass of the iron in a ship can thus be considered as the sum total or resultant of many small magnets, some of which are permanent (hard iron), some of which are induced and change each time the ship alters course (horizontal soft iron) and some of which also change with change of latitude (vertical soft iron).

8. The various separate deviating effects on the magnetic compass can thus be summarized as follows:

(a) That due to the magnetism of the hard iron in the ship, which was acquired during the building stage and which, after 'settling down', can be regarded as permanent.

(b) That due to magnetism induced into the horizontal soft iron of the ship by the horizontal component of the earth's magnetic field. This changes every time the ship alters course.

(c) That due to magnetism induced in the vertical soft iron of the ship by the vertical component of the earth's magnetic field. It changes with each alteration of course and with change of latitude, altering its sign on crossing the magnetic equator.

9. Considering paragraph 8(a), at a well placed compass (i.e. one on the centre line and with the ship's iron symetrically placed about it), the deviation due to the *fore-and-aft* component of the ship's permanent magnetism follows a sine curve. It is zero when the ship's head is north or south and a maximum when it is east or west (see figure 2). The deviation due to the *athwartship* componment of the ship's permanent magnetism follows a cosine curve and is zero when the ship's head is east or west and a maximum when it is north or south (see figure 3). Such deviation curves are called semicircular.

10. At a well placed compass the deviation due to 8(b) also follows a sine law but is zero on the four cardinal points, north, south, east and west, and a maximum on the half-cardinal points, NE, SE, SW and NW (thus it varies as the sine of twice the course). This is called quadrantal deviation (see figure 4) and its effect is readily distinguishable from the semicircular deviation.

11. The deviation due to 8(c) also follows a sine law and is semicircular. It is similar to that produced by the fore-and-aft component of the permanent magnetism (8(a)). Thus from observations in any one latitude it is not possible to separate the two effects. As, however, the deviating effect of 8(c), which is due to induction in the vertical soft iron, will alter with change of latitude, the two effects may be separated by making observations in two widely separated latitudes.

12. *Heeling error.* When a ship heels, although the compass card remains horizontal the iron in the ship moves around it. The deviating effect on the compass will therefore alter. Permanent (hard-iron) magnetism acting directly below or above the compass,

which has no effect on the compass when the ship is upright, will now exert a deviating attraction; the magnetism induced in the soft iron, particularly in the vertical soft iron, will also change and so will the deviating effect it has on the compass. In practice it is found that the alteration in the deviation of the compass when a ship heels can be considerable. Thus, as the *direction* of the resulting deviation depends on the direction in which the ship heels, when a ship is rolling heavily from side to side the compass may be caused to oscillate violently on either side of the mean course.

13. A ship is *swung* in order to observe the deviation (error) of the compass on each heading, so that courses and bearings taken from that compass can be corrected for use in navigating the ship. This is done by turning the ship slowly round through 360° and noting the error of the compass with the ship's head on each of the 16 or 32 points of the compass (or as frequently as may be desired). If the compass is to be adjusted, (paragraphs 14-17) this is done first, and the ship is then swung to observe the residual deviations.

14. *Adjusting the Compass*. In iron ships where deviations of the compass will inevitably be significant, it is customary to introduce correctors which remove or reduce these errors so that the compass is as nearly correct as possible. These correctors are designed to counteract the disturbing magnetic fields of the ship's iron and are placed near the compass, in or on the binnacle. When a compass is adjusted, it is clearly desirable that it should remain accurate when the ship changes its magnetic latitude, and this is achieved by correcting the ship's permanent magnetism by permanent magnets, whilst the soft iron effects are corrected by soft iron correctors. This principle is described as correcting 'like with like'. If a compass has its semicircular errors (paragraphs 8(a) and (c)) corrected by magnets *alone* it will be accurate in the latitude where the adjustment is made but will become increasingly inaccurate as the ship changes latitude. Quadrantal deviation (paragraph 8(b)) can only be effectively corrected by soft-iron correctors.

15. The following types of corrector are normally employed, working on the principle of correcting like with like:

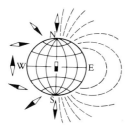

Figure 1 Lines of force from the earth's magnetic field, showing the angle of dip of a magnetic needle at the surface.

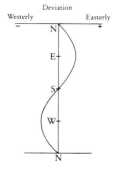

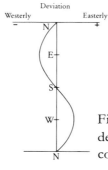

Figure 2 Semicircular deviation, depending on the sine of the course.

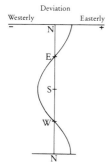

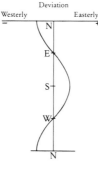

Figure 3 Semicircular deviation, depending on the cosine of the course.

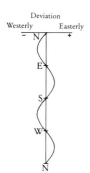

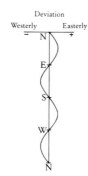

Figure 4 Quadrantal deviation, depending on the sine of twice the course.

(a) *Permanent magnets,* placed horizontally, fore and aft and athwartship, to counteract the ship's permanent horizontal magnetism (paragraph 8(a))

(b) *Soft-iron spheres,* normally placed on either side and on a level with the compass, to counteract the magnetism induced in the horizontal soft iron of the ship (paragraph 8(b)), acting on a level with the compass. In practice, the magnetic needles of the compass also induce magnetism in the spheres and this assists the correction.

(c) *A Flinders bar,* which is a bar of vertical soft iron, normally placed on the foreside of the compass with its upper end on a level with the needle, to counteract the magnetism induced in the vertical soft iron of the ship (paragraphs 8(c) and 11). NB: The correct length of this bar can only be determined by making observations in two widely separated latitudes (see paragraph 11).

(d) *Permanent magnets* placed vertically below the compass to correct healing error by counteracting the effects of the vertical components of the ship's permanent magnetism and of the magnetism induced in the soft iron by the vertical component of the earth's field (paragraph 12). In this instance it is not possible entirely to correct like with like. Heeling error must therefore be readjusted on change of latitude.

16. It is important to note that these correctors are placed so as to counteract the effect of the ship's magnetism at the position of the compass. Although it is customary to talk about correcting the compass, it is really the compass position that is being corrected, to allow the compass to operate correctly in that position. A compass placed in any other part of the ship will read quite differently and a different adjustment of the correctors will be needed to correct it.

17. When the correctors have been placed and adjusted it is customary to swing the ship to observe and tabulate the (small) residual amounts of deviation remaining on each heading (paragraph 13).

NOTES

APPENDIX I

[1] This subject is treated in depth in many publications of which the following is a selection: *Admiralty Manual of Navigation,* Vol. 3, chaps 23–24, HMSO; A. Hine, *Magnetic Compasses and Magnetometers,* Bristol, Adam Hilger, 1968; and *The Theory of the Deviations of the Magnetic Compass,* HMSO, 1948.

Admiralty Memorandum,
11 April 1843

The Lords Commissioners of the Admiralty having had under their consideration the importance of carefully preserving the Standard Compasses supplied to Her Majesty's Ships and Vessels from the Compass Department, are pleased to direct, that in future they shall be placed under the charge of the Captain, or Commanding Officer, similarly to Chronometers, who will be required to certify on the Master's final bill for full-pay, 'that the Standard Compass has been properly attended to, and duly returned to the Dock-yard at – by the Master.'

Whenever it shall be found requisite to move the said Instrument to or from the shore, or from ship to ship, it is always to be done in the presence of the Master or a Commissioned Officer.

The Master Attendants of the Dock-yards or their Assistants have been directed minutely to inspect each Compass, immediately on its return from the Ship or Vessel to which it has been supplied, and to report to the Superintendent of the Compass Department, its state and condition, the number of Cards, Azimuth Circles, &c. in order that he may be advertised of any unusual or unaccounted for dilapidation, and take the necessary steps to ascertain the cause from the Captain or Commanding Officer before the Certificate for its return shall be given, which Certificate from the Superintendent of the Compass Department will be required to be produced by the Captain or Commanding Officer, before he can receive his final bill for full-pay, – the same to be lodged in the Hydrographer's Office.

Where Marine Barometers shall have been issued to Her Majesty's Ships, the charge and return of these Instruments are to be subject to the same regulation, and to be issued with the Certificate for Chronometers and Charts.

By Command of their Lordships,
SIDNEY HERBERT

To all Captains, Commanders, and Commanding Officers of Her Majesty's Ships and Vessels

Admiralty Circular, No. 9 (20 November, 1845) Memorandum

With reference to the several orders which from time to time have been issued respecting the removal of Iron from the vicinity of the Compasses, placing the Binnacles and Standard Compasses on board Her Majesty's Ships, &c, and with the view of comprising these orders in one Circular for the guidance of the Officers concerned, my Lords Commissioners of the Admiralty are pleased to direct –

That no Iron of any kind shall be placed nor be suffered to remain within the distance of 7 feet of the Binnacle or Standard Compasses, when it is practicable according to the size and construction of the vessel to remove it; and that mixed metal, or copper, be substituted for iron in the bolts, keys, and dowels, in the scarphs of beams, coamings and head-ledges, and also the hoops of the gaffs and booms, and belaying pins, which come within the distance of 7 feet of the said Compasses.

The Spindles and Knees of the Steering Wheels which come within the distance of 7 feet of the Compasses are also to be of mixed metal.

Iron Tillars which work forward from the rudder-head are not to range within 7 feet of the Compasses and in vessels which have Iron Tillars working abaft the rudder-head, the Binnacles are to be placed as far forward from the wheel as may be convenient for the helmsman to steer by.

The Boat's Iron Davits are to be placed as far as may be practicable and convenient from the Compasses.

All vertical Iron Stanchions, such as those for the support of the Deck, or for the Awnings, &c, and likewise the Armstands are to be kept beyond the distance of 14 *feet* from the Compasses in use, so far as the size of the vessel will admit.

All Steam Vessels are to be fitted with hollow pillars for the support of their Standard Compasses except in such cases as the Superintendent of the Compass Department shall point out, in which instances a solid wood pillar, or mixed metal stanchions for the support of a copper binnacle head, is to be prepared, and these pillars, or supports, are to be so placed that the said binnacle head will be in the midship line, and in such a position forward, or aft, as the Superintendent upon consultation with the master-shipwright shall think most advisable, according to the construction of the vessel and nature of her armament.

In Ships of the Line, and Frigates, it having been found more convenient to place the Standard Compass in a copper binnacle, supported by mixed metal stanchions or a solid wood pillar, these are to be prepared according to the application of the Superintendent of the Compass Department.

In Brigs or other Vessels where the Main Boom may prevent a Standard or Azimuth Compass from being constantly kept at the proper elevation for observations, a solid pillar, made so as to unship; or a sliding tube, constructed so as to be capable of being lowered upon a short pillar, is to be prepared; whichever plan may be considered most suitable to the vessel, according to her equipment and armament.

The Binnacles for the steering Compasses are to be constructed upon a given plan, with tops made to take off, and in order to prevent improper materials from being deposited therein, they are not to be fitted with doors.

As the vicinity of the Compasses when the Binnacles are too close together, has been found materially to affect their accuracy, in all ships where there are two Binnacles they are to be separated as much as the diameter of the wheel will permit, and so as the helmsman may see the Compass conveniently; but in no case are they to be allowed to be nearer than 4 feet, 6 inches.

For the better preservation of the Compasses, in every Ship a Closet is to be constructed in a dry place, sufficiently large for the reception of the Ships' establishment of Compasses, and it is to be appropriated to that purpose *exclusively*, the key being kept by the Master; and in order that the spare Compass Cards may never be kept with poles of the same name nearest to each other, Cases, which prevent the possibility of their being packed improperly (specimens of which have been sent to each yard) are to be prepared.

These Regulations are to be alike applicable to ships ordered to be built, and to those directed to be prepared for commission; and the previous orders on this subject are to be considered cancelled.

By Command of their Lordships,

H. CORRY

To all Captains and Commanding Officers of Her Majesty's Ships and Vessels

Report on the Compass Observatory at Woolwich, 1855

In accordance with the Board minute, 'The Hydrographer to report on the present state of the Compass Establishment adding thereto any propositions he may have to offer for its future management', the following brief report is noted:

1. Owing to the bad state of the compasses of the Navy in 1820 Professor Barlow was requested to examine and report on them. He did so and condemned them all as not trustworthy.

2. A compass committee was formed the result of whose labours was the production of a much improved compass now called the Standard Compass. The committee further recommended that a Compass Observatory should be established, all compasses to be used in the Navy should be tested at the Observatory and that every ship should be swung to ascertain local deviation.

3. The Compass Observatory was established in 1844. The late Captain Edward J. Johnson was Superintendent of it and Mr J. Brunton storekeeper and Inspector of compasses. Since that period every compass issued to the fleet has been tested at the Observatory, and every ship swung.

4. About the year 1848 the labour of swinging ships at the several outports became so heavy that Commander Strange was employed to assist in the work. After about two years the Board decided that Commander Strange's services were no longer necessary but the Masters of the Flagships at the outports should swing the ships, those in the yard at Woolwich being swung by Capt. Johnson who was also required to visit the outports once every quarter and oftener if necessary to see that all was conducted in order.

5. In October 1853 Capt. Johnson died, since which period the duty of the Observatory and the swinging of ships at Greenhithe has entirely devolved on Mr Brunton who as far as lay in his power has carried on the work in a most creditable manner.

6. The duties of the Superintendent of the Compass Observatory are:

1. To examine and test every compass issued to the Fleet

2. To keep up a supply of tested compasses at all the outports ready for any demand

3. To point out the particular sort of compass best adapted to a class of vessel as screw gunboats, mortar vessels, fast steam packets, etc.

4. To determine the best position in the ship for the standard compass

5. To decide upon all repairs to the compasses and to check the maker's bills.

6. To superintend the swinging of all HM ships and hired transports at Greenhithe.

7. To examine the deviation tables of the ships swung at outports and when re-swung in any other ports of the globe, and to call for explanations of any error or discrepancy in them.

8. To examine and report upon all inventions and improvements relative to the compass, (fresh proposals being sent in about once a fortnight).

9. To test the Standard Compasses ordered in England by foreign Governments, (a large order for the United States having been recently executed).

10. To form a collection of specimens from all the best compasses made in the different parts of Europe and America, such a collection being now at Woolwich.

11. To answer questions on the subjects of compasses frequently made by foreign Governments who are gradually adopting the English Standard Compass, and to conduct a large correspondence with the Admiralty, the Dockyard, the Makers and Repairers of compasses, the Masters who swing ships at the outports, etc.

12. To keep himself informed of all advances in the science of Magnetism with a view to its application to the improvement of compasses, or for neutralising the effects of the extensive use of iron in screw steamers, iron ships, etc.

7. The highly respectable individual who for the last eighteen months has been entrusted with these responsible duties has the rank and education of a Sergeant of Artillery.

8. Compasses are no longer what they were fifteen years ago. The enlightened views and liberality of the Board of Admiralty in 1842 sanctioned the introduction of an almost perfect instrument, the present standard compass, at a cost of £25 each. It is a delicate but at the same time a thoroughly practical instrument. It should be handled as a chronometer or barometer, and its adjustments before leaving the Observatory require to be most carefully attended to.

9. The already great use and the possible more extended adoption of iron in our ships, and the speed with which steamers now dash along at a rate of 10 to 12 miles an hour render the preservation and improvement of the compass still more important. The wrecks of the *Conqueror* and *Alliance* off Boulogne in 1842 were most probably caused by the error in local deviation of their compasses. The main cause of the wreck of the *Birkenhead* troop ship at the Cape of Good Hope, the packet ship *Philadelphia* last year on the Cape Race in Newfoundland and the *Tayleur* off Lanbay in the Irish Sea.

10. The questions and discussions and differences of opinion between High Authorities as to the use of magnets to correct compasses for local deviation has assumed a formidable aspect. The Astronomer Royal and Dr Scoresby are entirely opposed to each other on this subject. The discussion occupied one section of the British Association nearly its whole sitting at Liverpool in September last. A committee has been established at that port to investigate the subject and they naturally would apply as they had already applied, to the Admiralty for information. To whom shall they be referred?

11. The fate of the boats compasses in the Navy also requires to be carefully looked into. The Common Boats Compasses, three of which are supplied to each ship, are utterly worthless. They swing round as peg tops at every stroke of the oars. Owing to trusting to one of these Captain Cooper Key of the *Amphion* and a boats crew were nearly lost last year in a fog off Riga.

12. Were it only for the minor financial view of the case, the subject deserves to be considered. There are about 3,500 compasses in the Navy, at the value of £19,000. New compasses and repairs cost about £600 a year. The number of compasses supplied to our ships – fifteen to a line of battleship and 13 to a frigate – might probably be much reduced if that question were carefully gone into.

13. In the Baltic the compass is our chief guide, the chronometer is hardly used from one end of the season to the other. The steam

screw gunboats, mortar vessels and especially the floating batteries, covered as they are with iron will all require the most careful placing of their compasses. A case in point has just occurred in swinging the gunboat *Ruby*. It appeared that within two points from south to south-south-west local deviation jumps from 2° West to 9° East, or one whole point. In standing up the Kattegat on these courses a run of two hours would place the ship ashore if this error were not carefully allowed for when shaping the course. I therefore respectfully but urgently submit to Their Lordships favourable consideration that a Naval Officer of the rank of Master be appointed forthwith as Superintendent of Compasses, and the Compass Observatory, and that his first and immediate duty be to make every arrangement that time will permit for selecting the best sort of compass and placing it in the best position on board this particular class of vessels now fitting for the Baltic Sea.

Signed J. Washington, 12 March 1855

To accompany this report, Washington sent a letter which read:

Should Their Lordships approve of the above suggestions, I would further submit for approval the name of Mr Frederick Evans, Master RN, long employed in the survey service and the officer who seems to be best qualified for these duties. His name is already on the books of the Fisguard for the surveying service, where I propose it should be continued for on going on board ships to swing it is an advantage to be recognised as on full pay.

When not engaged in the actual duties of the Observatory, he should be attached as aforesaid to the Hydrographic Office and to receive yearly the same specialist pay of 10/- a day as the other officers for which estimates are already taken in the vote for 1855–6.

Note: Mr Evans to be appointed *Signed* R. O.

Note: Is it intended that Mr Evans should only be appointed additional to Fisguard for the duties of the Compass Observatory, or is he to have a separate civil appointment? *Signed* Woolley

The Hydrographer writes: I suggest he be appointed additional to Fisguard as Superintendent of the Compass Observatory. No civil appointment is necessary. *Signed* W., 17 March 1855

(The whole operation took less than a week.)

Magnetic Coefficients

Archibald Smith's coefficients can be briefly explained as follows:

Coefficient A: A constant deviation on all headings, which may be *real* (e.g. due to unsymetrical soft iron) or *apparent* (e.g. due to an index error in the compass).

Coefficients B and C: These are due to the combined effects of the permanent magnetism of the hard iron – normally called the semicircular effects. B represents that part acting in a fore-and-aft direction and C that part acting in an athwartship direction.

Coefficients D and E: These are due to the horizontal induction in the soft iron and produce a quadrantal deviation, D having four maxima on the intercardinal points and E on the cardinal points

At a well-placed compass A and E are generally small and can be disregarded. On any course (ζ), the deviation (δ) of the compass, reckoned positive when the north point of the needle deviates to the east, is given by the expression:

$$\delta = A + B \sin \zeta + C \cos \zeta + D \sin 2\zeta + E \cos 2\zeta$$

While this formula is only approximate it may be considered sufficiently accurate provided the deviation does not exceed about 20°. When dealing with larger deviations, the more precise formula and coefficients must be used, details of which are given in the papers and publications referred to in the text.

List of patents standing in the name of Commander Louis W.P. Chetwynd, or in his name in conjunction with others

In his own name

25965/1906 A liquid compass with reduced-diameter card and lubber's point extending from the side to it.

1397/1907 A binnacle in which the corrector magnets are raised or lowered on chains.

25639/1907 Oscillations of card of liquid compass damped by a closed vessel, partly filled with liquid, attached to the underside of the card.

4761/1912 A means of holding the card of a liquid compass while a course indicator is adjusted on it.

17768/1912 A liquid compass with a compartment of variable depth at the base so that the drag of the oil with which the compartment is partially filled may be increased in order to curb the oscillation of the bowl.

24768/1912 A liquid compass in which the oil-filled compartment at the base does not cover the whole bottom of the bowl, so that light can shine up through the flat glass surrounding it and be deflected down upon the card by an annular reflector round the verge. The pivot to be cushioned on horsehair and an ususual arrangement of gimbals used.

With D. Buckney

7543/1907 An azimuth circle with rollers to make it turn easily on the verge ring.

With Kelvin & White, and F. W. Clarke

18509/1908 A method of fitting the verge glass in a liquid compass.

18510/1908 An adjustable steering prism.

20185/1908 An Azimuth Instrument with claws to take on the verge ring.

21634/1908 and 16607/1909 Liquid Compasses for use ashore

19057/1909 A liquid compass in which the float has positive buoyancy (as in Crow's compass) and 'bilge keels' to prevent it rocking.

25718/1909 A liquid compass in which the pivot can be extracted through the base.

29719/1909 A liquid compass in which the diaphragm between bowl and expansion chamber is made of skin, parchment or waterproofed silk instead of metal.

9347/1911 An optical arrangement for viewing at a distance above the compass an enlarged image of the card.

With Dent & Co., and Johnson Ltd

6703/1913 A compass with lubber's point pivoted to keep it on a level with the card.

Description of Dr. Anschütz-Kaempfe's Gyro Direction Indicator by Commander The Hon. L.W.P. Chetwynd, September 1905

The instrument consists of a system of three electrically driven gyroscopes, one, the main gyro, to maintain the direction relative to the meridian, and two smaller gyros mounted with their axes vertical, in the plane of the gimbal rings, to overcome any tendency to displacement of the main system owing to the rolling or pitching of a ship.

The main gyro is suspended in a frame in such a manner, that its axis can change inclination in the vertical plane with reference to the frame, but not in a horizontal direction, consequently any change of position of axis in the horizontal plane is communicated to the frame, which in turn is suspended, by a flexible connection, to a ball bearing the support for which is fixed to the inner gimbal ring.

The spindle carrying the main gyro frame is continued above the flexible joint and ball bearing, and at its upper end is secured a compass card, and a circular frame with radial bars.

The ball bearing is given a continual reversing rotary motion by means of electrically driven differential mitre wheels, the object of such motion being to keep the bearing surface 'alive'.

The two balancing gyros, the rotary motion motor and a small motor with necessary gearing for adjusting the direction of the main gyro axis in the horizontal plane, are all fixed to the inner ring of an ordinary system of gimballing.

To the frame carrying the main gyro, is fixed an additional weight, by means of which the position of the centre of gravity of the system can be adjusted relative to the centre of rotation or Cardan point.

This adjustment of the position of the centre of gravity constitutes one of the principal adjustments of the instrument.

In the moveable part of the main gyro frame (i.e. that part which moves in the vertical plane) is a contact point which on the precession of the axis amounting to one degree, (and the axis is therefore tilting in the vertical plane), makes contact with an attachment on the upper part of the frame and completing a circuit causes the adjustment motor to actuate a lever which, engaging in one of the radial bars, changes the direction of the axis until it is again horizontal, when contact is broken.

Thus the precessing of the axis of the gyro, due to the rotation of the earth is continually adjusted and can never be more than a degree in error.

The speed at which the main gyro revolves is stated to be 8000 revolutions per minute.

The price of the instrument is quoted at £600.

The first rules for placing a compass in an aeroplane, January 1911

1. Whenever possible, position should be in the exact 'Fore and Aft' axis of machine.

2. Compass in a position to be easily read by the pilot; a reflector or prism could be arranged to assist in this.

3. As little magnetic material as possible should be used within a radius of three feet.

4. It is essential that all moveable parts within this radius (3 feet) should be made of some non magnetic material, such as brass, gunmetal, aluminium, duralumin etc.

5. As far as possible from engine and magneto.

6. As soon as a satisfactory pattern of instrument has been decided on, a regular fitting for securing it down should be settled. Probably the most suitable would be a $\frac{3}{4}$ inch piece of wood 7 inches in diameter if round, covered with felt. This should be placed in the chosen spot by the makers of the machine and looked on as an essential part of it.

It should be placed parallel to the normal horizontal axis of the machine when in flight – not at rest on ground.

7. Screw compass down to block, being very careful to see that the pointer or 'lubber line' is on fore side of bowl and exactly in line with the 'fore and aft' axis of the machine.

The Manor of Ditton is first mentioned in Domesday Book (1086), when it was held by 'William, sone of Ansculf' and his brother Walter, and was valued at 30 shillings. Walter's descendants held the property for 400 years and one of them, Richard de Ditton, married Cecilia de Stoke in 1205, which explains why the parish of Stoke Poges, six miles distant, included Ditton Park until the boundaries were revised during the 1960s.

In 1331 Sir John de Molyns was granted a licence by Edward III to fortify his 'mansun of Ditton', and, four years later, to 'build a park of 38 acres'. The central tower of the house is still known as de Molyns tower, and is probably a perpetuation of the original fourteenth-century edifice. In 1472 Ditton reverted to the Crown, and was at one time the residence of Cardinal Wolsey. In 1532 Ann Boleyn was 'Keeper of Ditton Park', an emolument worth £180 a year. Eighty years afterwards, in 1615, when Sir Ralph Winwood, Secretary of State, held a similar appointment, he was granted the property which, by then, incorporated some 250 acres. He promptly rebuilt the mansion around de Molyns tower and greatly enlarged the moat so that it enclosed much of the present garden. Sir Ralph's granddaughter Ann married Edward, Baron Montagu of Boughton, later Duke of Montagu. Passing often through the distaff side the property remained in the Montagu family until bought by the Admiralty in 1917.

In 1812 the Winwood house was burnt down, and the following year the present mansion, modelled on the former one, was built by the then owner, Henry, Duke of Buccleuch, as a dower house.

Organization of the Compass Department at the Admiralty Compass Observatory, 1957

10

Director of the Compass Department (DCD)

DDCD

AD (R & D)

AD (Production)

Compasses

Drawing Office

Instruments (including SINS)

Procurement, inspection and tests; Finance

Workshops

Ship-fitting Superintendents of gyro-compasses

Staff Requirements, central services

Air liaison

Naval Assistants

Instruction

Admiralty Transmitting Magnetic Compasses

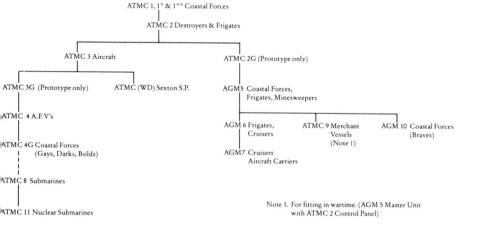

ATMC 1, 1* & 1** Coastal Forces

ATMC 2 Destroyers & Frigates

ATMC 3 Aircraft

ATMC 2G (Prototype only)

ATMC 3G (Prototype only)

ATMC (WD) Sexton S.P.

AGM5 Coastal Forces, Frigates, Minesweepers

ATMC 4 A.F.V's

AGM 6 Frigates, Cruisers

ATMC 9 Merchant Vessels (Note 1)

AGM 10 Coastal Forces (Braves)

ATMC 4G Coastal Forces (Gays, Darks, Bolds)

AGM7 Cruisers Aircraft Carriers

ATMC 8 Submarines

ATMC 11 Nuclear Submarines

Note 1. For fitting in wartime. (AGM 5 Master Unit with ATMC 2 Control Panel)

Note on the improved accuracy of SINS Mark 2 over SINS Mark 1

SINS Mark 1 was designed as an analogue system and gyro-corrections were provided by steady currents which had to be held to a high degree of stability. For this reason it was necessary to arrange that the three gyros should each sense a constant input rate which had, therefore, to be either zero or full earth rate. The configuration of the gimbals and gyros used ensured that the longitude gyro would sense full earth rate (i.e. its 'input' axis pointed at the north celestial pole) and this was compensated for by a fixed torque, applied mechanically in the gyro itself. The other two gyros sensed no earth rate about their input axes. However, this configuration introduced gravity-related errors as the vessel changed latitude (e.g. at the equator the input axis of the longitude gyro was horizontal whereas at the pole it was vertical).

By using digital techniques it was possible to supply pulse-torque corrections to all three gyros with sufficient accuracy to cope with any value between zero and full earth rate. SINS Mark 2 therefore has gyros which maintain a fixed orientation with respect to gravity at all times and the bothersome errors which affected SINS Mark 1 with change of latitude are not effective.

Bibliography

EARLY COMPASS HISTORY

1. Evans, F. J. O. and Smith, A. *Admiralty Manual for Ascertaining and Applying the Deviations of the Compass.* Printed by J. D. Potter, London, 1862.

2. Hitchins, H. L. and May, W. E. *From Lodestone to Gyro-Compass.* Hutchinson, London, 1952.

3. Johnson, E. J. *Practical Illustrations of the Necessity of Ascertaining the Deviations of the Compass* George Barclay, London, 1847.

4. Lecky, S. T. S. *Wrinkles in Practical Navigation.* George Philip and Son, Ltd, London. 1881 (Many subsequent editions).

5. May, W. E. *History of Marine Navigation.* G. T. Foulis and Co. Ltd, Henley-on-Thames. 1973.

6. Scoresby, W. *Journal of a Voyage to Australia and Round the World for Magnetical Research.* Longman, London. 1859.

7. *Reports of the Liverpool Compass Committee to the Board of Trade.* HMSO 1961.

MODERN COMPASSES AND SINS

8. Broxmeyer, Charles. *Inertial Navigation Systems.* McGraw-Hill Book Co., New York. 1964.

9. Chaffer, C. *Admiralty Handbook of the Gyroscopic Compass.* HMSO 1925.

10. Grant, G. A. A. and Klinkert, J. *The Ship's Compass.* Routledge and Kegan Paul, London and Henley, 1952.

11. Hine, A. *Magnetic Compasses and Magnetometres.* Adam Hilger Ltd, London. 1968.

12. Rawlings, A. L. *The Theory of the Gyroscopic Compass.* MacMillan and Co. Ltd, London. 1929.

BIOGRAPHIES

13. Airy, Wilfred. (edited). *Autobiography of Sir George Biddell Airy.* 1896.

14. Dawson, L. S. *Memoirs of Hydrography.* (1985. Reprinted by Cornmarket Press Ltd, London. 1969).

15. Fisher, A. J. *Records.* Hodder and Stoughton Ltd, London, 1919.

16. Friendly, Alfred. *Beaufort of the Admiralty*. Hutchinson, London. 1977.

17. Hughes, T. P. *Elmer Sperry, Inventer and Engineer*. John Hopkins Press, Baltimore. 1971.

18. Ross, J. C. *A Voyage of Discovery in the Southern and Antartic Seas*. John Murray, London. 1847.

19. Ross, M. J. *Ross of the Antartic*. Caedmon of Whitby. 1982.

20. Thompson, Sylvanus P. *The Life of Lord Kelvin*. MacMillan and Co. Ltd, London. 1910.

21. Watt, Robert Watson. *Three Stages to Victory*. Odhams Ltd, London. 1957.

Index